Ready® | 8

Mathematics
PRACTICE AND
PROBLEM SOLVING
Teacher Guide

Program Authors

Mark Ellis, Ph.D.
Department Chair and Professor, Education, CSU Fullerton
Board of Directors, Executive Committee, NCTM
National Board Certified Teacher

Gladis Kersaint, Ph.D.
Professor, Mathematics Education, USF
Board of Directors, Executive Committee, NCTM
Board of Directors, Association of Mathematics Teacher Educators

Acknowledgments

Vice President–Product Development: Adam Berkin
Editorial Director: Cynthia Tripp
Executive Editor: Kathy Kellman
Editors: Stacie Cartwright, Pamela Halloran, Lauren Van Wart
Project Manager: Grace Izzi
Cover Design: Matt Pollock
Book Designer: Scott Hoffman

Table of Contents

Mathematics Lessons

	Lesson		Standards	Embedded SMPs
Unit 1	**Expressions and Equations (Exponents) and the Number System**			
1	Properties of Integer Exponents	1	8.EE.A.1	1, 2, 3, 6, 7, 8
2	Square Roots and Cube Roots	5	8.EE.A.2	2, 5, 6, 7, 8
3	*Understand* Rational and Irrational Numbers . .	9	8.NS.A.1, 8.NS.A.2	2, 4, 6, 7, 8
4	Scientific Notation	12	8.EE.A.3	2, 5, 6
5	Operations and Scientific Notation	16	8.EE.A.4	1, 6, 8

Student Book includes a Family Letter for every lesson and Unit Vocabulary for every unit.

Mathematics Lessons *continued*

Student Book includes a Family Letter for every lesson and Unit Vocabulary for every unit.

Mathematics Lessons *continued*

		Standards	Embedded SMPs

Student Book includes a Family Letter for every lesson and Unit Vocabulary for every unit.

Mathematics Lessons *continued*

Student Book includes a Family Letter for every lesson and Unit Vocabulary for every unit.

Mathematics Lessons *continued*

		Standards	Embedded SMPs

Unit 5   Statistics and Probability

Lesson

Teacher Resource Blackline Masters

Teacher Resource blackline masters are provided for use with the collaborative practice games in *Ready Practice and Problem Solving*. Full instructions for use of these teacher resources can be found in the Step by Step for each unit game.

Student Book includes a Family Letter for every lesson and Unit Vocabulary for every unit.

Ready® Program Overview

Ready Mathematics prepares students for mastery of rigorous national and state standards through a balance of conceptual understanding, procedural skills, fluency, and application. Use *Ready's* clear, thoughtful pedagogy to support rich classroom instruction in which meaningful reasoning, mathematical discourse, and a range of mathematical practices thrive.

Built for the new standards. Not just aligned.

For Students

Ready Instruction provides whole class and small group instruction and independent practice of concepts and skills for every standard. Interim assessments give frequent opportunities for standards mastery monitoring.

Ready Practice and Problem Solving complements *Ready Instruction* through rich practice, games, and performance tasks that develop understanding of and fluency with key skills and concepts.

Ready Assessments provides three full-length benchmark assessments that match the latest consortia guidance.

For Teachers

The *Ready Teacher Resource Book* and *Ready Practice and Problem Solving Teacher Guide* support teachers with point-of-use strategies and tips, step-by-step guidance, and best practices for implementing rigorous standards.

Ready Teacher Toolbox provides online access to prerequisite lessons from previous grades, student-led center activities differentiated for three levels, and teacher-led activities for students requiring additional instruction on prerequisite or on-level skills.

Ready Program Features

 Built with **all-new content** written specifically for rigorous national and state standards

 Uses a research-based, **gradual release** instructional model

 Requires **higher-order thinking** and complex reasoning to solve problems

 Integrates **Standards for Mathematical Practice** throughout every lesson

 Embeds thoughtful **teacher support**

 Encourages students to develop **deeper understanding** of concepts and to understand and use a variety of mathematical strategies and models

 Promotes **fluency** and connects hands-on learning with clearly articulated models throughout

What's in *Ready*® Practice and Problem Solving

Building on **Ready Instruction, Ready Practice and Problem Solving** encourages students to reason, use strategies, solve extended problems, and engage in collaborative work to extend classroom learning. Designed for flexibility, **Ready Practice and Problem Solving** can be used for homework, independent classroom practice, and in after-school settings.

Lesson Features

Practice specific to each part of every *Ready Instruction* lesson gives students multiple opportunities to reinforce procedural fluency and synthesize concepts and skills learned in the classroom. Lesson practice pages can be used at the end of a lesson or after completing each part of a lesson.

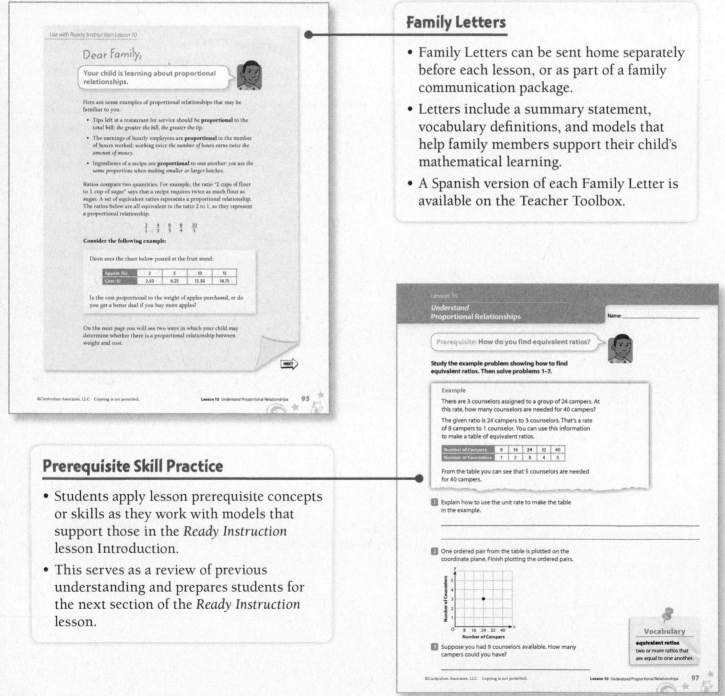

Family Letters

- Family Letters can be sent home separately before each lesson, or as part of a family communication package.

- Letters include a summary statement, vocabulary definitions, and models that help family members support their child's mathematical learning.

- A Spanish version of each Family Letter is available on the Teacher Toolbox.

Prerequisite Skill Practice

- Students apply lesson prerequisite concepts or skills as they work with models that support those in the *Ready Instruction* lesson Introduction.

- This serves as a review of previous understanding and prepares students for the next section of the *Ready Instruction* lesson.

A10

Find Unit Rates

Study the example problem showing how to find a unit rate. Then solve problems 1–6.

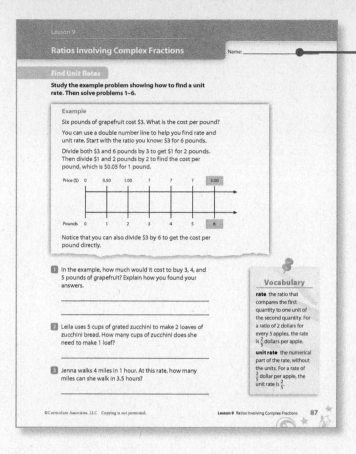

Example

Six pounds of grapefruit cost $3. What is the cost per pound?

You can use a double number line to help you find rate and unit rate. Start with the ratio you know: $3 for 6 pounds.

Divide both $3 and 6 pounds by 3 to get $1 for 2 pounds. Then divide $1 and 2 pounds by 2 to find the cost per pound, which is $0.05 for 1 pound.

Price ($) 0   0.50   1.00   ?   ?   ?   3.00

Pounds   0   1   2   3   4   5   6

Notice that you can also divide $3 by 6 to get the cost per pound directly.

1 In the example, how much would it cost to buy 3, 4, and 5 pounds of grapefruit? Explain how you found your answers.

_____

_____

2 Leila uses 5 cups of grated zucchini to make 2 loaves of zucchini bread. How many cups of zucchini does she need to make 1 loaf?

_____

3 Jenna walks 4 miles in 1 hour. At this rate, how many miles can she walk in 3.5 hours?

_____

Vocabulary

rate the ratio that compares the first quantity to one unit of the second quantity. For a ratio of 2 dollars for every 5 apples, the rate is $\frac{2}{5}$ dollars per apple.

unit rate the numerical part of the rate, without the units. For a rate of $\frac{2}{5}$ dollar per apple, the unit rate is $\frac{2}{5}$.

Solve.

4 It takes 30 cups of milk to make 4 sticks of butter. Use this ratio to complete the double number line. Describe the unit rate.

Cups of Milk   0   □   □   □   30   □   □

Sticks of Butter   0   □   □   □   4   □   □

_____

5 Rashid is paid by the hour. He earned $50 for a 4-hour workday. How much does he earn for a $5\frac{1}{2}$-hour workday?

Show your work.

Solution: _____

6 Ace Bike Rentals rents bikes for $28 per day. Renters can keep the bike for 8 hours. Bart's Bikes rents bikes for $30 per day. Renters can keep the bike for 10 hours. Which company charges a lower hourly rate? How much lower?

Show your work.

Solution: _____

_____

_____

Skills and Concepts Practice

- **Two pages of skills and concept practice** are provided after each Modeled and Guided Instruction section and each Guided Practice section of a *Ready Instruction* lesson. These can be used in class, after school, or at home.

- **Worked-out examples** support and reinforce students' classroom learning. They also provide family members assisting at home helpful explanations of the lesson content.

- Problems are **differentiated** to provide maximum flexibility when assigning practice as independent classwork or homework. The differentiation is marked in the Teacher Guide as basic **B**, medium **M**, or challenging **C**.

- **Vocabulary** is defined at helpful points in the lesson.

- Students are encouraged to show their work and **use models and strategies** they learned in the *Ready Instruction* lesson.

- Lessons conclude with **mixed practice** problems that vary in type, including multiple choice, yes-no, true-false formats, and open-ended questions.

Unit Features

Unit materials cover multiple skills and concepts, helping students make connections across standards. Use Unit Games, Unit Practice, Unit Performance Tasks, and Unit Vocabulary after completing each unit to apply and integrate skills and to consolidate learning.

Unit Game

- Unit Games are engaging, collaborative experiences designed to encourage students to use **strategic thinking** as they play with a partner.

- Students record the mathematics of each game to **promote fluency** and reinforce learning. The recording sheet also serves as an opportunity for informal assessment for teachers to monitor students' work.

- These partner games can be used at classroom centers and/or sent home for play with a family member.

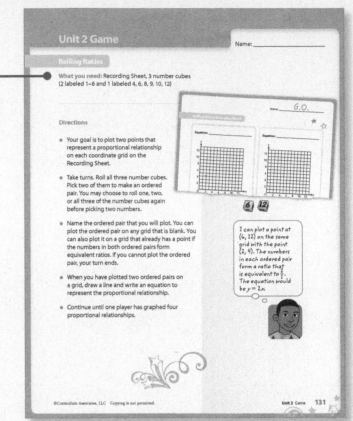

Unit Practice

- The Unit Practice provides **mixed practice** of lesson skills and concepts.

- The first page references the Self-Check chart in the *Ready Instruction* Unit Opener. This helps students quickly identify the lesson(s) to revisit for additional support.

- Unit Practice problems **integrate multiple skills**.

- These pages present problems with a **variety of formats**, including multiple choice and constructed response, to help students become familiar with items they will encounter on their state tests.

- The unit practice pages can be assigned as homework, used as independent or small group practice, or for whole class discussion.

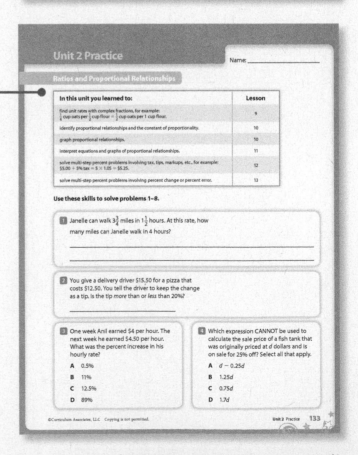

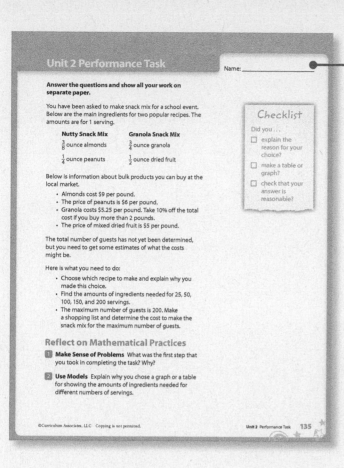

Unit 2 Performance Task

Name: _____

Answer the questions and show all your work on separate paper.

You have been asked to make snack mix for a school event. Below are the main ingredients for two popular recipes. The amounts are for 1 serving.

Nutty Snack Mix
$\frac{3}{8}$ ounce almonds
$\frac{1}{4}$ ounce peanuts

Granola Snack Mix
$\frac{3}{4}$ ounce granola
$\frac{1}{2}$ ounce dried fruit

Below is information about bulk products you can buy at the local market.
- Almonds cost $9 per pound.
- The price of peanuts is $6 per pound.
- Granola costs $5.25 per pound. Take 10% off the total cost if you buy more than 2 pounds.
- The price of mixed dried fruit is $5 per pound.

The total number of guests has not yet been determined, but you need to get some estimates of what the costs might be.

Here is what you need to do:
- Choose which recipe to make and explain why you made this choice.
- Find the amounts of ingredients needed for 25, 50, 100, 150, and 200 servings.
- The maximum number of guests is 200. Make a shopping list and determine the cost to make the snack mix for the maximum number of guests.

Reflect on Mathematical Practices

1 **Make Sense of Problems** What was the first step that you took in completing the task? Why?

2 **Use Models** Explain why you chose a graph or a table for showing the amounts of ingredients needed for different numbers of servings.

Checklist
Did you ...
☐ explain the reason for your choice?
☐ make a table or graph?
☐ check that your answer is reasonable?

©Curriculum Associates, LLC Copying is not permitted.   **Unit 2** Performance Task   135

Unit Performance Task

- Real-world Unit Performance Tasks require students to **integrate skills and concepts**, apply higher-order thinking, and explain their reasoning.

- Engaging real-world tasks encourage students to become active participants in their learning by requiring them to organize and manage mathematical content and processes.

- **Performance Task Tips** help students organize their thinking.

- Students are asked to reflect on **Mathematical Practices** after they have completed the Performance Task.

Unit 2 Vocabulary

Name: _____

My Examples

rate
the ratio that compares the first quantity to one unit of the second quantity; for a ratio of 2 dollars for every 5 apples, the rate is $\frac{2}{5}$ dollars per apple

unit rate
the numerical part of the rate, without the units; for a rate of $\frac{2}{5}$ dollar per apple, the unit rate is $\frac{2}{5}$

equivalent ratios
two or more ratios that are equal to one another

proportional relationship
the relationship among a group of ratios that are equivalent

©Curriculum Associates, LLC Copying is not permitted.   **Unit 2** Vocabulary   137

Unit Vocabulary

- The Unit Vocabulary is a way for students to integrate vocabulary into their learning. Vocabulary pages provide a **student-friendly definition** for each new and review vocabulary term in the unit.

- Students are given space to write **examples** for each term to help them connect the term to their own understanding.

- After students have completed these pages, they can use them as a reference.

- Students are also given opportunities to further personalize their acquisition of mathematics vocabulary by selecting terms they want to define.

Fluency Practice

Throughout instruction, use Fluency Skills and Fluency Repeated Reasoning worksheets to reinforce procedural fluency.

Skills Practice

- Fluency practice worksheets in multiple formats provide flexibility and promote the **use of grade-appropriate strategies and algorithms**.
- These worksheets address grade-level facts and operations and can be used any time after the skill has been taught.

Repeated Reasoning

- Repeated Reasoning worksheets encourage students to **make use of structure and look for regularity** as part of their development of grade-level fluency.
- In this type of fluency practice, students identify and describe patterns in the relationship between the answers and the problems. This develops their **abstract reasoning** and mental math skills.

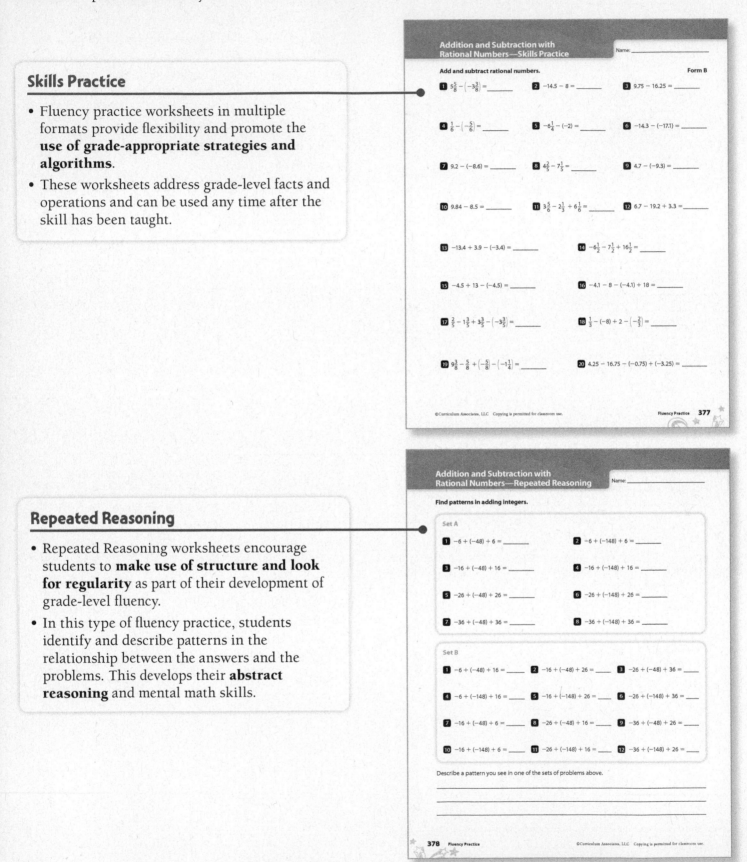

Addition and Subtraction with Rational Numbers—Skills Practice

Name: _____

Add and subtract rational numbers.   Form B

1 $5\frac{5}{8} - \left(-3\frac{3}{8}\right) =$ _____ 2 $-14.5 - 8 =$ _____ 3 $9.75 - 16.25 =$ _____

4 $\frac{1}{6} - \left(-\frac{5}{6}\right) =$ _____ 5 $-6\frac{1}{4} - (-2) =$ _____ 6 $-14.3 - (-17.1) =$ _____

7 $9.2 - (-8.6) =$ _____ 8 $4\frac{2}{5} - 7\frac{1}{5} =$ _____ 9 $4.7 - (-9.3) =$ _____

10 $9.84 - 8.5 =$ _____ 11 $3\frac{5}{6} - 2\frac{1}{3} + 6\frac{1}{6} =$ _____ 12 $6.7 - 19.2 + 3.3 =$ _____

13 $-13.4 + 3.9 - (-3.4) =$ _____ 14 $-6\frac{1}{2} - 7\frac{1}{2} + 16\frac{1}{2} =$ _____

15 $-4.5 + 13 - (-4.5) =$ _____ 16 $-4.1 - 8 - (-4.1) + 18 =$ _____

17 $\frac{2}{5} - 1\frac{3}{5} + 3\frac{3}{5} - \left(-3\frac{3}{5}\right) =$ _____ 18 $\frac{1}{3} - (-8) + 2 - \left(-\frac{2}{3}\right) =$ _____

19 $9\frac{3}{8} - \frac{5}{8} + \left(-\frac{5}{8}\right) - \left(-1\frac{1}{4}\right) =$ _____ 20 $4.25 - 16.75 - (-0.75) + (-3.25) =$ _____

©Curriculum Associates, LLC   Copying is permitted for classroom use.   Fluency Practice **377**

Addition and Subtraction with Rational Numbers—Repeated Reasoning

Name: _____

Find patterns in adding integers.

Set A

1 $-6 + (-48) + 6 =$ _____ 2 $-6 + (-148) + 6 =$ _____

3 $-16 + (-48) + 16 =$ _____ 4 $-16 + (-148) + 16 =$ _____

5 $-26 + (-48) + 26 =$ _____ 6 $-26 + (-148) + 26 =$ _____

7 $-36 + (-48) + 36 =$ _____ 8 $-36 + (-148) + 36 =$ _____

Set B

1 $-6 + (-48) + 16 =$ _____ 2 $-16 + (-48) + 26 =$ _____ 3 $-26 + (-48) + 36 =$ _____

4 $-6 + (-148) + 16 =$ _____ 5 $-16 + (-148) + 26 =$ _____ 6 $-26 + (-148) + 36 =$ _____

7 $-16 + (-48) + 6 =$ _____ 8 $-26 + (-48) + 16 =$ _____ 9 $-36 + (-48) + 26 =$ _____

10 $-16 + (-148) + 6 =$ _____ 11 $-26 + (-148) + 16 =$ _____ 12 $-36 + (-148) + 26 =$ _____

Describe a pattern you see in one of the sets of problems above.

_____

_____

_____

378 Fluency Practice   ©Curriculum Associates, LLC   Copying is permitted for classroom use.

Correlation Charts

Common Core Standards in *Ready® Practice and Problem Solving*

The tables below show the standards addressed in *Ready Practice and Problem Solving*, all of which correspond to *Ready Instruction*. Use this information to plan and focus meaningful practice.

Common Core State Standards for Grade 8 — Mathematics Standards		Content Emphasis	Ready® Practice and Problem Solving Lesson(s)
The Number System			
Know that there are numbers that are not rational, and approximate them by rational numbers.			
8.NS.A.1	Know that numbers that are not rational are called irrational. Understand informally that every number has a decimal expansion; for rational numbers show that the decimal expansion repeats eventually, and convert a decimal expansion which repeats eventually into a rational number.	Supporting/ Additional	3
8.NS.A.2	Use rational approximations of irrational numbers to compare the size of irrational numbers, locate them approximately on a number line diagram, and estimate the value of expressions (e.g., π^2). *For example, by truncating the decimal expansion of $\sqrt{2}$, show that $\sqrt{2}$ is between 1 and 2, then between 1.4 and 1.5, and explain how to continue on to get better approximations.*	Supporting/ Additional	3
Expressions and Equations			
Work with radicals and integer exponents.			
8.EE.A.1	Know and apply the properties of integer exponents to generate equivalent numerical expressions. *For example, $3^2 \times 3^{-5} = 3^{-3} = \frac{1}{3^3} = \frac{1}{27}$.*	Major	1
8.EE.A.2	Use square root and cube root symbols to represent solutions to equations of the form $x^2 = p$ and $x^3 = p$, where p is a positive rational number. Evaluate square roots of small perfect squares and cube roots of small perfect cubes. Know that $\sqrt{2}$ is irrational.	Major	2
8.EE.A.3	Use numbers expressed in the form of a single digit times an integer power of 10 to estimate very large or very small quantities, and to express how many times as much one is than the other. *For example, estimate the population of the United States as 3×10^8 and the population of the world as 7×10^9, and determine that the world population is more than 20 times larger.*	Major	4
8.EE.A.4	Perform operations with numbers expressed in scientific notation, including problems where both decimal and scientific notation are used. Use scientific notation and choose units of appropriate size for measurements of very large or very small quantities (e.g., use millimeters per year for seafloor spreading). Interpret scientific notation that has been generated by technology.	Major	5
Understand the connections between proportional relationships, lines, and linear equations.			
8.EE.B.5	Graph proportional relationships, interpreting the unit rate as the slope of the graph. Compare two different proportional relationships represented in different ways. *For example, compare a distance-time graph to a distance-time equation to determine which of two moving objects has greater speed.*	Major	11
8.EE.B.6	Use similar triangles to explain why the slope m is the same between any two distinct points on a non-vertical line in the coordinate plane; derive the equation $y = mx$ for a line through the origin and the equation $y = mx + b$ for a line intercepting the vertical axis at b.	Major	12

The Standards for Mathematical Practice are integrated throughout the lessons, unit practices, performance tasks, and unit games.

Common Core State Standards for Grade 8 — Mathematics Standards	Content Emphasis	*Ready* Practice and Problem Solving Lesson(s)
Expressions and Equations (*continued*)		
Analyze and solve linear equations and pairs of simultaneous linear equations.		
8.EE.C.7 Solve linear equations in one variable.	Major	13, 14
8.EE.C.7a Give examples of linear equations in one variable with one solution, infinitely many solutions, or no solutions. Show which of these possibilities is the case by successively transforming the given equation into simpler forms, until an equivalent equation of the form $x = a$, $a = a$, or $a = b$ results (where a and b are different numbers).	Major	14
8.EE.C.7b Solve linear equations with rational number coefficients, including equations whose solutions require expanding expressions using the distributive property and collecting like terms.	Major	13
8.EE.C.8 Analyze and solve pairs of simultaneous linear equations.	Major	15, 16, 17
8.EE.C.8a Understand that solutions to a system of two linear equations in two variables correspond to points of intersection of their graphs, because points of intersection satisfy both equations simultaneously.	Major	15
8.EE.C.8b Solve systems of two linear equations in two variables algebraically, and estimate solutions by graphing the equations. Solve simple cases by inspection. *For example, $3x + 2y = 5$ and $3x + 2y = 6$ have no solution because $3x + 2y$ cannot simultaneously be 5 and 6.*	Major	16
8.EE.C.8c Solve real-world and mathematical problems leading to two linear equations in two variables. *For example, given coordinates for two pairs of points, determine whether the line through the first pair of points intersects the line through the second pair.*	Major	17
Functions		
Define, evaluate, and compare functions.		
8.F.A.1 Understand that a function is a rule that assigns to each input exactly one output. The graph of a function is the set of ordered pairs consisting of an input and the corresponding output.	Major	6
8.F.A.2 Compare properties of two functions each represented in a different way (algebraically, graphically, numerically in tables, or by verbal descriptions). *For example, given a linear function represented by a table of values and a linear function represented by an algebraic expression, determine which function has the greater rate of change.*	Major	7
8.F.A.3 Interpret the equation $y = mx + b$ as defining a linear function, whose graph is a straight line; give examples of functions that are not linear. *For example, the function $A = s^2$ giving the area of a square as a function of its side length is not linear because its graph contains the points (1,1), (2,4) and (3,9), which are not on a straight line.*	Major	8
Use functions to model relationships between quantities.		
8.F.B.4 Construct a function to model a linear relationship between two quantities. Determine the rate of change and initial value of the function from a description of a relationship or from two (x, y) values, including reading these from a table or from a graph. Interpret the rate of change and initial value of a linear function in terms of the situation it models, and in terms of its graph or a table of values.	Major	9
8.F.B.5 Describe qualitatively the functional relationship between two quantities by analyzing a graph (e.g., where the function is increasing or decreasing, linear or nonlinear). Sketch a graph that exhibits the qualitative features of a function that has been described verbally.	Major	10

Common Core State Standards for Grade 8 — Mathematics Standards	Content Emphasis	Ready® Practice and Problem Solving Lesson(s)
Geometry		
Understand congruence and similarity using physical models, transparencies, or geometry software.		
8.G.A.1 Verify experimentally the properties of rotations, reflections, and translations:	Major	18
8.G.A.1a Lines are taken to lines, and line segments to line segments of the same length.	Major	18
8.G.A.1b Angles are taken to angles of the same measure.	Major	18
8.G.A.1c Parallel lines are taken to parallel lines.	Major	18
8.G.A.2 Understand that a two-dimensional figure is congruent to another if the second can be obtained from the first by a sequence of rotations, reflections, and translations; given two congruent figures, describe a sequence that exhibits the congruence between them.	Major	19
8.G.A.3 Describe the effect of dilations, translations, rotations, and reflections on two-dimensional figures using coordinates.	Major	19, 20
8.G.A.4 Understand that a two-dimensional figure is similar to another if the second can be obtained from the first by a sequence of rotations, reflections, translations, and dilations; given two similar two-dimensional figures, describe a sequence that exhibits the similarity between them.	Major	20
8.G.A.5 Use informal arguments to establish facts about the angle sum and exterior angle of triangles, about the angles created when parallel lines are cut by a transversal, and the angle-angle criterion for similarity of triangles. *For example, arrange three copies of the same triangle so that the sum of the three angles appears to form a line, and give an argument in terms of transversals why this is so.*	Major	21, 22
Understand and apply the Pythagorean Theorem.		
8.G.B.6 Explain a proof of the Pythagorean Theorem and its converse.	Major	23
8.G.B.7 Apply the Pythagorean Theorem to determine unknown side lengths in right triangles in real-world and mathematical problems in two and three dimensions.	Major	24
8.G.B.8 Apply the Pythagorean Theorem to find the distance between two points in a coordinate system.	Major	25
Solve real-world and mathematical problems involving volume of cylinders, cones, and spheres.		
8.G.C.9 Know the formulas for the volumes of cones, cylinders, and spheres and use them to solve real-world and mathematical problems.	Supporting/ Additional	26, 27
Statistics and Probability		
Investigate patterns of association in bivariate data.		
8.SP.A.1 Construct and interpret scatter plots for bivariate measurement data to investigate patterns of association between two quantities. Describe patterns such as clustering, outliers, positive or negative association, linear association, and nonlinear association.	Supporting/ Additional	28
8.SP.A.2 Know that straight lines are widely used to model relationships between two quantitative variables. For scatter plots that suggest a linear association, informally fit a straight line, and informally assess the model fit by judging the closeness of the data points to the line.	Supporting/ Additional	29
8.SP.A.3 Use the equation of a linear model to solve problems in the context of bivariate measurement data, interpreting the slope and intercept. *For example, in a linear model for a biology experiment, interpret a slope of 1.5 cm/hr as meaning that an additional hour of sunlight each day is associated with an additional 1.5 cm in mature plant height.*	Supporting/ Additional	30
8.SP.A.4 Understand that patterns of association can also be seen in bivariate categorical data by displaying frequencies and relative frequencies in a two-way table. Construct and interpret a two-way table summarizing data on two categorical variables collected from the same subjects. Use relative frequencies calculated for rows or columns to describe possible association between the two variables. *For example, collect data from students in your class on whether or not they have a curfew on school nights and whether or not they have assigned chores at home. Is there evidence that those who have a curfew also tend to have chores?*	Supporting/ Additional	31

Unit Correlations in *Ready Practice and Problem Solving*

Unit Correlations	
Unit	**Common Core State Standards**
Unit 1	
Game: Triple E: Equivalent Exponential Expressions	8.EE.A.1
Unit Practice	8.NS.A.1, 8.NS.A.2, 8.NS.A.3, 8.NS.A.4, 8.EE.A.1, 8.EE.A.2, 8.EE.A.3, 8.EE.A.4
Performance Task	8.EE.A.3, 8.EE.A.4
Unit 2	
Game: Slippery Slope	8.F.B.4
Unit Practice	8.F.A.1, 8.F.A.2, 8.F.B.3, 8.F.B.4, 8.F.B.5
Performance Task	8.F.A.1, 8.F.A.2
Unit 3	
Game: It's Systematic	8.EE.C.8a, 8.EE.C.8b
Unit Practice	8.EE.B.5, 8.EE.B.6, 8.EE.C.7a, 8.EE.C.7b, 8.EE.C.8b, 8.EE.C.8c
Performance Task	8.EE.C.7a, 8.EE.C.7b
Unit 4	
Game: Pythagorean Puzzler	8.G.B.8
Unit Practice	8.G.A.2, 8.G.A.3, 8.G.A.4, 8.G.A.5, 8.G.B.7, 8.G.B.8, 8.G.C.9
Performance Task	8.G.B.7, 8.NS.A.2
Unit 5	
Game: Scatter Plot Association	8.SP.A.1, 8.SP.A.2
Unit Practice	8.SP.A.2, 8.SP.A.3, 8.SP.A.4
Performance Task	8.SP.A.1, 8.SP.A.2, 8.SP.A.3

Lesson 1

Properties of Integer Exponents

Name: _____

Prerequisite: Evaluate Numerical Exponential Expressions

Study the example problem showing how to write and evaluate expressions with exponents. Then solve problems 1–9.

Example

Jacob decides to save money for a new tablet. He will save $3 the first week and then triple the amount he has saved each week for 5 weeks. Write and evaluate an exponential expression to find how much money Jacob will have in his savings in Week 5.

Represent the problem with repeated multiplication and exponential expressions.

Week 1	Week 2	Week 3	Week 4	Week 5
$3 = 3^1$	$3 \cdot 3 = 3^2$	$3 \cdot 3 \cdot 3 = 3^3$	$3 \cdot 3 \cdot 3 \cdot 3 = 3^4$	$3 \cdot 3 \cdot 3 \cdot 3 \cdot 3 = 3^5$

Week 5 expression: 3^5

Evaluate the expression: $3^5 = 3 \cdot 3 \cdot 3 \cdot 3 \cdot 3 = 243$

Jacob will have $243 in his savings in Week 5.

B 1 Look at the table. How many times greater is the amount in Jacob's savings in Week 3 than in Week 2?

three times greater

B 2 How much will Jacob have in his account in Week 3?

$27

M 3 Jacob thinks that 3^5 is $5 \cdot 5 \cdot 5$, or 125. Explain what Jacob is doing wrong.

Jacob is confusing the base and the exponent.

M 4 Margo's dad offers to give her 5¢ on Sunday. Then for each day of the week, he offers to give her 5 times the amount from the previous day. How much will he give her on Saturday? Write an expression to show how much Margo's dad gives her on Saturday.

$5^7 = 78,125$¢ or $781.25

Vocabulary

base the number being used as a factor in an exponential expression.

5 is the base. → 5^3

exponent the number that shows how many times a base is used as a factor.

5^3 ← 3 is the exponent.

③ Lesson 1 Properties of Integer Exponents

©Curriculum Associates, LLC Copying is not permitted.

Solve.

B 5 Is 2^4 equal to $2 \cdot 4$? Explain.

No; 2^4 means 2 used as a factor 4 times, or $2 \cdot 2 \cdot 2 \cdot 2 = 16$, but $2 \cdot 4 = 8$.

M 6 A bacterium cell splits into 2 cells every hour. Write and evaluate an exponential expression to find how many cells there will be in 6 hours. Then use your answer to help you find the number of hours it will take for there to be 1,024 cells.

Show your work.

Possible work: 6 hours: $2^6 = 2 \cdot 2 \cdot 2 \cdot 2 \cdot 2 \cdot 2 = 64$

1,024 cells: $2^6 = 64$, $2^7 = 64 \cdot 2 = 128$, $2^8 = 128 \cdot 2 = 256$,
$2^9 = 256 \cdot 2 = 512$, $2^{10} = 512 \cdot 2 = 1,024$

Solution: _In 6 hours, there will be 64 cells. There will be 1,024 cells in 10 hours._

M 7 The population of California is about 39 million. Is this greater than or less than 10^7? Explain.

Greater than; $10^7 = 10,000,000$ and $39,000,000 > 10,000,000$.

M 8 Write each of the numbers 1, 8, 27, 64, and 125 as a base raised to the third power.

$1 = \boxed{1}^3$ $8 = \boxed{2}^3$ $27 = \boxed{3}^3$

$64 = \boxed{4}^3$ $125 = \boxed{5}^3$

C 9 The exponential expression 2^8 has a value of 256. Write two other exponential expressions that have a value of 256. Explain how you got your answers. (Begin by writing out 2^8 as the product of 2s.)

Possible answers: 4^4 and 16^2. Possible explanation: I know that $2 \cdot 2 \cdot 2 \cdot 2 \cdot 2 \cdot 2 \cdot 2 \cdot 2 = 256$. If I put the 2s in groups of 2, I get $(2 \cdot 2) \cdot (2 \cdot 2) \cdot (2 \cdot 2) \cdot (2 \cdot 2)$ or $4 \cdot 4 \cdot 4 \cdot 4 = 256$. If I put the 4s in groups of 2, I get $(4 \cdot 4) \cdot (4 \cdot 4)$ or $16 \cdot 16 = 256$.

④ Lesson 1 Properties of Integer Exponents

©Curriculum Associates, LLC Copying is not permitted.

Key

B Basic   **M** Medium   **C** Challenge

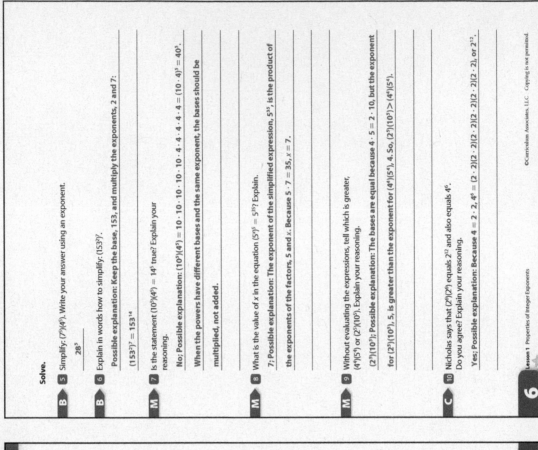

Solve.

5 Simplify: $(7^3)(4^3)$. Write your answer using an exponent.

28^3

6 Explain in words how to simplify: $(153^2)^7$.

Possible explanation: Keep the base, 153, and multiply the exponents, 2 and 7:

$(153^2)^7 = 153^{14}$

7 Is the statement $(10^5)(4^5) = 14^5$ true? Explain your reasoning.

No; Possible explanation: $(10^5)(4^5) = 10 \cdot 10 \cdot 10 \cdot 10 \cdot 10 \cdot 4 \cdot 4 \cdot 4 \cdot 4 \cdot 4 = (10 \cdot 4)^5 = 40^5$.

When the powers have different bases and the same exponent, the bases should be multiplied, not added.

8 What is the value of x in the equation $(5^x)^5 = 5^{35}$? Explain.

7; Possible explanation: The exponent of the simplified expression, 5^{35}, is the product of the exponents of the factors, 5 and x. Because $5 \cdot 7 = 35, x = 7$.

9 Without evaluating the expressions, tell which is greater, $(4^4)(5^4)$ or $(2^5)(10^5)$. Explain your reasoning.

$(2^5)(10^5)$; Possible explanation: The bases are equal because $4 \cdot 5 = 2 \cdot 10$, but the exponent for $(2^5)(10^5)$, 5, is greater than the exponent for $(4^4)(5^4)$, 4. So, $(2^5)(10^5) > (4^4)(5^4)$.

10 Nicholas says that $(2^6)(2^6)$ equals 2^{12} and also equals 4^6. Do you agree? Explain your reasoning.

Yes; Possible explanation: Because $4 = 2 \cdot 2, 4^6 = (2 \cdot 2)(2 \cdot 2)(2 \cdot 2)(2 \cdot 2)(2 \cdot 2)(2 \cdot 2)$, or 2^{12}.

Name: _____

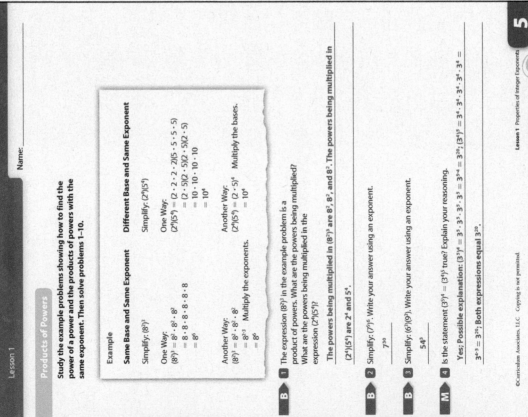

Lesson 1

Products of Powers

Study the example problems showing how to find the power of a power and the products of powers with the same exponent. Then solve problems 1–10.

Example

Same Base and Same Exponent

Simplify: $(8^2)^3$

One Way:

$(8^2)^3 = 8^2 \cdot 8^2 \cdot 8^2$

$= 8 \cdot 8 \cdot 8 \cdot 8 \cdot 8 \cdot 8$

$= 8^6$

Another Way:

$(8^2)^3 = 8^{2 \cdot 3}$ Multiply the exponents.

$= 8^6$

Different Base and Same Exponent

Simplify: $(2^4)(5^4)$

One Way:

$(2^4)(5^4) = (2 \cdot 2 \cdot 2 \cdot 2)(5 \cdot 5 \cdot 5 \cdot 5)$

$= (2 \cdot 5)(2 \cdot 5)(2 \cdot 5)(2 \cdot 5)$

$= 10 \cdot 10 \cdot 10 \cdot 10$

$= 10^4$

Another Way:

$(2^4)(5^4) = (2 \cdot 5)^4$ Multiply the bases.

$= 10^4$

1 The expression $(8^2)^3$ in the example problem is a product of powers. What are the powers being multiplied? What are the powers being multiplied in the expression $(2^4)(5^4)$?

The powers being multiplied in $(8^2)^3$ are 8^2, 8^2, and 8^2. The powers being multiplied in $(2^4)(5^4)$ are 2^4 and 5^4.

2 Simplify: $(7^5)^6$. Write your answer using an exponent.

7^{30}

3 Simplify: $(6^3)(9^3)$. Write your answer using an exponent.

54^3

4 Is the statement $(3^5)^4 = (3^4)^5$ true? Explain your reasoning.

Yes; Possible explanation: $(3^5)^4 = 3^5 \cdot 3^5 \cdot 3^5 \cdot 3^5 = 3^{5 \cdot 4} = 3^{20}$; $(3^4)^5 = 3^4 \cdot 3^4 \cdot 3^4 \cdot 3^4 \cdot 3^4 = 3^{4 \cdot 5} = 3^{20}$; Both expressions equal 3^{20}.

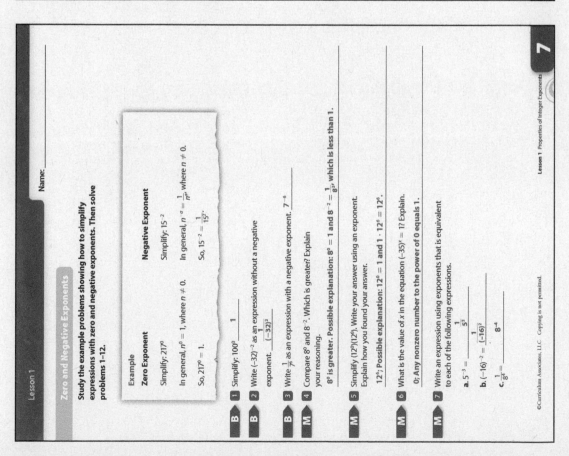

Lesson 1

Name: _____

Zero and Negative Exponents

Study the example problems showing how to simplify expressions with zero and negative exponents. Then solve problems 1–12.

Example

Zero Exponent	Negative Exponent
Simplify: 217^0	Simplify: 15^{-2}
In general, $n^0 = 1$, where $n \neq 0$.	In general, $n^{-a} = \frac{1}{n^a}$, where $n \neq 0$.
So, $217^0 = 1$.	So, $15^{-2} = \frac{1}{15^2}$.

B 1 Simplify: 100^0 ___1___

B 2 Write $(-32)^{-2}$ as an expression without a negative exponent. $\dfrac{1}{(-32)^2}$

B 3 Write $\frac{1}{7^6}$ as an expression with a negative exponent. 7^{-6}

M 4 Compare 8^0 and 8^{-2}. Which is greater? Explain your reasoning.
8^0 is greater. Possible explanation: $8^0 = 1$ and $8^{-2} = \frac{1}{8^2}$, which is less than 1.

M 5 Simplify $(12^0)(12^0)$. Write your answer using an exponent. Explain how you found your answer.
12^0; Possible explanation: $12^0 = 1$ and $1 \cdot 12^0 = 12^0$.

M 6 What is the value of x in the equation $(-35)^x = 1$? Explain.
0; Any nonzero number to the power of 0 equals 1.

M 7 Write an expression using exponents that is equivalent to each of the following expressions.
a. $5^{-3} =$ $\dfrac{1}{5^3}$
b. $(-16)^{-2} =$ $\dfrac{1}{(-16)^2}$
c. $\dfrac{1}{8^4} =$ 8^{-4}

Solve.

B 8 Simplify the expression 52^{-5}. Then write it as repeated multiplication.
$\frac{1}{52^5}$; $\frac{1}{52} \cdot \frac{1}{52} \cdot \frac{1}{52} \cdot \frac{1}{52} \cdot \frac{1}{52}$

M 9 Write an exponential expression that is equivalent to $(4^{14})^{-2}$.
Possible answers: 4^{-28}, $\frac{1}{(4^{14})^2}$, or $\frac{1}{4^{28}}$

M 10 Is 6^{-2} positive or negative? Explain.
positive; Possible answer: $6^{-2} = \frac{1}{6^2} = \frac{1}{36}$, which is positive.

M 11 Write 9^0, 9^3, and 9^{-2} in order from least to greatest.
Show your work.
$9^0 = 1$
9^3 is greater than 1.
$9^{-2} = \frac{1}{9^2}$, which is less than 1.
Solution: $9^{-2}, 9^0, 9^3$

C 12 Lizbeth says that $(-12)^{-3}$ equals a positive number because the product of two negative integers is a positive integer. Do you agree? Use what you know about exponential expressions to explain.
No; Possible explanation: To simplify an exponential expression, you do not multiply the exponent and the base. $(-12)^{-3} = \frac{1}{(-12)^3} = \frac{1}{-12 \cdot -12 \cdot -12}$ and the product of 3 negative numbers is a negative number.

Name: _____

Lesson 1

Simplify Expressions with Exponents

Solve the problems.

1 Look at the equations below. Tell whether each equation is *True* or *False*.

a. $3^5 \cdot 3^7 = 3^{35}$ ☐ True   ☒ False

b. $(6^2 \cdot 3^3)^2 = 18^6$ ☒ True   ☐ False

c. $7^{-6} \cdot \frac{1}{7} = \frac{1}{7^{10}}$ ☒ True   ☐ False

d. $4^4 \cdot 4^2 = 4^6$ ☒ True   ☐ False

e. $\frac{13^{-4}}{13^4} = 13^0$ ☐ True   ☒ False

f. $(2^3 \cdot 8)^0 = 16^9$ ☐ True   ☒ False

You may have to apply more than one rule when working with exponents.

2 Tyler simplified the expression $5^4 \cdot 5^{-9}$. All of his work except his answer is shown below.

$5^4 \cdot 5^{-9} = 5^{4+(-9)}$
$= 5^{-5}$
$= ?$

Which expression is the correct answer for Tyler's work?

A 5^5

B $\frac{1}{5^5}$ (circled)

C $\frac{1}{5^{-5}}$

D 5

Remember what you know about negative exponents.

3 Complete the table.

Expression	$10^4 \cdot 10^{-2}$	$5^4 \cdot 7^4$	$(2^3 \cdot 4^2)^3$
Simplified Expression	10^2	35^4	8^{21}

Are the bases equal? Are the exponents equal?

Solve.

4 Simplify $\frac{32^{-1}}{32^6}$. Write your answer with a positive exponent.

Show your work.

Possible answer:

$\frac{32^{-1}}{32^6} = 32^{-1-6}$
$= 32^{-7}$
$= \frac{1}{32^7}$

Solution: $\frac{32^{-1}}{32^6} = \frac{1}{32^7}$

The expression is a quotient of powers.

5 Write 9^6 as a power with a base of 3.

$9^6 = (3^2)^6 = 3^{12}$

What are the factors of 9?

6 Which expression is equivalent to $(3^4 \cdot 5^4)^{-3}$?

A $\frac{1}{15^5}$

B 15^{-48}

C $\frac{1}{15^{12}}$ (circled)

D 15^5

Tania chose **B** as the correct answer. How did she get that answer?

Possible answer: Tania did not use the order of operations or the rules for working with exponents. She multiplied the bases and multiplied all the exponents.

Remember the order of operations. Simplify the expression within the parentheses first.

Lesson 2

Square Roots and Cube Roots

Prerequisite: Understand Solutions to Equations

Study the example problem showing how to write and solve an equation. Then solve problems 1–7.

Example

Isabella has filled 3 album pages with photos. Each page has the same number of photos. Isabella has 24 photos. Write and solve an equation to find how many photos are on one album page.

Choose a variable to represent the number of photos on one page. → p

Write an expression to describe the total number of photos on the pages. → $3p$

Write an equation to compare the expression and the number of photos Isabella has. → $3p = 24$

Draw a bar model to represent the equation.

24		
p	p	p

You multiply 3 by 8 to get 24.

There are 8 photos on one album page.

Vocabulary

equation a statement that tells you two expressions are equivalent.

$4 + 5 = 9$ $2b = 14$

B 1 What does the variable p represent in the example problem?

The variable p represents the number of photos on each page of the album.

B 2 What is the solution to the equation $3p = 24$?

p equals 8.

M 3 Then Isabella filled 3 more pages with 36 photos which she evenly divided between the pages. Is the number of photos on one of those pages be more or less than the number in the example problem? Explain.

more than; Possible explanation: $36 > 24$, so there would be more than 8 photos on each album page.

©Curriculum Associates, LLC   Copying is not permitted.

Lesson 2 Square Roots and Cube Roots **13**

Solve.

B 4 Alberto is saving money to buy a pair of shoes that cost $58. He has already saved $32. He still needs to save d dollars.

a. Write an equation so that one side of the equation represents the cost of the shoes.

$32 + d = 58$

b. Explain how to solve your equation to find how much more money Alberto needs to save. How much more does he need to save?

I must find the amount that when added to 32 gives me 58. Because $32 + 26 = 58$,

I know Alberto needs to save another $26.

M 5 The bar model illustrates a division equation. What is the equation? Explain how you know.

s				
8	8	8	8	8

$s \div 5 = 8$; The model shows a quantity s divided into 5 equal parts, and each part equals 8.

M 6 In the equation $10n = 120$, is $n = 10$? How do you know?

No; Possible explanation: If $n = 10$, the expression $10n$ equals 100, not 120.

C 7 Write an equation that has a solution of 7, includes a variable, and uses multiplication. Write a real-world problem that you could represent with your equation. Show how you know that 7 is the solution.

Possible answer: $6x = 42$; Erika buys 6 movie tickets. The total cost of the tickets is $42.

What is the cost of each movie ticket? $7 is the solution because $6 \cdot \$7 = \$42$.

©Curriculum Associates, LLC   Copying is not permitted.

14 Lesson 2 Square Roots and Cube Roots

Key

B Basic   **M** Medium   **C** Challenge

Lesson 2

Name: _____

Find Cube Roots

Study the example problem showing how to find a cube root. Then solve problems 1–8.

Example

Each edge of a cube is x centimeters long. The volume of the cube is 343 cm³. What is the length of each edge of the cube?

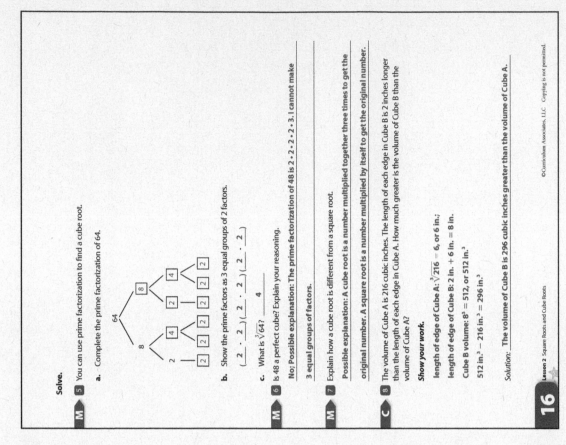

Volume = 343 cm³

Use the formula for the volume of a cube.

$x^3 = V$	Write the formula.
$x^3 = 343$	Substitute x for b and 343 for V.
$x = \sqrt[3]{343}$	Find the cube root of 343.
$x = 7$	Simplify.

Each edge of the cube is 7 centimeters long.

Vocabulary

cube root any number that is multiplied together three times to get the original number.

$\sqrt[3]{8} = 2$

2 is the cube root of 8.

perfect cube the product of an integer multiplied together three times.

$3^3 = 27$

27 is a perfect cube.

B 1 What is the relationship of the volume of the cube to its edge length?

The volume is the cube of the length of an edge.

B 2 What is the relationship of the edge length of the cube to its volume?

The length of an edge is the cube root of the volume.

M 3 The volume of a cube is 8 ft³. What is the length of each edge of the cube?

Each edge of the cube is 2 feet long.

M 4 Explain the difference between a number that is a cube and a number that is a cube root.

Possible explanation: A cube is the product of three identical factors. A cube root is the factor that is used three times to get a cube.

15

Solve.

M 5 You can use prime factorization to find a cube root.

a. Complete the prime factorization of 64.

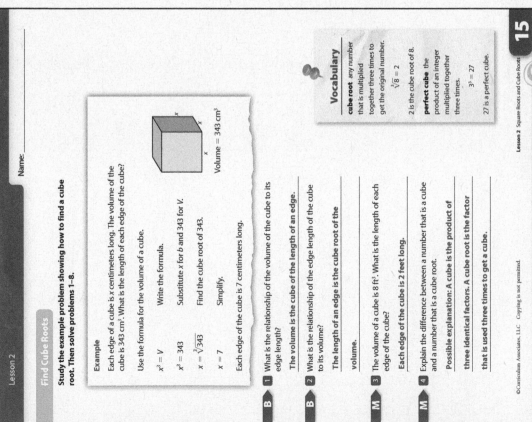

b. Show the prime factors as 3 equal groups of 2 factors.

(2 · 2)(2 · 2)(2 · 2)

c. What is $\sqrt[3]{64}$? _____ 4

M 6 Is 48 a perfect cube? Explain your reasoning.

No; Possible explanation: The prime factorization of 48 is 2 · 2 · 2 · 2 · 3. I cannot make 3 equal groups of factors.

M 7 Explain how a cube root is different from a square root.

Possible explanation: A cube root is a number multiplied together three times to get the original number. A square root is a number multiplied by itself to get the original number.

C 8 The volume of Cube A is 216 cubic inches. The length of each edge in Cube B is 2 inches longer than the length of each edge in Cube A. How much greater is the volume of Cube B than the volume of Cube A?

Show your work.

length of edge of Cube A: $\sqrt[3]{216} = 6$, or 6 in.;

length of edge of Cube B: 2 in. + 6 in. = 8 in.

Cube B volume: $8^3 = 512$, or 512 in.³

512 in.³ − 216 in.³ = 296 in.³

Solution: _The volume of Cube B is 296 cubic inches greater than the volume of Cube A._

16

Lesson 2

Name: _____

Solve Word Problems

Study the example problem showing how to use square roots and cube roots to solve word problems. Then solve problems 1–6.

Example

Markus walked halfway around a square park that has an area of 90,000 square meters. How many meters did Markus walk?

Use the formula for the area of a square to find the length of one side. Markus walked halfway around, so find the total length of two sides of the park to find the distance he walked.

$s^2 = A$ Write the formula.

$s^2 = 90,000$ Substitute 90,000 for A.

$s = \sqrt{90,000}$ Find the square root of 90,000.

$s = 300$ The length of each side is 300 m.

The length of 2 sides = $300 \cdot 2 = 600$

Markus walked 600 meters.

B **1** A smaller square park has an area of 3,600 square meters. What is the length of one side of the park?

60 meters

B **2** When completely full, a cube-shaped container will hold 8,000 cubic centimeters of water. What is the length of an edge of the container?

20 cm

M **3** A planter in the shape of a cube has a volume of 1,000 in.³. Is the area of the base of the cube greater than or less than 1 square foot? Explain.

Less than; The length of an edge is 10 in., so the area of the base is $10^2 = 100$ square inches. One square foot is $12^2 = 144$ square inches, and $100 < 144$.

Solve.

M **4** The distance d in feet that a dropped object falls in t seconds is given by the equation $d \div 16 = t^2$. How long does it take a dropped object to fall 64 feet?

Show your work.

$d \div 16 = t^2$

$64 \div 16 = t^2$

$4 = t^2$

$\sqrt{4} = t$

$2 = t$

Solution: __The object takes 2 seconds to fall 64 feet.__

M **5** The area of the top face of a small cube is 9 square centimeters. It takes 9 of these small cubes to make a larger cube. What is the volume of the larger cube?

Show your work.

$s^2 = 9; s = \sqrt{9} = 3$, so the length of each side is 3 cm;

$V = 3^3, V = 27$ cm³; $9 \cdot 27 = 243$, or 243 cm³

Solution: __The volume of the larger cube is 243 cubic centimeters.__

C **6** The diagram shows the dimensions of Taylor's deck. The area of the deck is 233 square feet. Taylor is going to put a railing along the longest edge. How many feet of railing will she need?

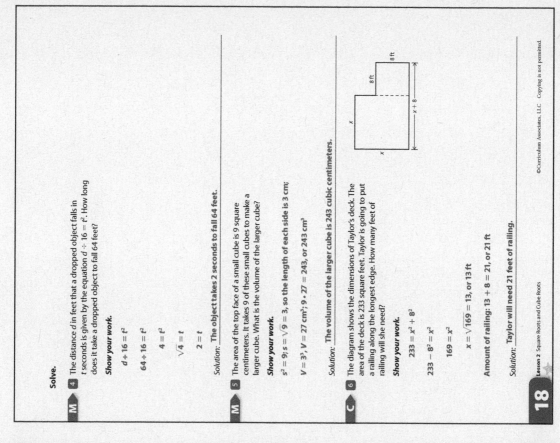

Show your work.

$233 = x^2 + 8^2$

$233 - 8^2 = x^2$

$169 = x^2$

$x = \sqrt{169} = 13$, or 13 ft

Amount of railing: $13 + 8 = 21$, or 21 ft

Solution: __Taylor will need 21 feet of railing.__

Lesson 2

Name: _____

Square Roots and Cube Roots

Solve the problems.

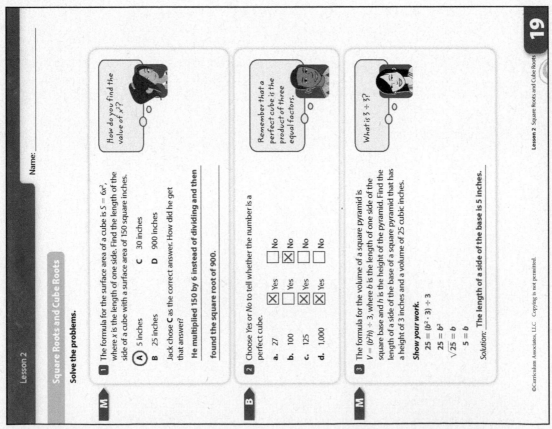

M 1 The formula for the surface area of a cube is $S = 6x^2$, where x is the length of one side. Find the length of the side of a cube with a surface area of 150 square inches.

(A) 5 inches   C 30 inches

B 25 inches   D 900 inches

How do you find the value of x^2?

Jack chose **C** as the correct answer. How did he get that answer?

He multiplied 150 by 6 instead of dividing and then found the square root of 900.

B 2 Choose *Yes* or *No* to tell whether the number is a perfect cube.

Remember that a perfect cube is the product of three equal factors.

a. 27   [X] Yes   [ ] No

b. 100   [ ] Yes   [X] No

c. 125   [X] Yes   [ ] No

d. 1,000   [X] Yes   [ ] No

M 3 The formula for the volume of a square pyramid is $V = (b^2h) \div 3$, where b is the length of one side of the square base and h is the height of the pyramid. Find the length of a side of the base of a square pyramid that has a height of 3 inches and a volume of 25 cubic inches.

What is $5 \div 5$?

Show your work.

$25 = (b^2 \cdot 3) \div 3$

$25 = b^2$

$\sqrt{25} = b$

$5 = b$

Solution: __The length of a side of the base is 5 inches.__

19

Solve.

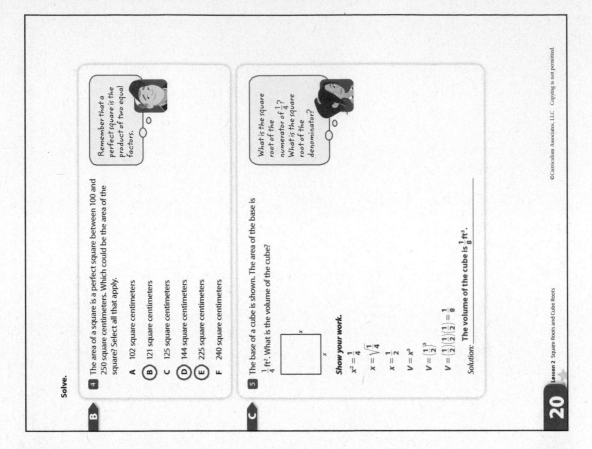

B 4 The area of a square is a perfect square between 100 and 250 square centimeters. Which could be the area of the square? Select all that apply.

Remember that a perfect square is the product of two equal factors.

A 102 square centimeters

(B) 121 square centimeters

C 125 square centimeters

(D) 144 square centimeters

(E) 225 square centimeters

F 240 square centimeters

C 5 The base of a cube is shown. The area of the base is $\frac{1}{4}$ ft². What is the volume of the cube?

What is the square root of the numerator of $\frac{1}{4}$? What is the square root of the denominator?

Show your work.

$x^2 = \frac{1}{4}$

$x = \sqrt{\frac{1}{4}}$

$x = \frac{1}{2}$

$V = x^3$

$V = \left(\frac{1}{2}\right)^3$

$V = \left(\frac{1}{2}\right)\left(\frac{1}{2}\right)\left(\frac{1}{2}\right) = \frac{1}{8}$

Solution: __The volume of the cube is $\frac{1}{8}$ ft³.__

20

Lesson 3
Understand Rational and Irrational Numbers

Name: _____

Prerequisite: How can you convert fractions to repeating or terminating decimals?

Study the example problem showing how to use division to express fractions as repeating decimals. Then solve problems 1–7.

Example

Erika uses division to write $\frac{1}{3}$ and $\frac{2}{3}$ as decimals.

First she estimates that because $\frac{1}{3}$ is between $\frac{1}{4}$ and $\frac{1}{2}$ it will be between 0.25 and 0.5. Likewise, because $\frac{2}{3}$ is between $\frac{1}{2}$ and $\frac{3}{4}$ it will be between 0.5 and 0.75. Then she divides as shown at the right.

$$\frac{1}{3} = 0.333\ldots \text{ or } 0.\overline{3} \qquad \frac{2}{3} = 0.666\ldots \text{ or } 0.\overline{6}$$

```
  0.333          0.666
3)1.000        3)2.000
 -9             -18
  10             20
  -9            -18
  10             20
  -9            -18
   1              2
```

B **1** Erika says that no matter how many decimal places she divides to when she divides 1 by 3, the digit 3 in the quotient will just keep repeating. Is she correct? Explain.

Yes; Possible explanation: She keeps subtracting 9 from 10 and dividing 10 by 3, so the digit 3 keeps repeating.

B **2** Is the decimal for $\frac{4}{3}$ a *repeating decimal*? Explain.

Yes; Possible explanation: When I divide 4 by 3, the 3 keeps repeating in the quotient.

M **3** How could Erika have used the decimal that she wrote for $\frac{1}{3}$ to find the decimal for $\frac{2}{3}$?

Possible answer: The decimal for $\frac{2}{3}$ is double the decimal for $\frac{1}{3}$, which makes sense because $\frac{2}{3}$ is twice as much as $\frac{1}{3}$.

> **Vocabulary**
> **repeating decimal** a decimal that never ends but instead repeats the same digit or group of digits over and over.
> 0.333... and 0.1666... are repeating decimals.

©Curriculum Associates, LLC   Copying is not permitted.

Solve.

B **4** Write the decimal for $\frac{1}{8}$. Explain why this decimal is called a *terminating decimal*.

0.125; Possible explanation: The decimal ends, or terminates.

M **5** Tell whether each statement below is true or false. If it is false, write an example that proves the statement is false.

All fractions can be written as repeating decimals.

false; Possible answer: $\frac{1}{4}$ can be written as a terminating decimal.

If a fraction can be written as a repeating decimal, only one digit can repeat over and over, without end.

false; Possible answer: $\frac{1}{11}$ can be written as .09090909..., which has two repeating digits.

> **Vocabulary**
> **terminating decimal** a decimal that ends, or terminates.
> 0.5; 4.08; 0.300

M **6** Raj is playing a game. He needs to find pairs of cards that have the same value. Which two pairs of cards does Raj have that express the same value?

Cards: $\frac{7}{9}$ $\frac{3}{8}$ $\frac{3}{5}$ 0.375 $0.\overline{5}$ $0.\overline{7}$ 0.675

$\frac{3}{8}$ and 0.375, $\frac{7}{9}$ and $0.\overline{7}$

C **7** Write each number in the appropriate box to show its placement along the number line.

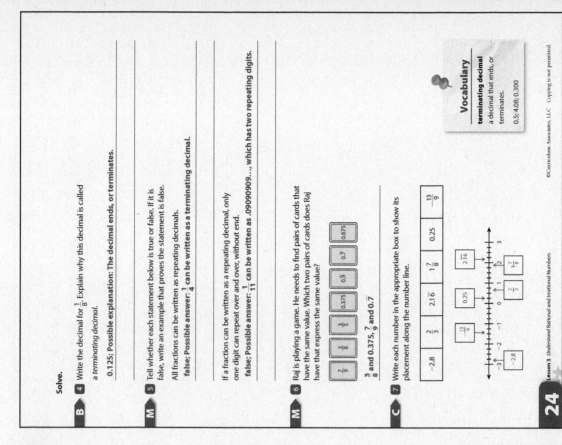

-2.8 $\frac{2}{3}$ $2.\overline{16}$ $1\frac{7}{8}$ 0.25 $\frac{13}{9}$

©Curriculum Associates, LLC   Copying is not permitted.

Key

B Basic   **M** Medium   **C** Challenge

Solve.

4 (B) Explain how a rational number and an irrational number are different.

Possible explanation: A rational number can be written as the quotient of two integers while an irrational number cannot.

5 (M) Describe how you would compare 3.6 and $\sqrt{12}$.

Possible answer: First I would find the two integers that $\sqrt{12}$ is between. It is between $\sqrt{9}$ and $\sqrt{16}$, or between 3 and 4, but a little closer to 3. Then I would find two decimals to the tenths that $\sqrt{12}$ is between: $3.4^2 = 11.56$ and $3.5^2 = 12.25$. So $\sqrt{12}$ is between 3.4 and 3.5.

Because $3.6 > 3.5$, $3.6 > \sqrt{12}$.

6 (M) Is 1.75 a reasonable estimate of the value of $\sqrt{8}$? Explain your reasoning.

No; Possible explanation: $\sqrt{8}$ is between $\sqrt{4}$ and $\sqrt{9}$, or between 2 and 3. Because 1.75 is less than 2, it is not a reasonable estimate.

7 (M) On a number line, will $\sqrt{20}$ be closer to 4.4 or 4.5? Explain your reasoning.

Closer to 4.5; Possible explanation: $4.4^2 = 19.36$ and $4.5^2 = 20.25$. 20.25 is closer to 20 than 19.36 is to 20.

8 (C) Look at the two points on the number line. Each number graphed is the square root of a whole number that is not a perfect square. Write the appropriate square root in each box. Explain how you found your answers.

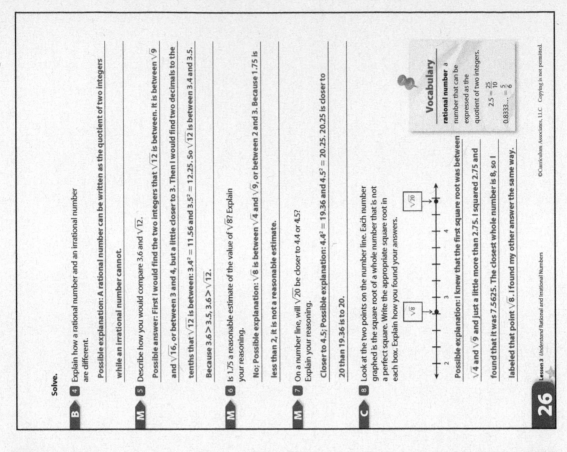

Possible explanation: I knew that the first square root was between $\sqrt{4}$ and $\sqrt{9}$ and just a little more than 2.75. I squared 2.75 and found that it was 7.5625. The closest whole number is 8, so I labeled that point $\sqrt{8}$. I found my other answer the same way.

Vocabulary
rational number a number that can be expressed as the quotient of two integers.
$2.5 = \dfrac{25}{10}$
$0.8333\ldots = \dfrac{5}{6}$

26

Lesson 3

Name: _____

Estimate Irrational Numbers

Study the example problem showing how to estimate the value of an irrational number. Then solve problems 1–8.

Example

Estimate the value of $\sqrt{6}$ to the nearest hundredth.

Because $\sqrt{6}$ is between $\sqrt{4}$, which equals 2, and $\sqrt{9}$, which equals 3, $\sqrt{6}$ is between 2 and 3, but it is closer to 2 than to 3.

Find the squares of tenths that are closer to 2 than to 3 in order to find which two tenths $\sqrt{6}$ is between.

$2.3^2 = 5.29$ $2.4^2 = 5.76$ $2.5^2 = 6.25$

Because 6 is almost exactly halfway between 5.76 and 6.25, $\sqrt{6}$ must be almost exactly halfway between 2.4 and 2.5. Now you can find which two hundredths $\sqrt{6}$ is between.

$2.44^2 = 5.9536$ and $2.45^2 = 6.0025$

$\sqrt{6}$ is between 2.44 and 2.45, but it is closer to 2.45.

1 (B) Mark a point at the approximate location of $\sqrt{6}$ to the hundredths place.

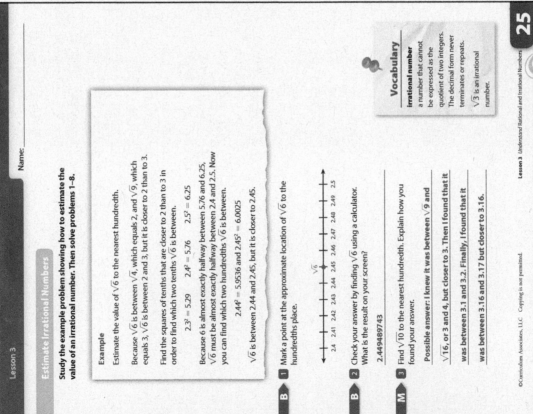

2 (B) Check your answer by finding $\sqrt{6}$ using a calculator. What is the result on your screen?

2.449489743

3 (M) Find $\sqrt{10}$ to the nearest hundredth. Explain how you found your answer.

Possible answer: I knew it was between $\sqrt{9}$ and $\sqrt{16}$, or 3 and 4, but closer to 3. Then I found that it was between 3.1 and 3.2. Finally, I found that it was between 3.16 and 3.17 but closer to 3.16.

Vocabulary
irrational number a number that cannot be expressed as the quotient of two integers. The decimal form never terminates or repeats.
$\sqrt{3}$ is an irrational number.

25

Lesson 3

Reason and Write

Study the example problem. Underline two parts that you think make it a particularly good answer and a helpful example.

Name: _____

Answers will vary. Note whether students incorporate the features they chose in their answer on the next page.

Example

Tell whether the following numbers are rational or irrational, and explain how you know.

$\frac{1}{9}$ $\sqrt{1.44}$

Write a decimal approximation for each number, and place it on the number line.

Show your work. Use decimal approximations, a number line, and words to explain your answers.

Possible answer:
$\frac{1}{9}$ is a rational number because it is the quotient of two integers. When I divide 1 by 9, I get a repeating decimal.

$$
\begin{array}{r}
0.111 \\
9\overline{)1.000} \\
-9 \\
\hline
10 \\
-9 \\
\hline
10 \\
-9 \\
\hline
1
\end{array}
$$

$\sqrt{1.44}$ is also a rational number. I know that $\sqrt{1.44}$ is between $\sqrt{1}$ and $\sqrt{4}$, or 1 and 2, but it is closer to 1. Then I can find two tenths that $\sqrt{1.44}$ is between: $1.1^2 = 1.21$ and $1.2^2 = 1.44$. Because $1.2^2 = 1.44$, I know that $\sqrt{1.44}$ must be 1.2, which is a rational number.

Where does the example ...
· identify whether the numbers are rational or irrational?
· include a decimal approximation?
· include a number line?
· use words to explain?

Lesson 3 *Understand Rational and Irrational Numbers*   **27**

Solve the problem. Use what you learned from the model.

Tell whether the following numbers are rational or irrational, and explain how you know.

$\sqrt{\frac{2}{8}}$ $\sqrt{2.56}$

Write a decimal approximation for each number, and place it on the number line.

Show your work. Use decimal approximations, a number line, and words to explain your answers.

Possible answer:
$\sqrt{\frac{2}{8}}$ is a rational number. I know that $\sqrt{\frac{2}{8}} = \sqrt{\frac{1}{4}}$ and that $\frac{1}{4} = \frac{1}{2} \cdot \frac{1}{2} = \left(\frac{1}{2}\right)^2$. This means that $\sqrt{\frac{1}{4}} = \sqrt{\left(\frac{1}{2}\right)^2} = \frac{1}{2}$.

$\sqrt{2.56}$ is also a rational number. I know that $\sqrt{2.56}$ is between $\sqrt{1}$ and $\sqrt{4}$, or 1 and 2, but it is a little closer to 2. Then I can find two tenths that $\sqrt{2.56}$ is between: $1.5^2 = 2.25$ and $1.6^2 = 2.56$. Because $1.6^2 = 2.56$, I know that $\sqrt{2.56}$ must be 1.6, which is a rational number.

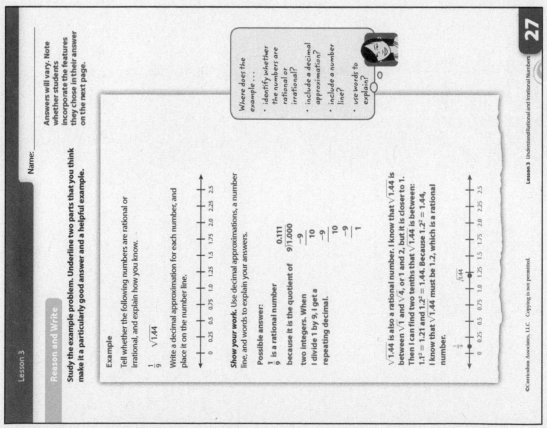

Did you ...
· identify whether the numbers are rational or irrational?
· include a decimal approximation?
· include a number line?
· use words to explain?

28 Lesson 3 *Understand Rational and Irrational Numbers*

Lesson 4

Scientific Notation

Prerequisite: Multiply and Divide by Powers of Ten

Study the example problem showing how to multiply a decimal number by a power of ten. Then solve problems 1–7.

Example

Find $1,000 \times 0.006$.

Start by breaking 1,000 into the product of tens. Then, multiply.

$$1,000 \times 0.006 = 10 \times 10 \times 10 \times 0.006$$
$$= 10 \times 10 \times 0.06$$
$$= 10 \times 0.6$$
$$= 6$$

This means that $1,000 \times 0.006 = 6$.

Vocabulary

power of ten a number that can be written as a product of tens.

$10 = 10$

$100 = 10 \times 10$

$1,000 = 10 \times 10 \times 10$

B 1 Write the missing powers of 10.

a. **1,000** $\times 0.005 = 5$ **100** $\times 0.005 = 0.5$

b. $0.09 \times$ **10** $= 0.9$ $0.009 \times$ **1,000** $= 9$

B 2 Jane says that multiplying a decimal by 100 is the same as multiplying the decimal by three factors of 10. Is Jane correct? Explain your answer.

No; Possible explanation: There are two factors of 10 in 100, so multiplying by 100 is the same as multiplying by two factors of 10.

B 3 Complete the equations.

a. $0.002 \times 100 =$ **0.2**

b. $0.05 \times 1,000 =$ **50**

Solve.

M 4 Remember that division is the inverse of multiplication. Complete the table below to show dividing 7 by powers of 10.

Ones	.	Tenths	Hundredths	Thousandths	
7	.	0	0	0	
0	.	7	0	0	$7 \div 10$
0	.	0	7	0	$7 \div 100$
0	.	0	0	7	$7 \div 1,000$

B 5 Daryl explains why $8.2 \div 10,000$ is 0.00082. Complete his explanation.

There are **four** factors of 10 in 10,000. Each time I divide a number by a factor of 10, the result is 10 times **less** than the original number.

For example, if I divide 8.2 by 10, the result is 0.82. This means that 0.82 is 10 times **less** than 8.2.

So, $8.2 \div 10,000$ is 0.00082.

M 6 Complete the equations.

a. $0.004 \times 100 = 0.004 \times 10^2 =$ ___**0.4**___

b. $0.4 \times 1,000 = 0.4 \times$ ___10^3___ $=$ ___**400**___

c. $600 \div 100 = 600 \div 10^2 =$ ___**6**___

d. $0.6 \div$ ___**10**___ $= 0.6 \div 10^1 =$ ___**0.06**___

C 7 Yara multiplies and divides a certain number by the same power of 10. The product she gets is 40,000 and the quotient she gets is 0.000004. Find Yara's number and the power of 10 she used. Explain your reasoning.

0.4 and 10^5; Possible explanation: You can start by noticing that 40,000 is a number in the ten thousands and 0.000004 is a number in the millionths, so you can divide and multiply them by a number that is between 10,000 and 1,000,000 to get Yara's number. If you divide 40,000 by 100,000, you get 0.4. If you multiply 0.000004 by 100,000, you get 0.4, so Yara used 0.4 and 100,000, or 10^5.

Key

B Basic   **M** Medium   **C** Challenge

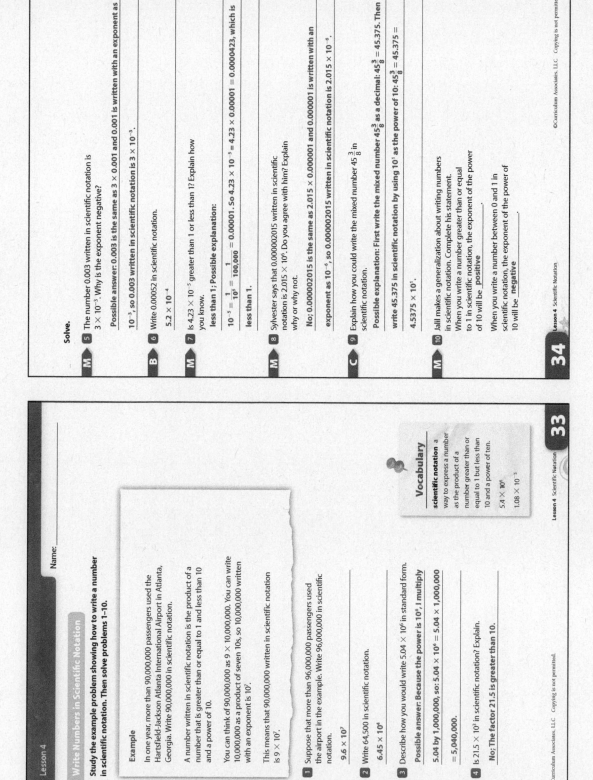

Lesson 4

Name: _____

Write Numbers in Scientific Notation

Study the example problem showing how to write a number in scientific notation. Then solve problems 1–10.

Example

In one year, more than 90,000,000 passengers used the Hartsfield-Jackson Atlanta International Airport in Atlanta, Georgia. Write 90,000,000 in scientific notation.

A number written in scientific notation is the product of a number that is greater than or equal to 1 and less than 10 and a power of 10.

You can think of 90,000,000 as 9 × 10,000,000. You can write 10,000,000 as a product of seven 10s, so 10,000,000 written with an exponent is 10^7.

This means that 90,000,000 written in scientific notation is $9 × 10^7$.

B 1 Suppose that more than 96,000,000 passengers used the airport in the example. Write 96,000,000 in scientific notation.

$9.6 × 10^7$

B 2 Write 64,500 in scientific notation.

$6.45 × 10^4$

M 3 Describe how you would write 5.04 × 10^6 in standard form.

Possible answer: Because the power is 10^6, I multiply 5.04 by 1,000,000, so: 5.04 × 10^6 = 5.04 × 1,000,000 = 5,040,000.

B 4 Is 21.5 × 10^3 in scientific notation? Explain.

No; The factor 21.5 is greater than 10.

> **Vocabulary**
> **scientific notation** a way to express a number as the product of a number greater than or equal to 1 but less than 10 and a power of ten.
> $5.4 × 10^6$
> $1.08 × 10^{-3}$

Lesson 4 Scientific Notation **33**

Solve.

M 5 The number 0.003 written in scientific notation is $3 × 10^{-3}$. Why is the exponent negative?

Possible answer: 0.003 is the same as 3 × 0.001 and 0.001 is written with an exponent as 10^{-3}, so 0.003 written in scientific notation is $3 × 10^{-3}$.

B 6 Write 0.00052 in scientific notation.

$5.2 × 10^{-4}$

M 7 Is 4.23 × 10^{-5} greater than 1 or less than 1? Explain how you know.

less than 1; Possible explanation:

$10^{-5} = \frac{1}{10^5} = \frac{1}{100,000} = 0.00001$. So 4.23 × 10^{-5} = 4.23 × 0.00001 = 0.0000423, which is less than 1.

M 8 Sylvester says that 0.000002015 written in scientific notation is 2.015 × 10^6. Do you agree with him? Explain why or why not.

No; 0.000002015 is the same as 2.015 × 0.000001 and 0.000001 is written with an exponent as 10^{-6}, so 0.000002015 written in scientific notation is 2.015 × 10^{-6}.

C 9 Explain how you could write the mixed number $45\frac{3}{8}$ in scientific notation.

Possible explanation: First write the mixed number $45\frac{3}{8}$ as a decimal: $45\frac{3}{8}$ = 45.375. Then write 45.375 in scientific notation by using 10^1 as the power of 10: $45\frac{3}{8}$ = 45.375 = 4.5375 × 10^1.

M 10 Jalil makes a generalization about writing numbers in scientific notation. Complete his statement.

When you write a number greater than or equal to 1 in scientific notation, the exponent of the power of 10 will be **positive**.

When you write a number between 0 and 1 in scientific notation, the exponent of the power of 10 will be **negative**.

34 Lesson 4 Scientific Notation

Name: _____

Lesson 4

Compare Numbers in Scientific Notation

Study the example problem showing how to compare two numbers written in scientific notation. Then solve problems 1–7.

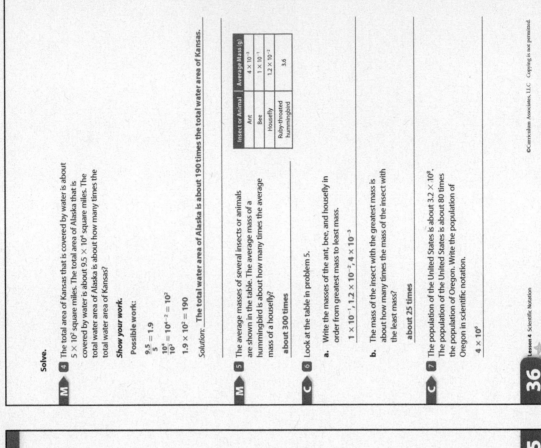

Example
The total area of Rhode Island is about 1.5×10^3 square miles. The total area of Georgia is about 6×10^4 square miles. The total area of Georgia is about how many times the total area of Rhode Island?

Use Standard Form	Use Scientific Notation
$1.5 \times 10^3 = 1,500$	Compare the parts of 1.5×10^3 and 6×10^4.
$6 \times 10^4 = 60,000$	
Compare by dividing: $\dfrac{60,000}{1,500} = 40$	$\dfrac{6}{1.5} = 4$ $\dfrac{10^4}{10^3} = 10^{4-3} = 10^1$
60,000 is 40 times 1,500.	Combine the results: $4 \times 10^1 = 40$.
	6×10^4 is 40 times 1.5×10^3.

The total area of Georgia is about 40 times the total area of Rhode Island.

B 1 Which of the two methods shown in the example problem do you prefer? Explain why.
Possible answer: I prefer the scientific notation method. The numbers you are comparing are smaller.

B 2 The total area of Ohio is about 4.5×10^4 square miles. The total area of Ohio is about how many times the total area of Rhode Island?
The total area of Ohio is about 30 times the total area of Rhode Island.

M 3 Which is greater, 9×10^{-2} or 3×10^{-4}? How many times greater is the number you chose than the other number? Explain your reasoning.
9×10^{-2}; Possible explanation: 9×10^{-2} is 300 times 3×10^{-4} because $0.09 \div 0.0003 = 300$.

Solve.

M 4 The total area of Kansas that is covered by water is about 5×10^2 square miles. The total area of Alaska that is covered by water is about 9.5×10^4 square miles. The total water area of Alaska is about how many times the total water area of Kansas?

Show your work.
Possible work:
$\dfrac{9.5}{5} = 1.9$
$\dfrac{10^4}{10^2} = 10^{4-2} = 10^2$
$1.9 \times 10^2 = 190$

Solution: The total water area of Alaska is about 190 times the total water area of Kansas.

M 5 The average masses of several insects or animals are shown in the table. The average mass of a hummingbird is about how many times the average mass of a housefly?
about 300 times

Insect or Animal	Average Mass (g)
Ant	4×10^{-3}
Bee	1×10^{-1}
Housefly	1.2×10^{-2}
Ruby-throated hummingbird	3.6

C 6 Look at the table in problem 5.
a. Write the masses of the ant, bee, and housefly in order from greatest mass to least mass.
$1 \times 10^{-1}, 1.2 \times 10^{-2}, 4 \times 10^{-3}$

b. The mass of the insect with the greatest mass is about how many times the mass of the insect with the least mass?
about 25 times

C 7 The population of the United States is about 3.2×10^8. The population of the United States is about 80 times the population of Oregon. Write the population of Oregon in scientific notation.
4×10^6

Lesson 4

Scientific Notation

Solve the problems.

1 Which of the following expressions is equivalent to 4,325,000,000?

A 4.325×10^{-9} C 4.325×10^{6}

B 4.325×10^{-6} (D) 4.325×10^{9}

Carson chose **A** as the correct answer. How did he get that answer?

He forgot that when you write a number greater than or equal to 1 in scientific notation, the exponent in the power of 10 will be positive.

> Will the exponent be positive or negative?

2 The mass of Earth's moon is about 7×10^{22} kilograms. The mass of Jupiter is about 1.89×10^{27} kilograms. The mass of Jupiter is about how many times the mass of Earth's moon?

Show your work.

Possible work: $\dfrac{1.89}{7} = 0.27$

$\dfrac{10^{27}}{10^{22}} = 10^{27-22} = 10^{5}$

$0.27 \times 10^{5} = 27{,}000$

Solution: Jupiter's mass is about 27,000 times the moon's mass.

> How can the parts of each number help you to compare?

3 Last year a restaurant chain spent 3.3×10^{6} dollars opening new restaurants. This year the restaurant will spend 9.9×10^{6} dollars. Which statement is true?

A The restaurant spent $330,000 dollars last year.

B This year the restaurant will spend $9,900,000.

C The restaurant spent 6.6×10^{6} dollars more this year than last year.

(D) This year the restaurant will spend about 0.3 times the amount it did last year.

> How can you write numbers in standard form?

Solve.

4 Which of the following numbers is NOT in scientific notation?

A 4.5×10^{-12}

B 3.025×10^{-9}

(C) 0.21×10^{7}

D 1.1×10^{10}

> What does it mean for a number to be in scientific notation?

5 Write 0.000003105 in scientific notation. Explain how you found your answer.

Show your work.

$0.000003105 = 3.105 \times 0.0000001$

$= 3.105 \times 10^{-7}$

0.000003105 is the same as 3.105×0.0000001 and 0.0000001 is written with an exponent as 10^{-7}, so 0.000003105 written in scientific notation is 3.105×10^{-7}.

Solution: 3.105×10^{-7}.

> Is the number between 0 and 1 or is it greater than 1? What does that tell you about the number in scientific notation?

6 The area of the Pacific Ocean is about 1.56×10^{8} square kilometers. The area of the East China Sea is about 1.2×10^{6} square kilometers. Tell whether each statement is *True* or *False*.

a. The area of the Pacific Ocean is about 15,600,000 square kilometers.   ☐ True   ☒ False

b. The area of the Pacific Ocean is about 130 times the area of the East China Sea.   ☒ True   ☐ False

c. The area of the East China Sea is about 130 times the area of the Pacific Ocean.   ☐ True   ☒ False

d. The area of the East China Sea is about 1,200,000 square kilometers.   ☒ True   ☐ False

> How do you compare numbers in scientific notation?

Lesson 5
Operations and Scientific Notation

Name: _____

Prerequisite: Write Numbers Using Scientific Notation

Study the example problem showing how to write numbers using scientific notation. Then solve problems 1–7.

Example

Five nanobytes is equivalent to 5 one-billionths of a byte, or 0.000000005 byte. Five gigabytes is equivalent to 5 billion bytes, or 5,000,000,000 bytes. Write 0.000000005 and 5,000,000,000 in scientific notation.

0.000000005   5,000,000,000

You can think of 0.000000005 as 5 × 0.000000001. Because 0.000000001 is a product of nine tenths, you can write it with an exponent as 10^{-9}. This means that 0.000000005 written in scientific notation is:

You can think of 5,000,000,000 as 5 × 1,000,000,000. Because 1,000,000,000 is a product of nine tens, you can write it with an exponent as 10^9. This means that 5,000,000,000 written in scientific notation is:

$$0.000000005 = 5 \times 0.000000001 \qquad 5,000,000,000 = 5 \times 1,000,000,000$$
$$= 5 \times 10^{-9} \qquad\qquad = 5 \times 10^9$$

B 1 In the example problem, 0.000000005 = 5 × 10^{-9}. What is the standard form of 10^{-9}?

0.000000001

B 2 Write a number that is greater than 1 in scientific notation. Explain how you know it is greater than 1.

Possible answer: 5.08 × 10^7; The exponent is positive.

M 3 Explain why you might want to write very large and very small numbers like the ones in the example problem in scientific notation.

Possible explanation: With scientific notation you do not have to count all of the zeros. Computations can be easier with scientific notation.

Vocabulary

scientific notation a way to express a number as the product of a number greater than or equal to 1 but less than 10 and a power of ten.

6.25 × 10^8

4.03 × 10^{-7}

Lesson 5 Operations and Scientific Notation **41**

Solve.

B 4 Write the numbers in scientific notation.

a. 0.000000608   6.08 × 10^{-7}

b. 0.000000092   9.2 × 10^{-8}

B 5 Write 2.06 × 10^{10} in standard form.

20,600,000,000

M 6 Use the information in the table to solve the problem.

Country	Estimated Population
China	1,390,000,000
Germany	82,700,000
Martinique	405,000

Write each population in scientific notation.

China _____ 1.39 × 10^9

Germany   8.27 × 10^7

Martinique   4.05 × 10^5

The population of Germany is about how many times the population of Martinique? Explain your reasoning.

about 200 times; Possible explanation: 8.27 is about 2 times as great as 4.05; 10^7 is 100 times as great as 10^5.

C 7 A scientist uses 2.8 × 10^{12} cells in one experiment, which is 2,000 times the number of cells she uses in a second experiment. Write the number of cells the scientist used in her second experiment in scientific notation. Explain your answer.

1.4 × 10^9; Possible explanation: I wrote 2,000 in scientific notation and then divided the number of cells in the first experiment, 2.8 × 10^{12}, by 2 × 10^3 to find the number of cells in the second experiment. (2.8 × 10^{12}) ÷ (2 × 10^3) = 1.4 × 10^9

42 Lesson 5 Operations and Scientific Notation

©Curriculum Associates, LLC Copying is not permitted.

Key

B Basic   **M** Medium   **C** Challenge

Lesson 5

Name: _____

Add and Subtract Numbers in Scientific Notation

Study the example problem showing how to add numbers expressed in scientific notation. Then solve problems 1–7.

Example
Evaluate: $(3.8 \times 10^5) + (2.4 \times 10^6)$.

$(3.8 \times 10^5) + (2.4 \times 10^6)$	Rewrite so that the powers of 10 are equal.
$= (3.8 \times 10^5) + (24 \times 10^5)$	
$= (3.8 + 24) \times 10^5$	Use the distributive property.
$= 27.8 \times 10^5$	Simplify.
$= 2.78 \times 10^6$	Write in scientific notation.

$(3.8 \times 10^5) + (2.4 \times 10^6) = 2.78 \times 10^6$

B 1 In the example problem, 2.4×10^6 was rewritten as 24×10^5. Explain why those expressions are equivalent.

Possible explanation: $2.4 \times 10^6 = 2.4 \times 10^{-1} \times 10^6 = 24 \times 10^5$

B 2 James rewrote the problem as $(0.38 \times 10^6) + (2.4 \times 10^6)$ and then added. Does his method work? Explain.

Yes; Possible explanation: It doesn't matter which number you rewrite, you just have to make sure that each power of 10 is written using the same exponent. Then you can add.

$(0.38 \times 10^6) + (2.4 \times 10^6) = (0.38 + 2.4) \times 10^6 = 2.78 \times 10^6$

M 3 You can use the same method to subtract numbers in scientific notation. Complete the steps to evaluate the subtraction expression $(2.1 \times 10^8) - (9.7 \times 10^7)$.

$(2.1 \times 10^8) - (9.7 \times 10^7) = ($ __210__ $\times 10^7) - (9.7 \times 10^7)$

$= ($ __210__ $-$ __9.7__ $) \times 10^7$

$=$ __200.3__ $\times 10^7$

$=$ __2.003__ $\times 10^9$

Solve.

B 4 Evaluate the expressions.

a. $(4.6 \times 10^9) + (1.7 \times 10^7)$ _____ 4.617×10^9

b. $(5.4 \times 10^5) - (1.4 \times 10^4)$ _____ 5.26×10^5

M 5 Explain one way that you could check your answer to problem 4b.

Possible explanation: I could write the standard form for each number, find the difference, and then compare that difference to the answer I got for problem 4b.

M 6 Find the perimeter of the rectangle in scientific notation.

Show your work.

$(2.4 \times 10^3) + (2.4 \times 10^3) + (8.2 \times 10^2) + (8.2 \times 10^2)$

$= (2.4 + 2.4) \times 10^3 + (8.2 + 8.2) \times 10^2$

$= (4.8 \times 10^3) + (16.4 \times 10^2)$

$= (48 \times 10^2) + (16.4 \times 10^2)$

$= (48 + 16.4) \times 10^2$

$= 64.4 \times 10^2$

$= 6.44 \times 10^3$

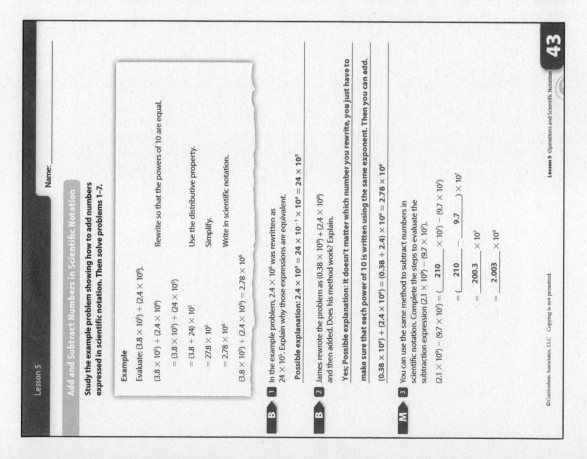

2.4×10^3 cm

8.2×10^2 cm

Solution: ___The perimeter is 6.44×10^3 cm.___

C 7 The area of the Southern Ocean is about 7.85×10^6 square miles. The difference between the areas of the Indian Ocean and the Southern Ocean is about 1.865×10^7 square miles. Explain how to find the area of the Indian Ocean. Then find the area.

Possible explanation: I can add the area of the Southern Ocean and the difference between the two areas. $(7.85 \times 10^6) + (1.865 \times 10^7) = (7.85 \times 10^6) + (18.65 \times 10^6) = (7.85 + 18.65) \times 10^6 = 26.5 \times 10^6 = 2.65 \times 10^7$; The area of the Indian Ocean is about 2.65×10^7 square miles.

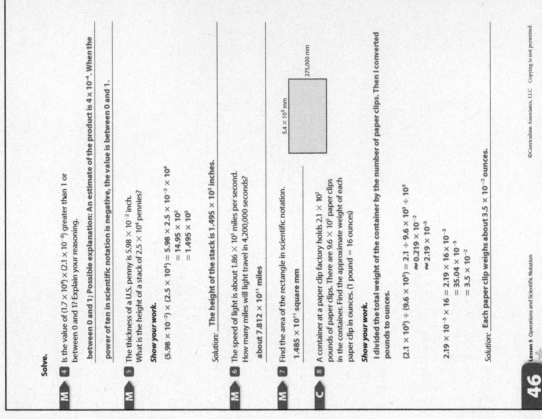

Lesson 5

Multiply Numbers in Scientific Notation

Study the example problem showing how to multiply numbers expressed in scientific notation. Then solve problems 1–8.

Example

Evaluate: $(5.3 \times 10^{-4}) \times (4.8 \times 10^{7})$.

$(5.3 \times 10^{-4}) \times (4.8 \times 10^{7})$

$= 5.3 \times 4.8 \times 10^{-4} \times 10^{7}$ Use the commutative property.

$= (5.3 \times 4.8) \times (10^{-4} \times 10^{7})$ Use the associative property to group the decimals and group the powers.

$= 25.44 \times 10^{3}$ Multiply.

$= 2.544 \times 10^{4}$ Write in scientific notation.

$(5.3 \times 10^{-4}) \times (4.8 \times 10^{7}) = 2.544 \times 10^{4}$

B **1** Explain why the product $(10^{-4} \times 10^{7})$ in the example problem equals 10^{3} and not 10^{-28}.

Possible answer: When you multiply two powers with the same base, you add the exponents rather than multiplying them.

B **2** Look at the example problem. Estimate the product $(5.3 \times 10^{-4}) \times (4.8 \times 10^{7})$ and show your work. Is your solution close to the estimate?

Yes; Possible estimate: $(5 \times 10^{-4}) \times (5 \times 10^{7}) = 25 \times 10^{3} = 2.5 \times 10^{4}$.

B **3** Estimate the product $0.047 \times (9.2 \times 10^{4})$. Then find the product. Is your solution close to your estimate?

Yes; Estimate: 0.047 is about 0.05 and 9.2×10^{4} is about 9×10^{4}; $0.05 \times (9 \times 10^{4}) =$

$0.45 \times 10^{4} = 4.5 \times 10^{3}$; Product: $0.047 = (4.7 \times 10^{-2}) \times (9.2 \times 10^{4}) =$

$(4.7 \times 9.2) \times (10^{-2} \times 10^{4}) = 43.24 \times 10^{2} = 4.324 \times 10^{3}$

Solve.

M **4** Is the value of $(1.7 \times 10^{4}) \times (2.1 \times 10^{-6})$ greater than 1 or between 0 and 1? Explain your reasoning.

between 0 and 1; Possible explanation: An estimate of the product is 4×10^{-4}. When the power of ten in scientific notation is negative, the value is between 0 and 1.

M **5** The thickness of a U.S. penny is 5.98×10^{-2} inch. What is the height of a stack of 2.5×10^{4} pennies?

Show your work.

$(5.98 \times 10^{-2}) \times (2.5 \times 10^{4}) = 5.98 \times 2.5 \times 10^{-2} \times 10^{4}$

$= 14.95 \times 10^{2}$

$= 1.495 \times 10^{3}$

Solution: _The height of the stack is 1.495×10^{3} inches._

M **6** The speed of light is about 1.86×10^{5} miles per second. How many miles will light travel in 4,200,000 seconds?

about 7.812×10^{11} miles

M **7** Find the area of the rectangle in scientific notation.

1.485×10^{11} square mm

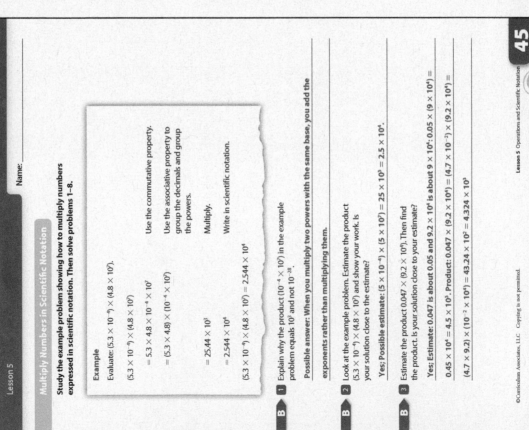

5.4×10^{5} mm

275,000 mm

C **8** A container at a paper clip factory holds 2.1×10^{3} pounds of paper clips. There are 9.6×10^{5} paper clips in the container. Find the approximate weight of each paper clip in ounces. (1 pound = 16 ounces)

Show your work.

I divided the total weight of the container by the number of paper clips. Then I converted pounds to ounces.

$(2.1 \times 10^{3}) \div (9.6 \times 10^{5}) = 2.1 \div 9.6 \times 10^{3} \div 10^{5}$

$\approx 0.219 \times 10^{-2}$

$\approx 2.19 \times 10^{-3}$

$2.19 \times 10^{-3} \times 16 = 2.19 \times 16 \times 10^{-3}$

$= 35.04 \times 10^{-3}$

$= 3.5 \times 10^{-2}$

Solution: _Each paper clip weighs about 3.5×10^{-2} ounces._

Name: _____

Lesson 5

Operations and Scientific Notation

Solve the problems.

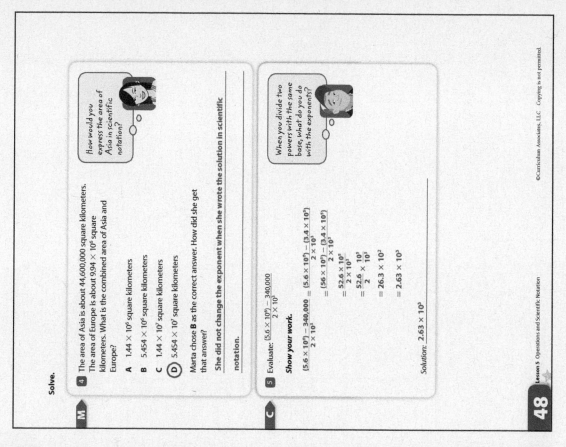

M 1 A glass marble factory produces 4.5×10^4 marbles in 1,800 minutes. What is the factory's unit rate of production in marbles per minute? Write the answer in scientific notation.

Show your work.

$1,800 = 1.8 \times 10^3$

$\dfrac{4.5 \times 10^4}{1.8 \times 10^3} = \dfrac{4.5}{1.8} \times \dfrac{10^4}{10^3}$

$= 2.5 \times 10^{4-3}$

$= 2.5 \times 10^1$

Solution: The factory produces 2.5×10^1 marbles per minute.

> Which operation do you need to use to solve this problem?

M 2 Jason incorrectly simplified the expression $(4.7 \times 10^2) \times (6.2 \times 10^4)$. Circle each step that shows an error. Then correct each of those steps so that the expression is correctly simplified.

A **Step 1.** $4.7 \times 6.2 \times 10^2 \times 10^4$

B **Step 2.** $(4.7 \times 6.2) \times (10^2 \times 10^6)$

C **Step 3.** 29.14×10^8 29.14×10^6

D **Step 4.** 2.914×10^6 2.914×10^7

> How do you multiply powers of 10?

B 3 Which is the **best** estimate for the product of 3.1×10^4 and 4.85×10^{-7}?

A 1.5×10^{-8}

B 1.2×10^{-8}

C 1.2×10^3

D 1.5×10^3

Solve.

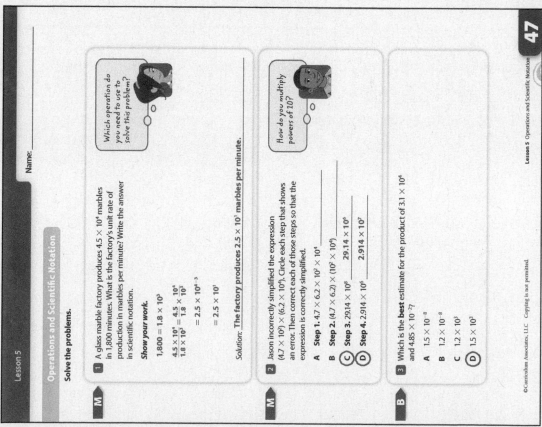

M 4 The area of Asia is about 44,600,000 square kilometers. The area of Europe is about 9.94×10^6 square kilometers. What is the combined area of Asia and Europe?

A 1.44×10^6 square kilometers

B 5.454×10^6 square kilometers

C 1.44×10^7 square kilometers

D 5.454×10^7 square kilometers

> How would you express the area of Asia in scientific notation?

Marta chose **B** as the correct answer. How did she get that answer?

_____

She did not change the exponent when she wrote the solution in scientific notation.

C 5 Evaluate: $\dfrac{(5.6 \times 10^6) - 340,000}{2 \times 10^3}$

> When you divide two powers with the same base, what do you do with the exponents?

Show your work.

$\dfrac{(5.6 \times 10^6) - 340,000}{2 \times 10^3} = \dfrac{(5.6 \times 10^6) - (3.4 \times 10^5)}{2 \times 10^3}$

$= \dfrac{(56 \times 10^5) - (3.4 \times 10^5)}{2 \times 10^3}$

$= \dfrac{52.6 \times 10^5}{2 \times 10^3}$

$= \dfrac{52.6}{2} \times \dfrac{10^5}{10^3}$

$= 26.3 \times 10^2$

$= 2.63 \times 10^3$

Solution: 2.63×10^3

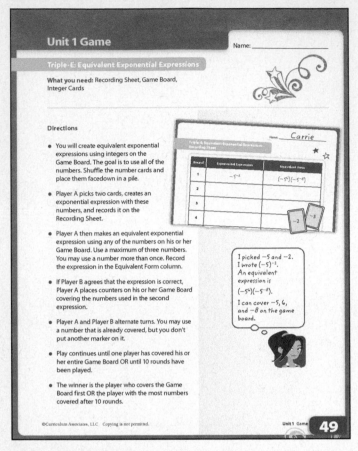

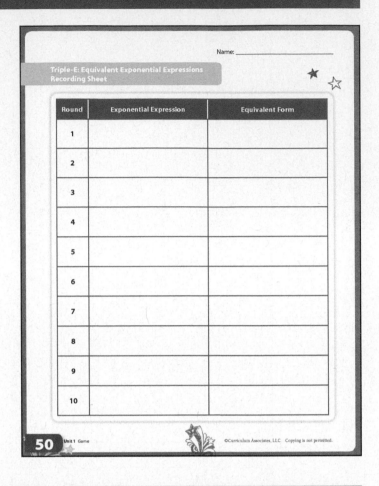

STEP BY STEP

CCSS Focus - 8.EE.A.1 *Embedded SMPs - 5, 6, 7, 8*	**Materials** For each pair: Recording Sheets (1 for each player) (TR 1), Game Board (1 for each player) (TR 2), 2 sets of Integer Cards (TR 3), 40 counters (20 for each player)
Objective • Use properties of integer exponents to generate equivalent expressions.	

- You will create equivalent exponential expressions using integers on the Game Board. The goal is to use all of the numbers. Shuffle the number cards and place them facedown in a pile.

- Player A picks two cards, creates an exponential expression with these numbers, and records it on the Recording Sheet.

- Player A then makes an equivalent exponential expression using any of the numbers on his or her Game Board. Use a maximum of three numbers. You may use a number more than once. Record the expression in the Equivalent Form column.

- If Player B agrees that the expression is correct, Player A places counters on his or her Game Board covering the numbers used in the second expression.

- Player A and Player B alternate turns. You may use a number already covered, but you don't put another marker on it.

- Play continues until one player has covered his or her entire Game Board OR until 10 rounds have been played.

- The winner is the player who covers the Game Board first OR the player with the most numbers marked after 10 rounds.

- Model Round 1 for students before they play. Discuss strategies for creating equivalent expressions.

Vary the Game Make equivalent expressions using up to 4 numbers from the Game Board.

Extra Support Play the same game using only positive and 0 integer cards, and make each number on the Game Board positive or 0.

Unit Practice

Unit 1

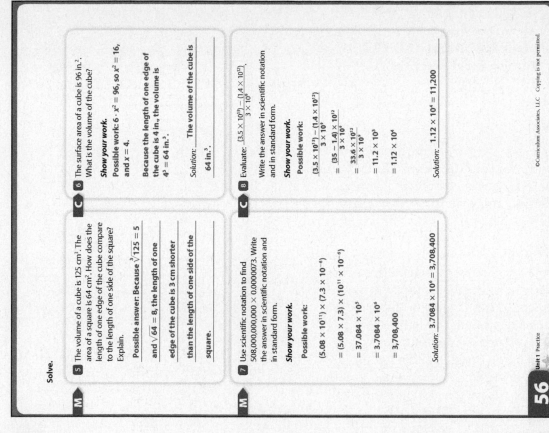

5 The volume of a cube is 125 cm³. The area of a square is 64 cm². How does the length of one edge of the cube compare to the length of one side of the square? Explain.

M

Possible answer: Because $\sqrt[3]{125} = 5$

and $\sqrt{64} = 8$, the length of one

edge of the cube is 3 cm shorter

than the length of one side of the

square.

6 The surface area of a cube is 96 in.². What is the volume of the cube?

C

Show your work.

Possible work: $6 \cdot x^2 = 96$, so $x^2 = 16$, and $x = 4$.

Because the length of one edge of the cube is 4 in., the volume is $4^3 = 64$ in.³.

Solution: __The volume of the cube is 64 in.³.__

7 Use scientific notation to find 508,000,000,000 × 0.0000073. Write the answer in scientific notation and in standard form.

M

Show your work.

Possible work:

$(5.08 \times 10^{11}) \times (7.3 \times 10^{-6})$

$= (5.08 \times 7.3) \times (10^{11} \times 10^{-6})$

$= 37.084 \times 10^{5}$

$= 3.7084 \times 10^{6}$

$= 3,708,400$

Solution: __3.7084 × 10⁶ = 3,708,400__

8 Evaluate: $\dfrac{(3.5 \times 10^{13}) - (1.4 \times 10^{12})}{3 \times 10^{9}}$.

C

Write the answer in scientific notation and in standard form.

Show your work.

Possible work:

$\dfrac{(3.5 \times 10^{13}) - (1.4 \times 10^{12})}{3 \times 10^{9}}$

$= \dfrac{(35 - 1.4) \times 10^{12}}{3 \times 10^{9}}$

$= \dfrac{33.6 \times 10^{12}}{3 \times 10^{9}}$

$= 11.2 \times 10^{3}$

$= 1.12 \times 10^{4}$

Solution: __1.12 × 10⁴ = 11,200__

Solve.

Unit 1 Practice

©Curriculum Associates, LLC   Copying is not permitted.

Unit 1 Practice

Name: _____

Expressions and Equations (Exponents) and the Number System

In this unit you learned to:

	Lesson
simplify numerical expressions that include integer exponents, for example: $(5^9)(5^6) = 5^{15}$.	1
solve equations of the form $p = x^2$ and $p = x^3$.	2
evaluate square roots of perfect squares and cube roots of perfect cubes, for example: $\sqrt[3]{27} = 3$.	2
write the repeating decimal that is equivalent to a rational number and the fraction that is equivalent to a repeating decimal, for example: $0.\overline{3} = \frac{1}{3}$.	3
estimate the value of irrational numbers.	3
use scientific notation to express very large or very small quantities and to add, subtract, multiply, or divide with numbers expressed in scientific notation.	4, 5

Use these skills to solve problems 1–8.

1 Which numbers are rational? Select all that apply.

B

(A) $1.\overline{45}$

B $\sqrt{10}$

C π

(D) $\sqrt{49}$

(E) 3.8

(F) $\frac{13}{19}$

2 Which of these is equivalent to 3^7? Select all that apply.

B

A $\frac{3^{8}}{3^{3}}$

B $\frac{6^{7}}{2}$

C $3^5 \cdot 3^3$

(D) $3 \cdot 3$

(E) $\frac{3^{12}}{3^{10}}$

(F) $\frac{3^{-3}}{3^{-5}}$

3 Express $0.\overline{54}$ as a fraction.

M

$\dfrac{54}{99}$ or $\dfrac{6}{11}$

4 Which pair shows items that have the same value?

B

A $\sqrt[3]{64}$ and $\sqrt{8}$

B $\sqrt[3]{27}$ and $\sqrt{81}$

C $\sqrt[3]{45}$ and $\sqrt{9}$

(D) $\sqrt[3]{216}$ and $\sqrt{36}$

55

Unit 1 Practice

©Curriculum Associates, LLC   Copying is not permitted.

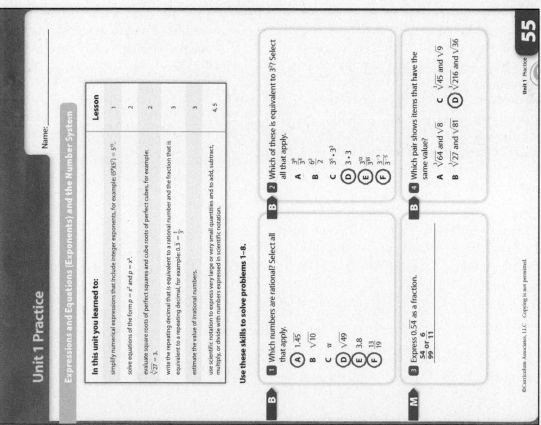

Key

B Basic	M Medium	C Challenge

TEACHER NOTES

Common Core Standards: 8.EE.A.3, 8.EE.A.4
Standards for Mathematical Practice: 1, 2, 3, 4, 5, 6, 7
DOK: 3
Materials: None

About the Task

To complete this task, students write numbers in scientific notation and compare them. The task requires them to analyze information about the distances of planets from the Sun and write a report using the information they found.

Getting Started

Read the problem out loud with students and go over the checklist. Review with students the fact that the orbits are not circular, so the planets' distances from the Sun vary. Consider having students locate an accurate visual representation of the solar system. Discuss the comparison questions that are given and have students describe how they could find the answers. Ask students how scientific notation will help them write their report. (**SMP 1, 4**)

Completing the Task

The directions tell students to first write the distances in scientific notation and then write the report. Ask students how they plan to work with the numbers. Some students may use estimation to help them understand and answer the comparison questions. Others may prefer to work with the exact quantities. Encourage students to work with scientific notation rather than standard form. Many students need to practice with scientific notation in order to gain comfort in using it. (**SMP 5, 6**)

Have each student choose a variety of questions for his or her report. Different questions require different skills and approaches. Students are free to answer questions other than the ones on the Student Book page. (**SMP 7**)

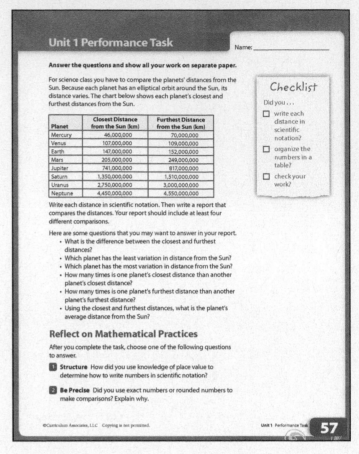

Have students present their reports. Discuss the different comparisons and discoveries students made. (**SMP 2, 3**)

Extension

If students have more time to spend on this problem, you can have them solve this extension:

Use the data that you generated to write an additional comparison that is not included in your report.

SAMPLE RESPONSE AND RUBRIC

4-Point Solution

Planet	Closest Distance from the Sun (km)	Furthest Distance from the Sun (km)	Difference (km)	Average (km)
Mercury	$46{,}000{,}000 = 4.6 \times 10^7$	$70{,}000{,}000 = 7 \times 10^7$	2.4×10^7	5.8×10^7
Venus	$107{,}000{,}000 = 1.07 \times 10^8$	$109{,}000{,}000 = 1.09 \times 10^8$	2×10^6	1.08×10^8
Earth	$147{,}000{,}000 = 1.47 \times 10^8$	$152{,}000{,}000 = 1.52 \times 10^8$	5×10^6	1.495×10^8
Mars	$205{,}000{,}000 = 2.05 \times 10^8$	$249{,}000{,}000 = 2.49 \times 10^8$	4.4×10^7	2.27×10^8
Jupiter	$741{,}000{,}000 = 7.41 \times 10^8$	$817{,}000{,}000 = 8.17 \times 10^8$	7.6×10^7	7.79×10^8
Saturn	$1{,}350{,}000{,}000 = 1.35 \times 10^9$	$1{,}510{,}000{,}000 = 1.51 \times 10^9$	1.6×10^8	1.43×10^9
Uranus	$2{,}750{,}000{,}000 = 2.75 \times 10^9$	$3{,}000{,}000{,}000 = 3.00 \times 10^9$	2.5×10^8	2.875×10^9
Neptune	$4{,}450{,}000{,}000 = 4.45 \times 10^9$	$4{,}550{,}000{,}000 = 4.55 \times 10^9$	1×10^8	4.5×10^9

Report: Each planet has its own orbit around the Sun. The closest planet is Mercury. Its average distance from the Sun is 5.8×10^7 kilometers. Neptune is the furthest, with an average distance of 4.5×10^9 kilometers from the Sun. Neptune's furthest distance is nearly 100 times further from the Sun than Mercury's closest distance.
$(4.55 \times 10^9) \div (4.6 \times 10^7) = \left(\frac{4.55}{4.6}\right) \times 10^2$, which is close to 1×10^2, or 100.

The difference between the furthest and closest distances gives the variation of the orbit. Venus's orbit has the least variation in it, only 2×10^6 kilometers. Uranus's orbit has the most variation as at 2.5×10^8 kilometers.

REFLECT ON MATHEMATICAL PRACTICES

1. Students' explanations should demonstrate understanding of the relationship between the place value system and powers of 10. (**SMP 7**)

2. Accept either answer, as long as students explain their decision using valid mathematical arguments. (**SMP 6**)

SCORING RUBRIC

4 points   All parts of the problem are complete and correct. Students correctly express each distance in scientific notation. The report contains at least 4 different comparisons and all are correct.

3 points   The student has completed all parts of the problem, with one or two errors. Possible errors might include incorrect or incomplete comparisons, incorrect scientific notation, or incorrect calculations.

2 points   The student has attempted all parts of the problem, with a number of errors. Some distances are not correctly expressed in scientific notation. Some calculations and/or comparisons are incorrect.

1 point   Much of the problem is incomplete, with several errors. Scientific notation and calculations are missing or incorrect. Comparisons are incorrect. The report is incomplete.

SOLUTION TO THE EXTENSION

Possible Solution

Earth's average distance from the Sun: 1.495×10^8

Saturn's average distance from the Sun: 1.43×10^9

If you divide, you find that Saturn's average distance is about 1×10^1 or 10 times greater than Earth's average distance from the Sun.

Lesson 6
Understand Functions

Name: _____

Prerequisite: How can you use an equation to represent a proportional relationship?

Study the example showing how to write equations for proportional relationships. Then solve problems 1–8.

Example

Kata is making pizza dough. For every 4 cups of flour, she needs 2 cups of water. Represent this relationship using a table and an equation.

The table represents this proportional relationship. All of the ratios are equivalent to $\frac{4}{2} = \frac{2}{1}$.

Flour, f	2	3	4	5	6	7	8
Water, w	1	1.5	2	2.5	3	3.5	4

You can also use an equation. The ratio of flour to water is $\frac{4}{2} = \frac{2}{1}$, so the constant of proportionality is $\frac{2}{1}$, or 2.

$$\underset{\text{of flour}}{\underset{\downarrow}{\text{amount}}} = \underset{\text{proportionality}}{\underset{\downarrow}{\text{constant of}}} \cdot \underset{\text{water}}{\underset{\downarrow}{\text{amount of}}}$$

$$f = 2 \cdot w$$

equation: $f = 2w$

Vocabulary

constant of proportionality the unit rate in a proportional relationship.

1 What does the constant of proportionality represent in terms of the problem?

Possible answer: You need 2 cups of flour for every cup of water.

2 Use the equation in the example to find the number of cups of water you need if you have 12 cups of flour.

$f = 2w$
$12 = 2w$
$6 = w$ You need 6 cups of water.

3 For a different pizza dough recipe, the equation $f = 2.5w$ represents the number of cups of flour, f, that you need for w cups of water. What is the constant of proportionality? Explain what it means in this context.

2.5; Possible explanation: For each cup of water, you need 2.5 cups of flour.

Lesson 6 *Understand Functions*   **65**

Solve.

B 4 Basir buys 4 small drinks for $6. Write an equation to represent the cost, c, for d small drinks.

$c = 1.5d$

M 5 A horse ran 800 meters in 40 seconds, 1,200 meters in 60 seconds, and 480 meters in 24 seconds. Is this a proportional relationship? If so, what is the constant of proportionality? What does it represent? Write an equation to represent the distance d, in meters, that the horse runs in t seconds.

Yes; Possible answer: The constant of proportionality is $\frac{20}{1}$, which means that the horse can run 20 meters in 1 second. The equation $d = 20t$ represents this situation.

M 6 The equation $c = 6.4w$ represents the cost c for w pounds of walnuts. Does a value of 2.5 for w make sense in this situation? Explain your reasoning.

Yes; Possible explanation: You can buy 2.5 pounds of walnuts.

C 7 Lina and Michele studied the data in the table. They each wrote an equation to represent the relationship between the number of miles and the number of hours ridden by a bicyclist.

Miles, m	Hours, h
27	3
45	5
18	2
54	6

Lina's equation: $m = 9h$

Michele's equation: $h = \frac{1}{9}m$

The teacher said that both equations were correct. Explain why.

Possible explanation: Lina's equation shows that the bicyclist rides 9 miles in 1 hour. Michele's equation shows that the bicyclist can ride 1 mile in $\frac{1}{9}$ of an hour. The equations are two different ways of expressing the same relationship.

M 8 Zach's car travels 21 miles on 1 gallon of gas. Write an equation to represent the relationship between the gas Zach's car uses and the distance he travels. Then solve the equation to see how far Zach travels on a trip if he uses 16 gallons of gas.

$d = 21g$; Zach travels $21(16) = 336$ miles if he uses 16 gallons of gas.

66 Lesson 6 *Understand Functions*

Key

B Basic   **M** Medium   **C** Challenge

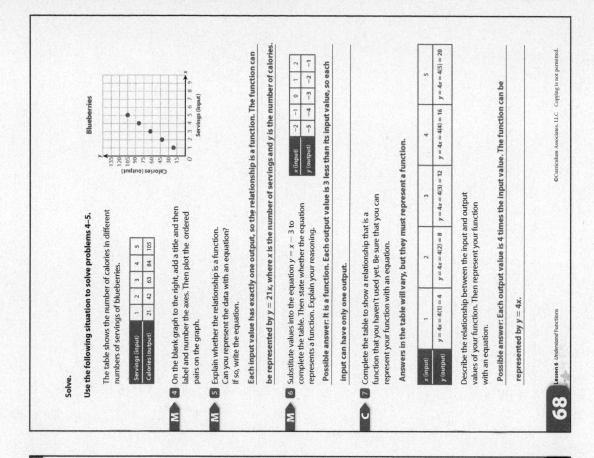

Solve.

Use the following situation to solve problems 4–5.

The table shows the number of calories in different numbers of servings of blueberries.

Servings (input)	1	2	3	4	5
Calories (output)	21	42	63	84	105

M 4 On the blank graph to the right, add a title and then label and number the axes. Then plot the ordered pairs on the graph.

Blueberries — Calories (output) axis: 15, 30, 45, 60, 75, 90, 105, 120, 135; Servings (input) axis: 0 1 2 3 4 5 6 7 8 9

M 5 Explain whether the relationship is a function. Can you represent the data with an equation? If so, write the equation.

Each input value has exactly one output, so the relationship is a function. The function can be represented by $y = 21x$, where x is the number of servings and y is the number of calories.

M 6 Substitute values into the equation $y = x - 3$ to complete the table. Then state whether the equation represents a function. Explain your reasoning.

Possible answer: It is a function. Each output value is 3 less than its input value, so each input can have only one output.

x (input)	-2	-1	0	1	2
y (output)	-5	-4	-3	-2	-1

C 7 Complete the table to show a relationship that is a function that you haven't used yet. Be sure that you can represent your function with an equation.

Answers in the table will vary, but they must represent a function.

x (input)	1	2	3	4	5
y (output)	$y = 4x = 4(1) = 4$	$y = 4x = 4(2) = 8$	$y = 4x = 4(3) = 12$	$y = 4x = 4(4) = 16$	$y = 4x = 4(5) = 20$

Describe the relationship between the input and output values of your function. Then represent your function with an equation.

Possible answer: Each output value is 4 times the input value. The function can be represented by

$y = 4x.$

Lesson 6 *Understand Functions*

68

Lesson 6

Name: _____

Identify Functions

Study the example problem showing how to determine whether a relationship is a function. Then solve problems 1–7.

Example

Describe the relationship shown in each table. Is the relationship a function? Explain.

The input identifies the hours, and the output gives the cost for those hours. The relationship is a function because there is only one output for each input.

Table A

Hours (input)	1	2	3	4	5
Cost (output)	$3	$6	$9	$12	$15

The input identifies the week and the output gives the growth for each week. The relationship is a function because there is only one output for each input.

Table B

Week (input)	1	2	3	4	5
Plant Growth in Inches (output)	4	3.25	2	2	1.75

B 1 Can you represent either of the functions in the example problem with an equation? Explain.

Possible answer: The function in Table A can be represented by $c = 3h$, where $c =$ cost and $h =$ hours.

B 2 Suppose you reverse the inputs and outputs in Table B. Would the relationship be a function? Explain.

No, it would not be a function. There would be two different outputs for the input 2.

B 3 The table shows the number of concert tickets sold by five students. Is the relationship a function? Explain.

Student (input)	1	2	3	4	5
Tickets (output)	12	18	12	22	16

Yes; There is only one output for each input.

Vocabulary

function a rule that produces exactly one output for each input.

Lesson 6 *Understand Functions*

67

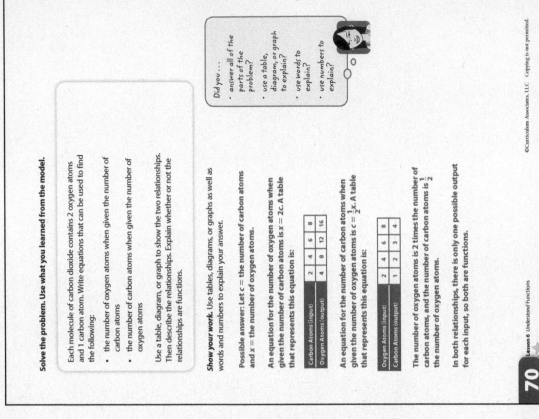

Solve the problem. Use what you learned from the model.

Each molecule of carbon dioxide contains 2 oxygen atoms and 1 carbon atom. Write equations that can be used to find the following:
- the number of oxygen atoms when given the number of carbon atoms
- the number of carbon atoms when given the number of oxygen atoms

Use a table, diagram, or graph to show the two relationships. Then describe the relationships. Explain whether or not the relationships are functions.

Show your work. Use tables, diagrams, or graphs as well as words and numbers to explain your answer.

Possible answer: Let c = the number of carbon atoms and x = the number of oxygen atoms.

An equation for the number of oxygen atoms when given the number of carbon atoms is $x = 2c$. A table that represents this equation is:

| Carbon Atoms (input) | 2 | 4 | 6 | 8 |
| Oxygen Atoms (output) | 4 | 8 | 12 | 16 |

An equation for the number of carbon atoms when given the number of oxygen atoms is $c = \frac{1}{2}x$. A table that represents this equation is:

| Oxygen Atoms (input) | 2 | 4 | 6 | 8 |
| Carbon Atoms (output) | 1 | 2 | 3 | 4 |

The number of oxygen atoms is 2 times the number of carbon atoms, and the number of carbon atoms is $\frac{1}{2}$ the number of oxygen atoms.

In both relationships, there is only one possible output for each input, so both are functions.

Did you . . .
- answer all of the parts of the problem?
- use a table, diagram, or graph to explain?
- use words to explain?
- use numbers to explain?

Name: _____

Answers will vary. Note whether students incorporate the features they chose in their answer on the next page.

Reason and Write

Study the example. Underline two parts that you think make it a particularly good answer and a helpful example.

Example
An object traveling at the speed of sound at sea level travels about 20 kilometers in 1 minute. Write equations that can be used to find the following:
- the distance when given the time
- the time when given the distance

Use a table, diagram, or graph to show the two relationships. Then describe the relationships. Explain whether or not the relationships are functions.

Show your work. Use a table, diagram, or graph as well as words and numbers to explain your answer.

Possible answer: Let d = distance and t = time.

An equation for the distance given the time is $d = 20t$ and an equation for the time given the distance is $t = \frac{1}{20}d$.

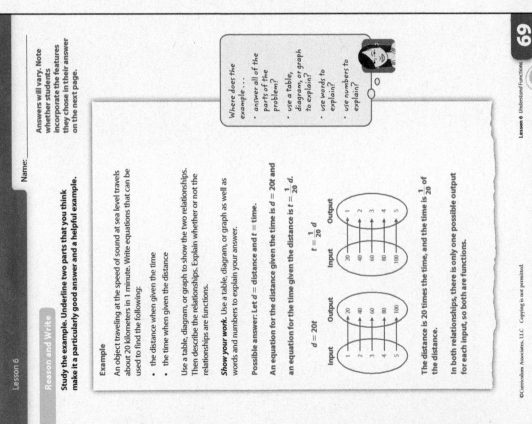

$d = 20t$ — Input: 1, 2, 3, 4, 5　Output: 20, 40, 60, 80, 100

$t = \frac{1}{20}d$ — Input: 20, 40, 60, 80, 100　Output: 1, 2, 3, 4, 5

The distance is 20 times the time, and the time is $\frac{1}{20}$ of the distance.

In both relationships, there is only one possible output for each input, so both are functions.

Where does the example . . .
- answer all of the parts of the problem?
- use a table, diagram, or graph to explain?
- use words to explain?
- use numbers to explain?

Lesson 7

Compare Functions

Name: _____

Prerequisite: Identify Functions

Study the example showing a function. Then solve problems 1–6.

Example

The table and graph show the relationship between the length of the sides of a square, in feet, and the perimeter of the square in feet.

Side Length (input)	1	2	3	4	5
Perimeter (output)	4	8	12	16	20

The relationship is a function because there is only one output value for each input value.

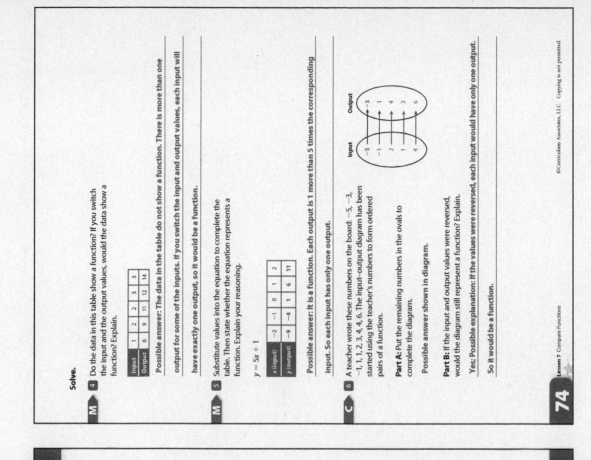

Perimeters of Squares

B 1 Describe the relationship between the input and output values in the example.

Possible answer: Each output value, which represents the perimeter, is 4 times the input value, which represents the side length of the square.

B 2 Can you represent the function in the example with an equation? If so, what equation can you write? If not, why not?

Yes; Possible explanation: The function can be represented by $y = 4x$, where y = perimeter and x = side length.

M 3 In the example function, could one side length ever produce two different perimeters? Explain.

No. Each side length produces only one perimeter. It's not possible to have two different perimeters for a given side length.

Solve.

M 4 Do the data in this table show a function? If you switch the input and the output values, would the data show a function? Explain.

Input	1	2	2	3	3
Output	6	9	11	12	14

Possible answer: The data in the table do not show a function. There is more than one output for some of the inputs. If you switch the input and output values, each input will have exactly one output, so it would be a function.

M 5 Substitute values into the equation to complete the table. Then state whether the equation represents a function. Explain your reasoning.

$y = 5x + 1$

x (input)	-2	-1	0	1	2
y (output)	-9	-4	1	6	11

Possible answer: It is a function. Each output is 1 more than 5 times the corresponding input. So each input has only one output.

C 6 A teacher wrote these numbers on the board: -5, -3, -1, 1, 2, 3, 4, 6. The input–output diagram has been started using the teacher's numbers to form ordered pairs of a function.

Part A: Put the remaining numbers in the ovals to complete the diagram.

Possible answer shown in diagram.

Part B: If the input and output values were reversed, would the diagram still represent a function? Explain.

Yes; Possible explanation: If the input and output values were reversed, each input would have only one output.

So it would be a function.

Vocabulary

function a rule that assigns exactly one output to each input.

input the number put into a function.

output the number that results from applying the function to the input.

Key

B Basic	M Medium	C Challenge

Solve.

M **4** The table shows the weight gain of a kitten over a 5-week period. The graph shows the weight gain of a second kitten over the same period. Compare the rates of change for these two functions.

Kitten A

Week	Weight (oz)
0	3
1	7
2	11
3	15
4	19
5	23

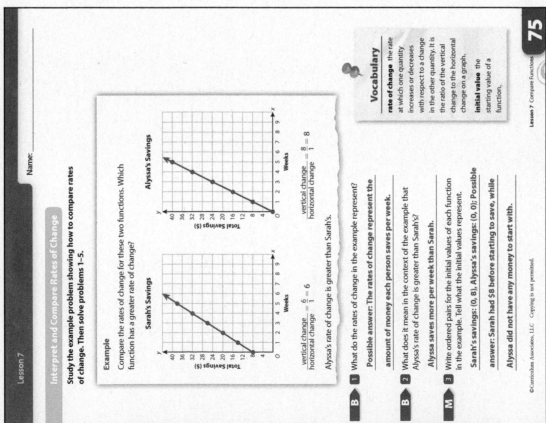

Kitten B

The rate of change for Kitten A is 4 oz per week, and the rate of change for Kitten B is

3 oz per week. Kitten A is gaining weight faster than Kitten B.

C **5** Sonya sells bracelets once a month at a flea market. The table shows her profits for a 5-month period.

Sonya

Month	1	2	3	4	5
Total Profit ($)	30	60	90	120	150

a. Kirsten sells bracelets once a month at a different flea market. The rate of change for her profits is $10 per month. Complete the table and the graph to show her total profits.

Kirsten

Month	1	2	3	4	5
Total Profit ($)	10	20	30	40	50

Kirsten

b. Sonya says that her profit is increasing 4 times as fast as Kirsten's profit. Do you agree? Explain.

No; Possible explanation: Sonya's rate of change is $30 per month, and Kirsten's rate of change is $10 per month. Sonya's profit is increasing 3 times as fast as Kirsten's.

Lesson 7

Interpret and Compare Rates of Change

Study the example problem showing how to compare rates of change. Then solve problems 1–5.

Example

Compare the rates of change for these two functions. Which function has a greater rate of change?

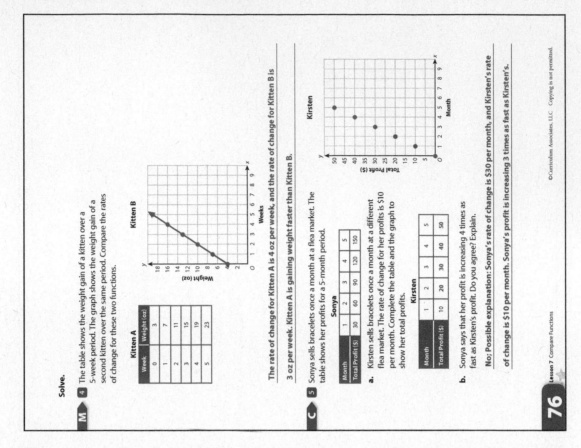

Sarah's Savings

Alyssa's Savings

$$\frac{\text{vertical change}}{\text{horizontal change}} = \frac{6}{1} = 6$$

$$\frac{\text{vertical change}}{\text{horizontal change}} = \frac{8}{1} = 8$$

Alyssa's rate of change is greater than Sarah's.

B **1** What do the rates of change in the example represent?

Possible answer: The rates of change represent the

amount of money each person saves per week.

B **2** What does it mean in the context of the example that Alyssa's rate of change is greater than Sarah's?

Alyssa saves more per week than Sarah.

M **3** Write ordered pairs for the initial values of each function in the example. Tell what the initial values represent.

Sarah's savings: (0, 8), Alyssa's savings: (0, 0); Possible

answer: Sarah had $8 before starting to save, while

Alyssa did not have any money to start with.

Vocabulary

rate of change the rate at which one quantity increases or decreases with respect to a change in the other quantity. It is the ratio of the vertical change to the horizontal change on a graph.

initial value the starting value of a function.

Lesson 7

Compare Negative and Positive Rates of Change

Study the example problem showing how to compare two functions. Then solve problems 1–6.

Example

Mr. Allen bought a new computer. His monthly payment plan is shown in the table.

Month	0	1	2	3	4	5	6	7
Amount Mr. Allen Owes ($)	560	480	400	320	240	160	80	0

Mr. Jessup buys a new computer for $400. He makes monthly payments of $40 until the computer is paid for. Compare the initial values and rates of change of each function.

You can graph both functions to show that the amount Mr. Allen owes starts at $560 and decreases $80 per month. The amount that Mr. Jessup owes starts at $400 and decreases $40 each month.

Mr. Allen's initial value is $160 more than Mr. Jessup's. Mr. Allen's rate of change is greater than Mr. Jessup's rate of change.

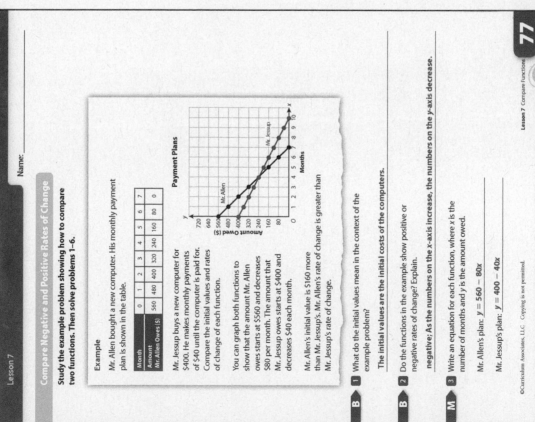

1 What do the initial values mean in the context of the example problem?

The initial values are the initial costs of the computers.

2 Do the functions in the example show positive or negative rates of change? Explain.

negative; As the numbers on the x-axis increase, the numbers on the y-axis decrease.

3 Write an equation for each function, where x is the number of months and y is the amount owed.

Mr. Allen's plan: $y = 560 − 80x$

Mr. Jessup's plan: $y = 400 − 40x$

Solve.

4 Below are two companies' rates to rent a bicycle. How much does it cost per hour to rent a bicycle at Company A? What is the cost to rent a bicycle for 6 hours from each company?

Company A: $c = 5h + 4$, where c = total cost (in dollars) and h = number of hours

Company B: $6 per hour per bicycle

It costs $5 per hour to rent a bicycle at Company A; At Company A when $h = 6$,

$c = 5(6) + 4 = 34$, so it costs $34 to rent a bike for 6 hours. At Company B, $6(6) = 36$,

so it costs $36 to rent a bike for 6 hours.

5 Roy wants to buy a new television for $300. Two stores offer different payment options. Compare the initial values and rates of change.

Store A Payment Plan

Month	0	1	2	3	4	5	6
Amount Owed ($)	300	250	200	150	100	50	0

Store B Payment Plan

Pay $100 at the time of purchase. Pay $50 per month until the television is paid for.

Show your work.

Possible work: Initial values: Store A is $300 in the table. Store B is $200 ($300 − $100). Rates of change: Store A is $50 and Store B is also $50.

Solution: Store A's initial value is $100 greater. The rates of change are the same.

6 Most plumbing companies charge a fee to come to your house plus a charge per hour of work. The fees and charges for two plumbing companies are shown.

Company A
Fee: $50
Charge per hour: $40

Company B
Fee: $25
Charge per hour: $50

Write an equation for each company, where c = total cost (in dollars) and h = number of hours. Explain what the initial values and rates of change mean in this context.

Company A: $c = 50 + 40h$

Company B: $c = 25 + 50h$

The initial value is the fee, and the charge per hour is the rate of change.

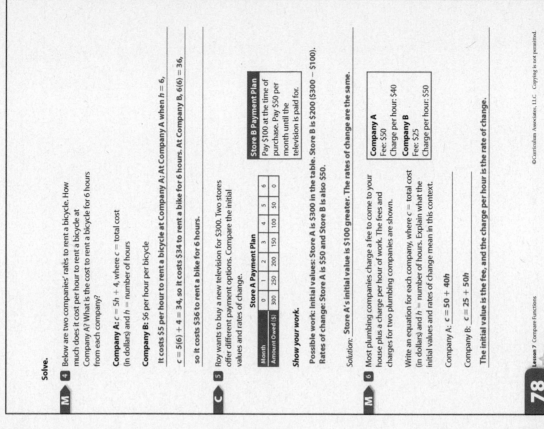

Practice Lesson 7 Compare Functions

Solve.

4 The rates for two airport shuttles are shown below.

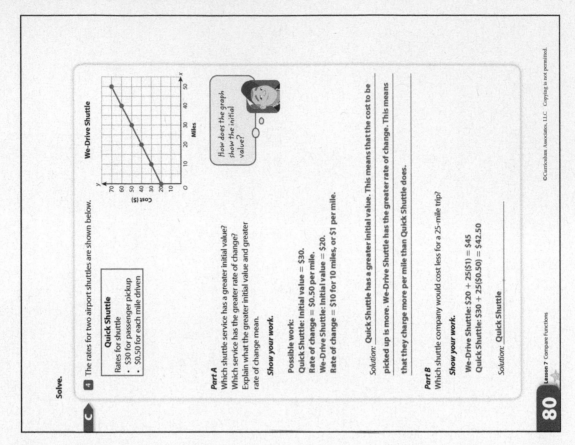

> How does the graph show the initial value?

We-Drive Shuttle

(graph: Cost ($) vs Miles, y-axis 10 20 30 40 50 60 70, x-axis 10 20 30 40 50)

Quick Shuttle
Rates for shuttle
- $30 for passenger pickup
- $0.50 for each mile driven

Part A
Which shuttle service has a greater initial value?
Which service has the greater rate of change?
Explain what the greater initial value and greater rate of change mean.

Show your work.

Possible work:
Quick Shuttle: Initial value = $30.
Rate of change = $0.50 per mile.
We-Drive Shuttle: Initial value = $20.
Rate of change = $10 for 10 miles, or $1 per mile.

Solution: Quick Shuttle has a greater initial value. This means that the cost to be

picked up is more. We-Drive Shuttle has the greater rate of change. This means

that they charge more per mile than Quick Shuttle does.

Part B
Which shuttle company would cost less for a 25-mile trip?

Show your work.

We-Drive Shuttle: $20 + 25($1) = $45
Quick Shuttle: $30 + 25($0.50) = $42.50

Solution: Quick Shuttle

Name: _____

Compare Functions

Solve the problems.

1 A hardware store charges a $30 rental fee and $15 per day to rent a power washer. Which equation correctly relates the total cost y to rent the washer for x days?

> What do the parts of each equation represent?

A $y = 15 + 30x$ C $y = 30 - \dfrac{x}{15}$

B $y = 30 + 15x$ D $y = 15 - \dfrac{x}{30}$

2 Tony drives 18 miles to pick up his friend at his house. Then he drives at a constant speed of 40 miles per hour to a state park to go hiking. Let y represent the number of miles that Tony drives after x hours. Which of the following statements are true? Select all that apply.

> How do you determine the initial value and rate of change?

A The relationship can be represented by the equation $y = 40x + 18$.

B If Tony travels for 1.5 hours, he will have driven a total of 60 miles.

C The initial value is 18 miles.

D The rate of change is negative.

3 Alma borrows money from her mom to buy a $150 bike. She gives her mom $40 at the time of purchase and continues to pay her $10 each month until the bike is paid for in full. Alma wrote this equation to represent the amount y that she will have paid her mom after x months.

> How does an equation show a rate of change?

Equation: $y = 40x + 10$

Is her equation correct? How did she get that equation? If it is not correct, write a correct equation.

No; Alma thought 40 was the rate of change and not the initial value. The correct

equation is $y = 10x + 40$.

Lesson 8
Understand
Linear Functions

Name: _____

> **Prerequisite: How can you compare two functions?**

Study the example problem showing how to compare rates of change for two functions. Then solve problems 1–6.

Example

Monte and Ramon are each saving all of the money they earn. Monte started with $3 and earns $8 an hour at his part-time job. The graph shows Ramon's total savings. Which function has a greater rate of change?

Make a table of values for Monte's savings.

Hours Worked	0	1	2	3	4	5
Total Savings ($)	3	11	19	27	35	43

You can use ordered pairs from the table to find Monte's rate of change.

Monte's rate of change: $\dfrac{\text{vertical change}}{\text{horizontal change}} = \dfrac{8}{1} = 8$, or $8/hr

You can use the graph to find Ramon's rate of change.

Ramon's rate of change: $\dfrac{\text{vertical change}}{\text{horizontal change}} = \dfrac{6}{1} = 6$, or $6/hr

The rate of change for Monte's savings is greater.

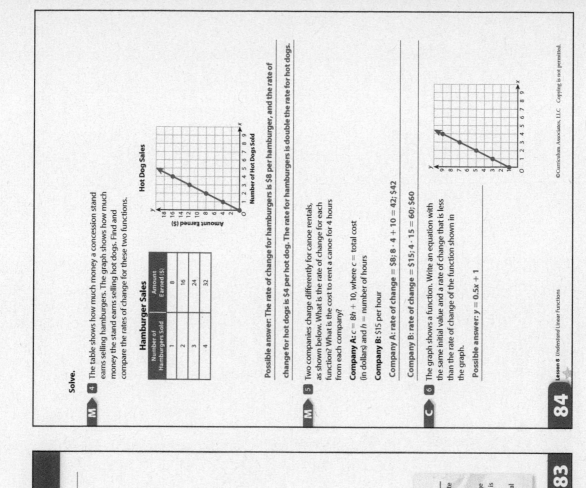

Ramon's Savings — Total Money ($) vs. Hours Worked

B 1 What do the rates of change represent?
Possible answer: The rates of change are the hourly wages, or the amounts of money earned per hour.

B 2 What does it mean in the context of the example to say that the rate of change for Monte's savings is greater?
Monte earns more money per hour.

M 3 Find the total savings after working 8 hours for each person.
Monte's savings: $67; Ramon's savings: $54

> **Vocabulary**
> **rate of change** the rate at which one quantity increases or decreases with respect to a change in the other quantity. It is the ratio of the vertical change to the horizontal change on a graph.

Lesson 8 *Understand* Linear Functions **83**

Solve.

M 4 The table shows how much money a concession stand earns selling hamburgers. The graph shows how much money the stand earns selling hot dogs. Find and compare the rates of change for these two functions.

Hamburger Sales

Number of Hamburgers Sold	Amount Earned ($)
1	8
2	16
3	24
4	32

Hot Dog Sales — Amount Earned ($) vs. Number of Hot Dogs Sold

Possible answer: The rate of change for hamburgers is $8 per hamburger, and the rate of change for hot dogs is $4 per hot dog. The rate for hamburgers is double the rate for hot dogs.

M 5 Two companies charge differently for canoe rentals, as shown below. What is the rate of change for each function? What is the cost to rent a canoe for 4 hours from each company?

Company A: $c = 8h + 10$, where c = total cost (in dollars) and h = number of hours

Company B: $15 per hour

Company A: rate of change = $8; $8 \cdot 4 + 10 = 42$; $42
Company B: rate of change = $15; $4 \cdot 15 = 60$; $60

C 6 The graph shows a function. Write an equation with the same initial value and a rate of change that is less than the rate of change of the function shown in the graph.

Possible answer: $y = 0.5x + 1$

84 Lesson 8 *Understand* Linear Functions

Key

B Basic   **M** Medium   **C** Challenge

Lesson 8

Name: _____

Identify Linear Functions

Study the example showing how to tell whether a function is linear. Then solve problems 1–6.

Example

Consider the equation $y = x + 2$. Use the equation to complete the table and then graph the equation.

Does the equation $y = x + 2$ represent a linear function?

Complete the table and graph the equation.

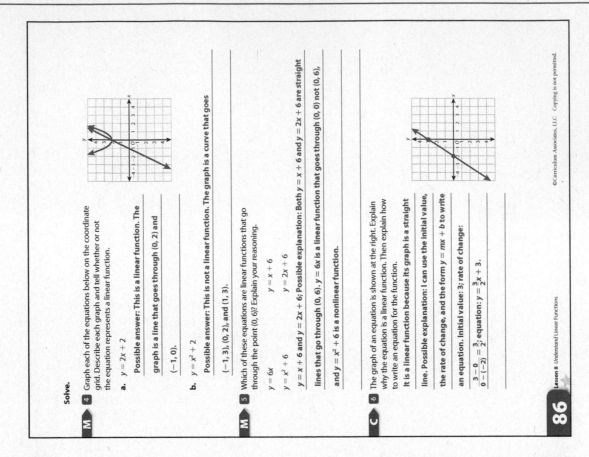

x	-2	-1	0	1	2
y	0	1	2	3	4

The graph is a straight line, so the equation $y = x + 2$ represents a linear function.

B 1 What is the initial value for the function in the example problem? What is the rate of change?

The initial value is 2. The rate of change is 1.

M 2 Linear functions can be written with equations in the forms $y = mx$ and $y = mx + b$. In which form is the linear function in the example problem? What are the values of m and b and what do they represent?

$y = mx + b$; In this form, m represents the rate of change and b represents the initial value. In this function, $m = 1$ and $b = 2$.

M 3 Do you think that the equation $y = 2x^2$ is a linear function? Explain why or why not.

No; Possible explanation: The equation is not in the form $y = mx$ or $y = mx + b$. It is in the form $y = mx^2$.

Vocabulary

linear function a function with a graph that is a non-vertical straight line, which can be represented by a linear equation in the form $y = mx + b$.

$y = x + 1$ is a linear function.

85   Lesson 8 *Understand* Linear Functions

Solve.

M 4 Graph each of the equations below on the coordinate grid. Describe each graph and tell whether or not the equation represents a linear function.

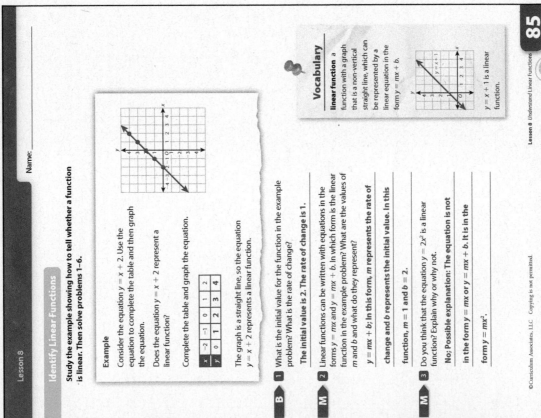

a. $y = 2x + 2$

Possible answer: This is a linear function. The graph is a line that goes through (0, 2) and (−1, 0).

b. $y = x^2 + 2$

Possible answer: This is not a linear function. The graph is a curve that goes through (−1, 3), (0, 2), and (1, 3).

M 5 Which of these equations are linear functions that go through the point (0, 6)? Explain your reasoning.

$y = 6x$ $y = x + 6$

$y = x^2 + 6$ $y = 2x + 6$

$y = x + 6$ and $y = 2x + 6$; Possible explanation: Both $y = x + 6$ and $y = 2x + 6$ are straight lines that go through (0, 6). $y = 6x$ is a linear function that goes through (0, 0) not (0, 6), and $y = x^2 + 6$ is a nonlinear function.

C 6 The graph of an equation is shown at the right. Explain why the equation is a linear function. Then explain how to write an equation for the function.

It is a linear function because its graph is a straight line. Possible explanation: I can use the initial value, the rate of change, and the form $y = mx + b$ to write an equation. Initial value: 3; rate of change: $\dfrac{3 - 0}{0 - (-2)} = \dfrac{3}{2}$; equation: $y = \dfrac{3}{2}x + 3$.

86   Lesson 8 *Understand* Linear Functions

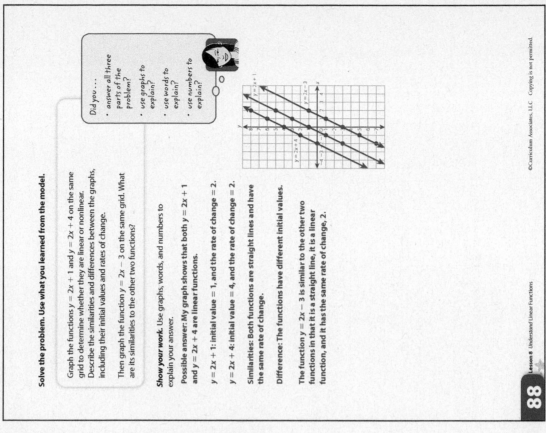

Solve the problem. Use what you learned from the model.

Graph the functions $y = 2x + 1$ and $y = 2x + 4$ on the same grid to determine whether they are linear or nonlinear. Describe the similarities and differences between the graphs, including their initial values and rates of change.

Then graph the function $y = 2x - 3$ on the same grid. What are its similarities to the other two functions?

Show your work. Use graphs, words, and numbers to explain your answer.

Possible answer: My graph shows that both $y = 2x + 1$ and $y = 2x + 4$ are linear functions.

$y = 2x + 1$: initial value = 1, and the rate of change = 2.

$y = 2x + 4$: initial value = 4, and the rate of change = 2.

Similarities: Both functions are straight lines and have the same rate of change.

Difference: The functions have different initial values.

The function $y = 2x - 3$ is similar to the other two functions in that it is a straight line, it is a linear function, and it has the same rate of change, 2.

> Did you . . .
> • answer all three parts of the problem?
> • use graphs to explain?
> • use words to explain?
> • use numbers to explain?

Lesson 8

Reason and Write

Study the example. Underline two parts that you think make it a particularly good answer and a helpful example.

Name:

Answers will vary. Note whether students incorporate the features they chose in their answer on the next page.

Example

Safina graphs the functions $y = x + 1$ and $y = \frac{x}{2}$ on the same grid. She says that $y = x + 1$ is linear but $y = \frac{x}{2}$ is not because it cannot be written as an equation in the form $y = mx + b$. Describe how you can check Safina's work and reasoning. Then tell whether Safina is correct or not.

Show your work. Use graphs, words, and numbers to explain your answer.

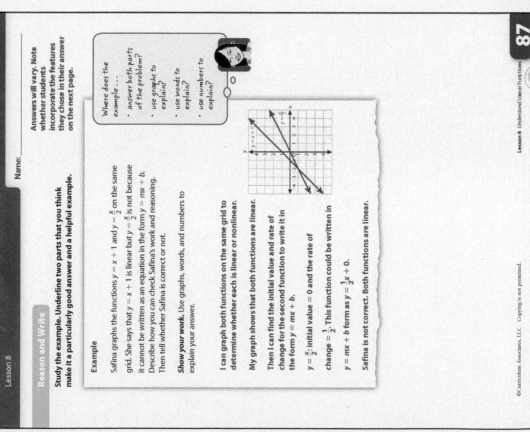

I can graph both functions on the same grid to determine whether each is linear or nonlinear.

My graph shows that both functions are linear.

Then I can find the initial value and rate of change for the second function to write it in the form $y = mx + b$.

$y = \frac{x}{2}$: initial value = 0 and the rate of change = $\frac{1}{2}$. This function could be written in $y = mx + b$ form as $y = \frac{1}{2}x + 0$.

Safina is not correct. Both functions are linear.

> Where does the example . . .
> • answer both parts of the problem?
> • use graphs to explain?
> • use words to explain?
> • use numbers to explain?

Lesson 9

Analyze Linear Functions

Prerequisite: Identify Linear Functions

Study the example problem showing a linear function. Then solve problems 1–6.

Example

An equation for the perimeter of an equilateral triangle with side length x is $y = 3x$. Does the equation $y = 3x$ represent a linear function?

Complete the table and graph the equation.

Side Length (units)	0	1	2	3	4	5
Perimeter (units)	0	3	6	9	12	15

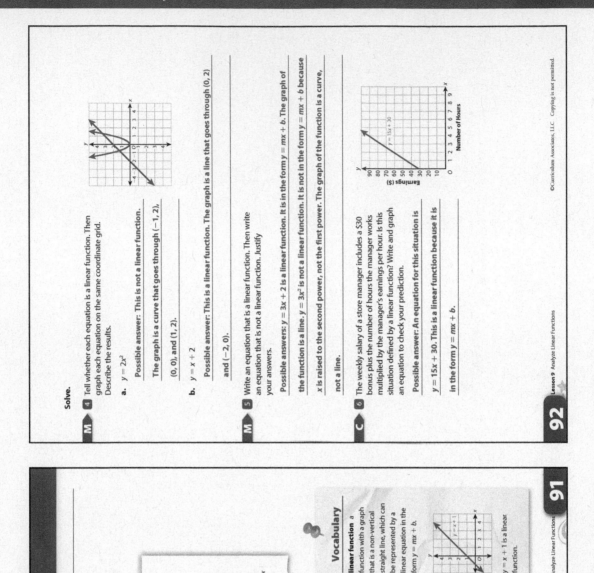

The graph is a straight line, so the equation $y = 3x$ represents a linear function.

B 1 In the example problem, what is the relationship between the perimeter and the side length of an equilateral triangle?

The perimeter is 3 times the side length.

B 2 What is the rate of change of the function? What does it represent?

3; It represents the rate at which the perimeter increases as the side length increases by 1 unit.

B 3 The equation $y = 3x$ is in the form $y = mx$. Jessie says that equations of the form $y = mx$ have no rate of change. Is Jessie correct?

No; equations of the form $y = mx$ have a rate of change of m and an initial value of 0.

Lesson 9 Analyze Linear Functions **91**

Vocabulary

linear function a function with a graph that is a non-vertical straight line, which can be represented by a linear equation in the form $y = mx + b$.

$y = x + 1$ is a linear function.

Solve.

M 4 Tell whether each equation is a linear function. Then graph each equation on the same coordinate grid. Describe the results.

a. $y = 2x^2$

Possible answer: **This is not a linear function.**

The graph is a curve that goes through $(-1, 2)$,

$(0, 0)$, and $(1, 2)$.

b. $y = x + 2$

Possible answer: **This is a linear function. The graph is a line that goes through $(0, 2)$**

and $(-2, 0)$.

M 5 Write an equation that is a linear function. Then write an equation that is not a linear function. Justify your answers.

Possible answers: $y = 3x + 2$ is a linear function. $y = 3x^2$ is not a linear function. It is in the form $y = mx + b$. The graph of

the function is a line. $y = 3x^2$ is not a linear function. It is not in the form $y = mx + b$ because

x is raised to the second power, not the first power. The graph of the function is a curve,

not a line.

C 6 The weekly salary of a store manager includes a $30 bonus plus the number of hours the manager works multiplied by the manager's earnings per hour. Is this situation defined by a linear function? Write and graph an equation to check your prediction.

Possible answer: An equation for this situation is

$y = 15x + 30$. This is a linear function because it is

in the form $y = mx + b$.

92 **Lesson 9** Analyze Linear Functions

Key

B Basic   **M** Medium   **C** Challenge

Lesson 9

Write an Equation Using Slope and y-Intercept

Study the example problem showing how to write an equation using the slope and the y-intercept. Then solve problems 1–7.

Example

Chuck's Appliance Repair charges a $25 service fee plus $35 for each hour the repair takes. Write an equation that relates the total cost y of a repair and the number of hours the repair takes x.

Use a table of values to find the slope and y-intercept. When $x = 0$, $y = 25$, so the y-intercept is 25. As x increases by 1, y increases by 35, so the slope is $\frac{35}{1}$, or 35.

You can write an equation for this function by substituting values for the slope m and the y-intercept b into the equation $y = mx + b$.

The equation is $y = 35x + 25$.

Hours, x	Total Cost ($), y
0	25
1	60
2	95
3	130
4	165

Vocabulary

slope the ratio $\frac{rise}{run}$ which tells you how many units a line goes up for every unit that it goes over.

y-intercept the y-coordinate of the point where a graph intersects the y-axis.

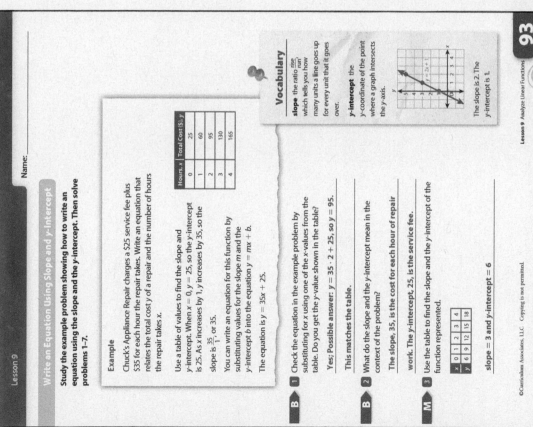

The slope is 2. The y-intercept is 1.

B 1 Check the equation in the example problem by substituting for x using one of the x-values from the table. Do you get the y-value shown in the table?

Yes; Possible answer: $y = 35 \cdot 2 + 25$, so $y = 95$.

This matches the table.

B 2 What do the slope and the y-intercept mean in the context of the problem?

The slope, 35, is the cost for each hour of repair work. The y-intercept, 25, is the service fee.

M 3 Use the table to find the slope and the y-intercept of the function represented.

x	0	1	2	3	4
y	6	9	12	15	18

slope = 3 and y-intercept = 6

Solve.

M 4 What are the slope and the y-intercept of the equation $y = 0.5x + 3$?

slope = 0.5 and y-intercept = 3

M 5 Write an equation for the table of values. Explain how you got your answer.

x	0	1	2	3	4
y	1	5	9	13	17

$y = 4x + 1$; Possible explanation: The table includes the ordered pair $(0, 1)$, so 1 is the y-intercept. Each y-value increases by 4 as each x-value increases by 1. The slope is $\frac{4}{1}$, or 4.

I substituted the slope and the y-intercept for m and b in $y = mx + b$.

M 6 An amusement park charges $8 for admission and $2 for each ride. Use the graph to find the slope and the y-intercept. Then write an equation for the function that relates the total cost to the number of rides.

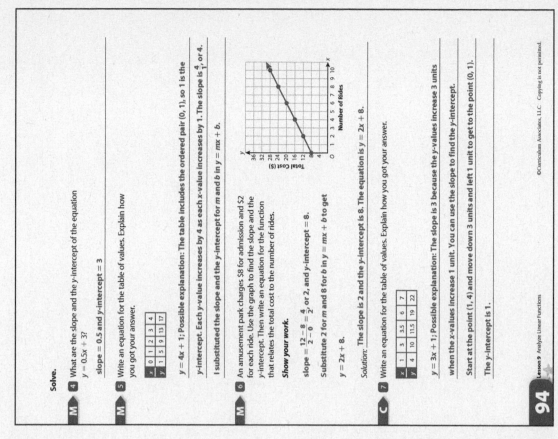

Show your work.

slope = $\frac{12 - 8}{2 - 0} = \frac{4}{2}$ or 2, and y-intercept = 8.

Substitute 2 for m and 8 for b in $y = mx + b$ to get

$y = 2x + 8$.

Solution: The slope is 2 and the y-intercept is 8. The equation is $y = 2x + 8$.

C 7 Write an equation for the table of values. Explain how you got your answer.

x	1	3.5	6	7
y	4	11.5	19	22

$y = 3x + 1$; Possible explanation: The slope is 3 because the y-values increase 3 units when the x-values increase 1 unit. You can use the slope to find the y-intercept.

Start at the point $(1, 4)$ and move down 3 units and left 1 unit to get to the point $(0, 1)$.

The y-intercept is 1.

Lesson 9

Name: _____

Use an Equation to Find Slope and y-Intercept

Study the example showing how to use an equation to find the slope and the y-intercept of a linear function. Then solve problems 1–8.

Example

A fitness club charges its members a sign-up fee and a weekly fee. The cost y of membership at the fitness club is given by the equation $y = 7.5x + 50$, where x is the number of weeks of membership. Make a table of values for the equation and find its slope and y-intercept.

Use the equation to make a table of values by substituting values of x into the equation and solving for y. Then find the slope and the y-intercept.

When $x = 0$, $y = 50$. The y-intercept is 50. As x increases by 10, y increases by 75, so the slope is $\frac{75}{10}$ or 7.5.

Number of Weeks, x	Total Cost ($), y
0	50
10	125
20	200
30	275
40	350
50	425

B **1** Use the table of values in the example problem to graph the function. Explain how to find the slope and the y-intercept from the graph.

The graph shows the point (0, 50), so 50 is the y-intercept. For the slope, use two points on the graph, $\frac{200 - 50}{20 - 0} = \frac{150}{20} = \frac{75}{10}$, or 7.5.

B **2** Explain how the equation $y = 7.5x + 50$ in the example problem shows the slope and the y-intercept.

The coefficient of x, or 7.5, is the slope. The constant, or 50, is the y-intercept.

B **3** What do the slope and the y-intercept mean in the context of the problem?

The slope, 7.5, is the cost for each week of membership. The y-intercept, 50, is the cost to join the fitness club.

©Curriculum Associates, LLC   Copying is not permitted.   Lesson 9 Analyze Linear Functions **95**

Solve.

M **4** A taxi service charges a pick-up fee plus a charge for each mile driven. The equation $y = 1.8x + 5$ gives the total cost y to travel x miles in the taxi. Complete the table. Explain how to use the table to find the slope and the y-intercept for this function.

x	0	10	20	30	40
y	5	23	41	59	77

The table shows that when $x = 0$, $y = 5$, so 5 is the y-intercept. The table also shows that as x increases by 10, y increases by 18. So the slope is $\frac{18}{10}$ or 1.8.

M **5** A different taxi service charges a pick-up fee of $4 plus a charge of $1.75 per mile driven. Write an equation for this function, and identify the slope and the y-intercept.

$y = 1.75x + 4$; slope = 1.75 and y-intercept = 4

M **6** Enrico is filling his pool. The pool has 3,000 gallons of water in it now. The water hose that Enrico uses puts 500 gallons per hour into the pool. Write an equation for the number of gallons y of water in the pool after x hours. Identify the slope and the y-intercept.

$y = 500x + 3{,}000$; slope = 500 and y-intercept = 3,000

M **7** The Peach Festival charges $12 for admission and $2.25 for each pound of peaches picked. Write an equation for the total cost if you pick x pounds of peaches. Use your equation to find the total cost of attending the festival and picking 5 pounds of peaches.

Show your work. Possible work:
Equation: $y = 2.25x + 12$
$y = 2.25(5) + 12$
$y = 11.25 + 12$
$y = 23.25$

Solution: __The cost of attending the festival and picking 5 pounds of peaches is $23.25.__

C **8** Write an equation for the function that passes through the points $\left(1, \frac{3}{2}\right)$ and $\left(\frac{3}{2}, 2\right)$.

$y = x + \frac{1}{2}$

96 Lesson 9 Analyze Linear Functions   ©Curriculum Associates, LLC   Copying is not permitted.

Lesson 9

Write Equations with Negative Slope

Study the example problem showing an equation with a negative slope. Then solve problems 1–7.

Example
Paolo is going to take part in a 20-kilometer walk. He makes this graph to show the relationship between time and remaining distance if he maintains his planned speed. Write an equation for this function.

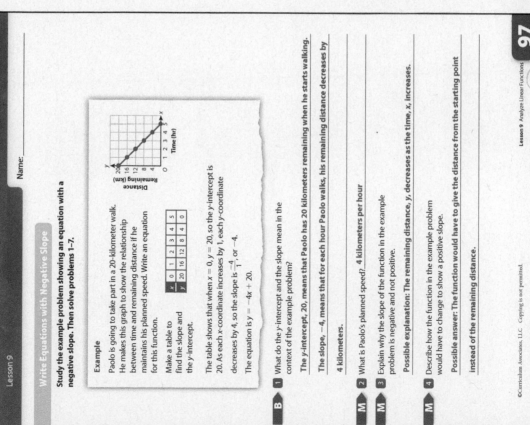

Make a table to find the slope and the y-intercept.

x	0	1	2	3	4	5
y	20	16	12	8	4	0

The table shows that when $x = 0$, $y = 20$, so the y-intercept is 20. As each x-coordinate increases by 1, each y-coordinate decreases by 4, so the slope is $\frac{-4}{1}$, or -4.

The equation is $y = -4x + 20$.

B 1 What do the y-intercept and the slope mean in the context of the example problem?

The y-intercept, 20, means that Paolo has 20 kilometers remaining when he starts walking.

The slope, −4, means that for each hour Paolo walks, his remaining distance decreases by 4 kilometers.

M 2 What is Paolo's planned speed? 4 kilometers per hour

M 3 Explain why the slope of the function in the example problem is negative and not positive.

Possible explanation: The remaining distance, y, decreases as the time, x, increases.

M 4 Describe how the function in the example problem would have to change to show a positive slope.

Possible answer: The function would have to give the distance from the starting point instead of the remaining distance.

Lesson 9 Analyze Linear Functions **97**

Solve.

B 5 Sasha is driving her car at an average rate of 60 miles per hour. She is driving directly to Atlanta and is 400 miles away. The equation $y = 400 - 60x$ can be used to represent the distance y Sasha is from Atlanta after x hours. Identify the slope and the y-intercept, and explain what they represent.

The slope, −60, represents the change in Sasha's distance from Atlanta each hour.

The y-intercept, 400, represents her current distance from Atlanta.

M 6 A restaurant has a container that holds 25 gallons of lemonade. They sell lemonade at a rate of about 2.5 gallons per hour. Suppose that the container is full. Write an equation that shows how much lemonade y (in gallons) is in the container after x hours. Identify the slope and the y-intercept.

Show your work.

Possible work:

Hours (x)	0	1	2	3	4
Gallons of Lemonade Left (y)	25	22.5	20	17.5	15

Start with 25 gallons. Subtract 2.5 gallons each hour.

Solution: $y = 25 - 2.5x$ or $y = -2.5x + 25$;

slope $= -2.5$ and y-intercept $= 25$

C 7 Write an equation for the function shown in the graph. Identify the slope and the y-intercept. Then graph a different linear function that has the same slope as the function shown. Write an equation for your function.

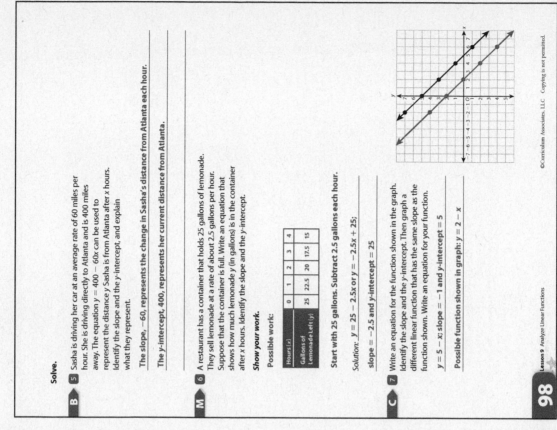

$y = 5 - x$; slope $= -1$ and y-intercept $= 5$

Possible function shown in graph: $y = 2 - x$

98 **Lesson 9** Analyze Linear Functions

Lesson 9

Analyze Linear Functions

Solve the problems.

M **1** Martin has an 18-cup container of flour that he uses for muffins only. He uses 3 cups of the flour for every batch of muffins he makes. Write an equation to show how much flour is left in the container after x batches of muffins. Then graph the function.

Show your work.

Possible answer:

18 cups is the initial amount, so the y-intercept is 18.

The amount in the container decreases by 3 for each

batch, so the slope is −3.

Solution: $y = 18 − 3x$ or $y = −3x + 18$

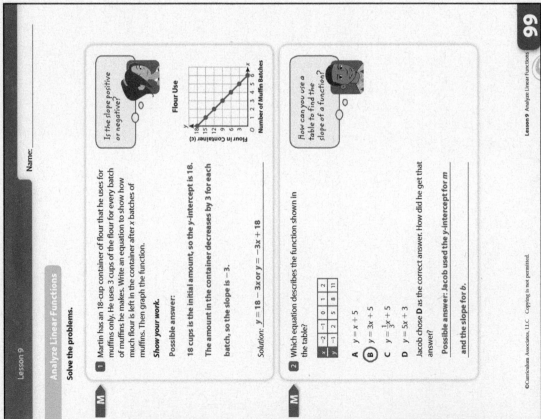

Is the slope positive or negative?

Flour Use

Flour in Container (c) — Number of Muffin Batches

M **2** Which equation describes the function shown in the table?

x	−2	−1	0	1	2
y	−1	1	2	5	8	11

A $y = x + 5$

B $y = 3x + 5$

C $y = \frac{1}{3}x + 5$

D $y = 5x + 3$

Jacob chose **D** as the correct answer. How did he get that answer?

Possible answer: Jacob used the y-intercept for m

and the slope for b.

How can you use a table to find the slope of a function?

Solve.

M **3** The cost of having a package delivered by Quick Bicycle Delivery is a function of the weight of the package. The graph of this function is shown.

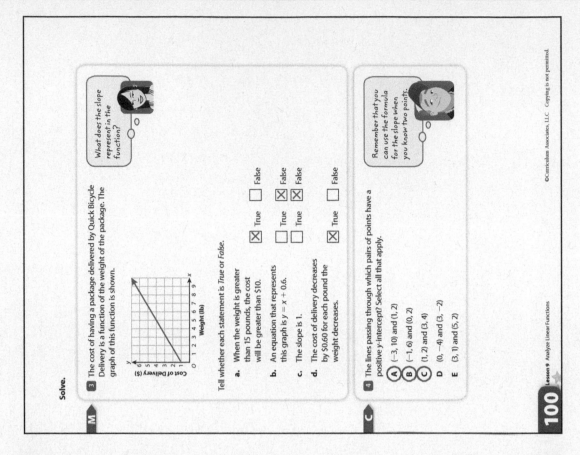

Cost of Delivery ($) — Weight (lb)

What does the slope represent in the function?

Tell whether each statement is *True* or *False*.

a. When the weight is greater than 15 pounds, the cost will be greater than $10.   ☒ True ☐ False

b. An equation that represents this graph is $y = x + 0.6$.   ☐ True ☒ False

c. The slope is 1.   ☐ True ☒ False

d. The cost of delivery decreases by $0.60 for each pound the weight decreases.   ☒ True ☐ False

C **4** The lines passing through which pairs of points have a positive y-intercept? Select all that apply.

Ⓐ $(−3, 10)$ and $(1, 2)$

Ⓑ $(−1, 6)$ and $(0, 2)$

Ⓒ $(1, 2)$ and $(3, 4)$

D $(0, −4)$ and $(3, −2)$

E $(3, 1)$ and $(5, 2)$

Remember that you can use the formula for the slope when you know two points.

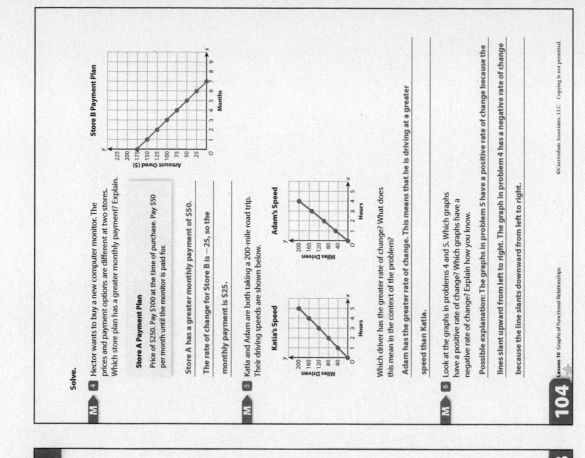

Lesson 10

Graphs of Functional Relationships

Prerequisite: Compare Rates of Change

Study the example problem showing ways to compare functions. Then solve problems 1–6.

Example

Carmen buys a new bicycle. Her weekly payment plan is shown in the table. Sam also buys a new bicycle. His weekly payment plan is shown in the graph. Find the rate of change for each function and explain what it represents.

Week:	0	1	2	3	4
Amount Carmen Owes ($)	200	150	100	50	0

The amount Carmen owes decreases by $50 each week, so her rate of change is −$50.

The amount Sam owes decreases by $25 each week, so his rate of change is −$25. Carmen pays more per week than Sam.

M 1 Graph Carmen's function on the same grid as Sam's function. Which line is steeper?

Carmen's line is steeper than Sam's.

B 2 How does the graph show that the rate of change is negative?

Possible explanation: As the x-values of each function increase, the y-values decrease. So, the lines slant downward from left to right.

M 3 Suppose Sam decides to pay for his bicycle in two equal weekly payments. How would that affect his rate of change? Would Sam pay more or less than Carmen each week?

Sam's rate of change would become −$62.50 instead of −$25. Sam would pay more than Carmen each week.

©Curriculum Associates, LLC   Copying is not permitted.

Lesson 10 Graphs of Functional Relationships **103**

Solve.

M 4 Hector wants to buy a new computer monitor. The prices and payment options are different at two stores. Which store plan has a greater monthly payment? Explain.

Store A Payment Plan
Price of $250. Pay $100 at the time of purchase. Pay $50 per month until the monitor is paid for.

Store B Payment Plan

Store A has a greater monthly payment of $50.

The rate of change for Store B is −25, so the monthly payment is $25.

M 5 Katia and Adam are both taking a 200-mile road trip. Their driving speeds are shown below.

Katia's Speed

Adam's Speed

Which driver has the greater rate of change? What does this mean in the context of the problem?

Adam has the greater rate of change. This means that he is driving at a greater speed than Katia.

M 6 Look at the graphs in problems 4 and 5. Which graphs have a positive rate of change? Which graphs have a negative rate of change? Explain how you know.

Possible explanation: The graphs in problem 5 have a positive rate of change because the lines slant upward from left to right. The graph in problem 4 has a negative rate of change because the line slants downward from left to right.

104 Lesson 10 Graphs of Functional Relationships

©Curriculum Associates, LLC   Copying is not permitted.

Key

B Basic   **M** Medium   **C** Challenge

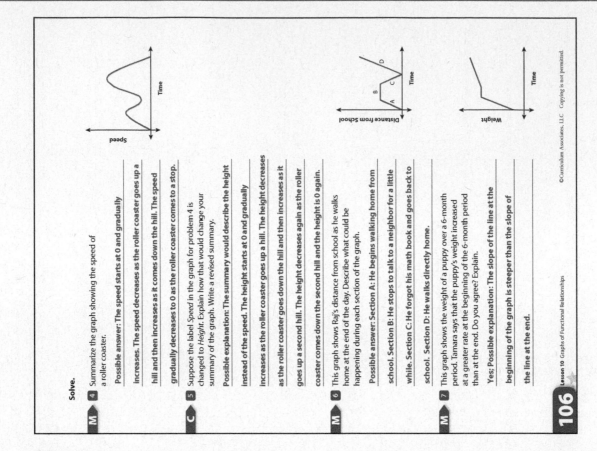

Solve.

M 4 Summarize the graph showing the speed of a roller coaster.

Possible answer: The speed starts at 0 and gradually increases. The speed decreases as the roller coaster goes up a hill and then increases as it comes down the hill. The speed gradually decreases to 0 as the roller coaster comes to a stop.

C 5 Suppose the label *Speed* in the graph for problem 4 is changed to *Height*. Explain how that would change your summary of the graph. Write a revised summary.

Possible explanation: The summary would describe the height instead of the speed. The height starts at 0 and gradually increases as the roller coaster goes up a hill. The height decreases as the roller coaster goes down the hill and then increases as it goes up a second hill. The height decreases again as the roller coaster comes down the second hill and the height is 0 again.

M 6 This graph shows Raj's distance from school as he walks home at the end of the day. Describe what could be happening during each section of the graph.

Possible answer: Section A: He begins walking home from school. Section B: He stops to talk to a neighbor for a little while. Section C: He forgot his math book and goes back to school. Section D: He walks directly home.

M 7 This graph shows the weight of a puppy over a 6-month period. Tamara says that the puppy's weight increased at a greater rate at the beginning of the 6-month period than at the end. Do you agree? Explain.

Yes; Possible explanation: The slope of the line at the beginning of the graph is steeper than the slope of the line at the end.

106 Lesson 10 Graphs of Functional Relationships

Lesson 10

Name: _____

Describe Qualitative Graphs

Study the example problem showing how to interpret a qualitative graph. Then solve problems 1–7.

Example

The graph shows the temperature for a day in a city. Summarize what the graph shows.

The temperature increases at the beginning of the day. It stays constant during the middle of the day. Then it decreases for the rest of the day.

B 1 Explain how the graph in the example shows that the temperature increases at the beginning of the day. What do you know about the slope of the line?

Possible answer: The line in the first part of the graph is gradually going up. It has a positive slope.

B 2 Explain how the graph in the example shows that the temperature stays constant for a while.

Possible answer: The line in the second part of the graph is a horizontal line.

M 3 This graph shows the speed of a car on a city street. Describe and interpret section C of the graph.

Possible answer: The car is not moving, so it could have stopped at a stop sign or traffic light.

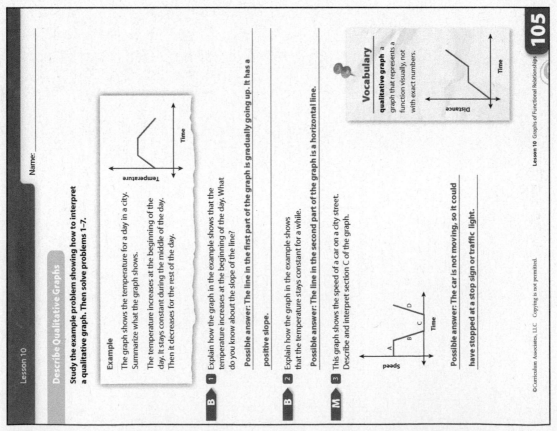

Vocabulary
qualitative graph a graph that represents a function visually, not with exact numbers.

105

Lesson 10 Graphs of Functional Relationships

Lesson 10

Name: _____

Draw Qualitative Graphs

Study the example showing how to draw a qualitative graph. Then solve problems 1–8.

Example

To draw a qualitative graph for a story, you can break a story into parts and then draw a section for each part. Shane is riding his bike from home to the store and back.

A From his house, he rides at a constant rate until he gets to the store.

B He is at the store for a little while and

C starts to go back home. On the way home,

D he stops at a friend's house,

E then he rides the rest of the way home.

The graph shows Shane's distance from home compared to time.

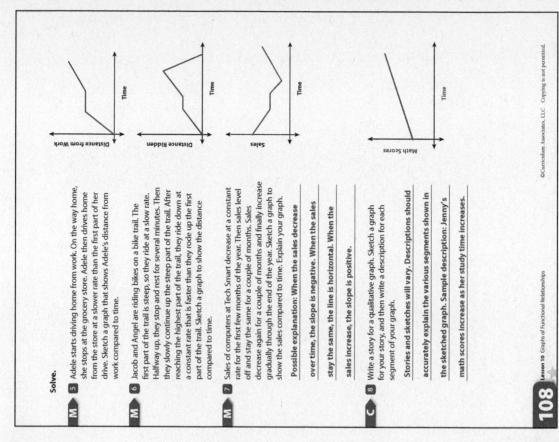

1 Why does the line in section A slant upward?

Possible answer: It shows that Shane's distance from home increases as the time increases.

2 Why are the lines in sections B and D horizontal?

They show that Shane stopped for a while, so his distance from home did not change.

3 The price of a cable company's service increases at a constant rate over time. Would a sketch of the graph show the price starting at 0? Explain why or why not. Then sketch a graph to show the price over time.

No; Possible explanation: The price would never have been $0.

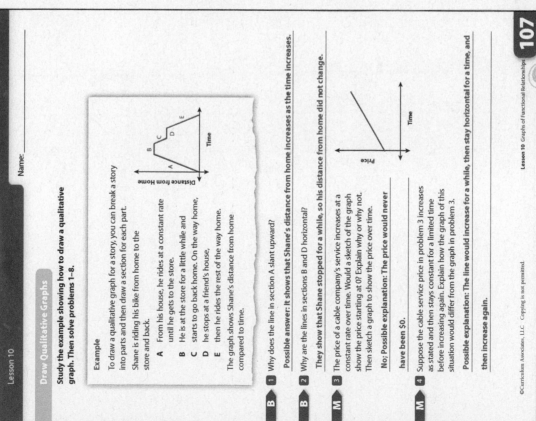

4 Suppose the cable service price in problem 3 increases as stated and then stays constant for a limited time before increasing again. Explain how the graph of this situation would differ from the graph in problem 3.

Possible explanation: The line would increase for a while, then stay horizontal for a while, and then increase again.

©Curriculum Associates, LLC Copying is not permitted.
Lesson 10 Graphs of Functional Relationships **107**

Solve.

5 Adele starts driving home from work. On the way home, she stops at the grocery store. Adele then drives home from the store at a slower rate than the first part of her drive. Sketch a graph that shows Adele's distance from work compared to time.

6 Jacob and Angel are riding bikes on a bike trail. The first part of the trail is steep, so they ride at a slow rate. Halfway up, they stop and rest for several minutes. Then they slowly continue up the steep part of the trail. After reaching the highest part of the trail, they ride down at a constant rate that is faster than they rode up the first part of the trail. Sketch a graph to show the distance compared to time.

7 Sales of computers at Tech Smart decrease at a constant rate for the first few months of the year. Then sales level off and stay the same for a couple of months. Sales decrease again for a couple of months and finally increase gradually through the end of the year. Sketch a graph to show the sales compared to time. Explain your graph.

Possible explanation: When the sales decrease over time, the slope is negative. When the sales stay the same, the line is horizontal. When the sales increase, the slope is positive.

8 Write a story for a qualitative graph. Sketch a graph for your story, and then write a description for each segment of your graph.

Stories and sketches will vary. Descriptions should accurately explain the various segments shown in the sketched graph. Sample description: Jenny's math scores increase as her study time increases.

108 Lesson 10 Graphs of Functional Relationships
©Curriculum Associates, LLC Copying is not permitted.

Lesson 10

Graphs of Functional Relationships

Solve the problems.

B **1** The graph represents Sophia's distance from home.

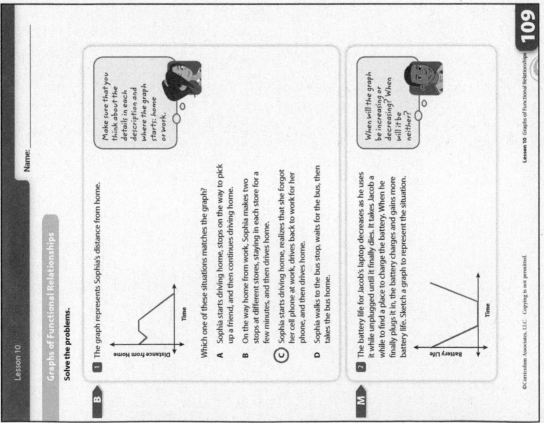

Which one of these situations matches the graph?

A Sophia starts driving home, stops on the way to pick up a friend, and then continues driving home.

B On the way home from work, Sophia makes two stops at different stores, staying in each store for a few minutes, and then drives home.

C Sophia starts driving home, realizes that she forgot her cell phone at work, drives back to work for her phone, and then drives home.

D Sophia walks to the bus stop, waits for the bus, then takes the bus home.

Make sure that you think about the detail in each description and where the graph starts: home or work.

M **2** The battery life for Jacob's laptop decreases as he uses it while unplugged until it finally dies. It takes Jacob a while to find a place to charge the battery. When he finally plugs it in, the battery charges and gains more battery life. Sketch a graph to represent the situation.

When will the graph be increasing or decreasing? When will it be neither?

©Curriculum Associates, LLC   Copying is not permitted.

Lesson 10 Graphs of Functional Relationships **109**

Solve.

M **3** Mica takes a train to visit a friend. The graph shows Mica's trip from his home in New Jersey to his friend's house in Maine.

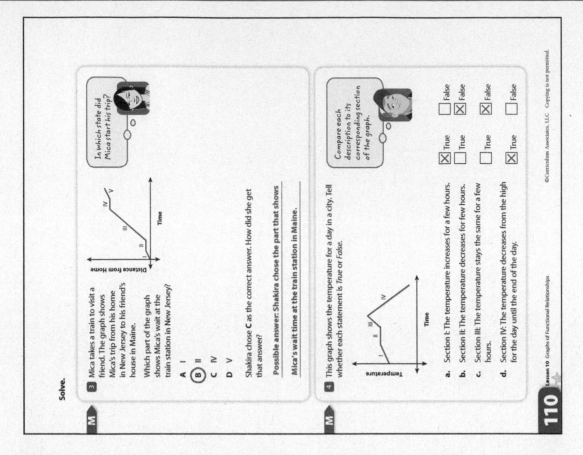

Which part of the graph shows Mica's wait at the train station in New Jersey?

A I

B II

C IV

D V

In which state did Mica start his trip?

Shakira chose **C** as the correct answer. How did she get that answer?

Possible answer: Shakira chose the part that shows Mica's wait time at the train station in Maine.

M **4** This graph shows the temperature for a day in a city. Tell whether each statement is *True* or *False*.

Compare each description to its corresponding section of the graph.

a. Section I: The temperature increases for a few hours.   [x] True   [ ] False

b. Section II: The temperature decreases for few hours.   [ ] True   [x] False

c. Section III: The temperature stays the same for a few hours.   [ ] True   [x] False

d. Section IV: The temperature decreases from the high for the day until the end of the day.   [x] True   [ ] False

©Curriculum Associates, LLC   Copying is not permitted.

110 Lesson 10 Graphs of Functional Relationships

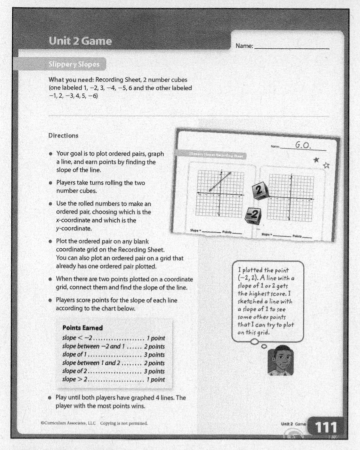

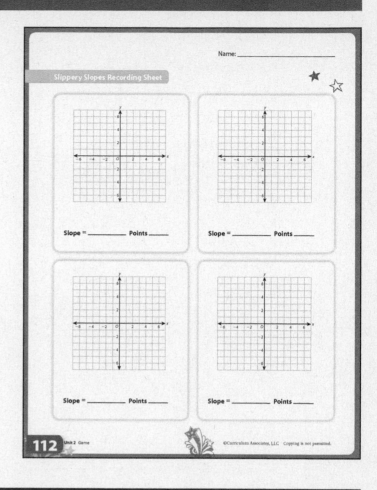

STEP BY STEP

CCSS Focus - 8.F.B.4 *Embedded SMPs* - 2, 4, 5, 7, 8	**Materials** For each pair: Recording Sheets (1 for each player)
Objective	(TR 4), 2 number cubes (one labeled 1, −2, 3, −4, −5, 6 and
• Plot ordered pairs, graph a line, and find its slope.	the other labeled −1, 2, −3, 4, 5, −6)

- Your goal is to plot ordered pairs, graph a line, and earn points by finding the slope of the line.

- Players take turns rolling the two number cubes.

- Use the rolled numbers to make an ordered pair, choosing which is the *x*-coordinate and which is the *y*-coordinate.

- Plot the ordered pair on any blank coordinate grid on the Recording Sheet. You can also plot an ordered pair on a grid that already has one ordered pair plotted.

- When there are two points plotted on a coordinate grid, connect them and find the slope of the line.

- Players score points for the slope of each line according to the chart provided.

- Play until both players have graphed 4 lines. The player with the most points wins.

- Model one round for students before they play. Help students brainstorm strategies for creating lines with slopes that score more points.

Vary the Game You can also plot one ordered pair on a grid that already has a line. If your point is on the line, score 5 points.

Challenge For a "bonus" round, roll to try to make a new line on each grid. Score 2 points if the line is parallel to the existing line. Score 3 points if it is perpendicular.

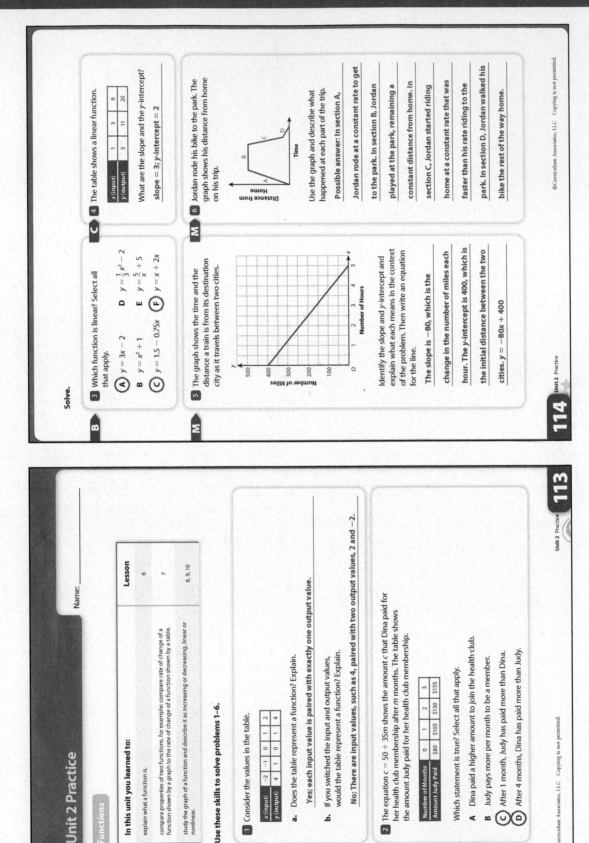

Unit 2 Practice

Functions

Name: _____

In this unit you learned to:

	Lesson
explain what a function is.	6
compare properties of two functions, for example: compare rate of change of a function shown by a graph to the rate of change of a function shown by a table.	7
study the graph of a function and describe it as increasing or decreasing, linear or nonlinear.	8, 9, 10

Use these skills to solve problems 1–6.

B **1** Consider the values in the table.

x (input)	-2	-1	0	1	2
y (output)	4	1	0	1	4

a. Does the table represent a function? Explain.

Yes; each input value is paired with exactly one output value.

b. If you switched the input and output values, would the table represent a function? Explain.

No; There are input values, such as 4, paired with two output values, 2 and −2.

M **2** The equation $c = 50 + 35m$ shows the amount c that Dina paid for her health club membership after m months. The table shows the amount Judy paid for her health club membership.

Number of Months	0	1	2	3
Amount Judy Paid	$80	$105	$130	$155

Which statement is true? Select all that apply.

A Dina paid a higher amount to join the health club.

B Judy pays more per month to be a member.

C After 1 month, Judy has paid more than Dina.

D After 4 months, Dina has paid more than Judy.

©Curriculum Associates, LLC   Copying is not permitted.
Unit 2 Practice **113**

B **3** Which function is linear? Select all that apply.

A $y = 3x - 2$ D $y = \frac{1}{3}x^3 - 2$

B $y = x^2 + 1$ E $y = \frac{5}{x} + 5$

C $y = 1.5 - 0.75x$ **F** $y = x + 2x$

C **4** The table shows a linear function.

x (input)	1	3	6
y (output)	5	11	20

What are the slope and the y-intercept?

slope = 3; y-intercept = 2

M **5** The graph shows the time and the distance a train is from its destination city as it travels between two cities.

Identify the slope and y-intercept and explain what each means in the context of the problem. Then write an equation for the line.

The slope is −80, which is the change in the number of miles each hour. The y-intercept is 400, which is the initial distance between the two cities. $y = -80x + 400$

M **6** Jordan rode his bike to the park. The graph shows his distance from home on his trip.

Use the graph and describe what happened at each part of the trip.

Possible answer: In section A, Jordan rode at a constant rate to get to the park. In section B, Jordan played at the park, remaining a constant distance from home. In section C, Jordan started riding home at a constant rate that was faster than his rate riding to the park. In section D, Jordan walked his bike the rest of the way home.

114 Unit 2 Practice
©Curriculum Associates, LLC   Copying is not permitted.

Key

B Basic   **M** Medium   **C** Challenge

©Curriculum Associates, LLC   Copying is not permitted.

TEACHER NOTES

Common Core Standards: 8.F.A.1, 8.F.A.2
Standards for Mathematical Practice: 1, 2, 3, 4, 5, 6, 7, 8
DOK: 3
Materials: grid paper (for Extension)

About the Task

To complete this task, students solve a multi-step problem that involves reasoning about how the rates of change for different functions are related. The task requires that they understand and utilize the functional relationship between the rate of water flow and the duration of the flow and make a decision based on their analysis of mathematical information.

Getting Started

Read the problem out loud with students and go over the checklist. Have them identify the goal. Have students predict which showerhead will use the least water and which will use the most. Invite students to explain their predictions using the information in the problem. Discuss approaches for solving the problem and the importance of the rate of change. **(SMP 1, 3)**

Completing the Task

Students will find that it is best to work through the steps of this problem in the order presented. They will use the result of each step in the next step. Some students may skip ahead and then need to go back and complete an earlier step. **(SMP 1)**

Students may approach this problem in different ways. Encourage them to use tools from this unit, such as graphing the relationship between shower duration and number of gallons used. They will find that the rate of change describes this relationship. It is the slope of the line that runs through the data points. **(SMP 4, 5, 7)**

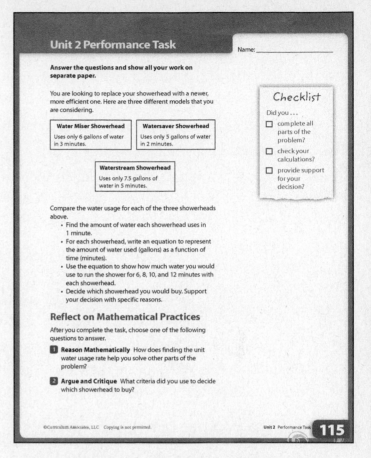

Have students discuss the benefits of finding the rate of change in this situation. It enables them to compare the amount of water used for any length of time rather than one specific length of time. **(SMP 6)**

Discuss students' findings and purchase decisions as a class. Have students note any patterns that they discovered. **(SMP 3, 8)**

Extension

If students have more time to spend on this problem, you can have them solve this extension:

Find how much water each showerhead would use for a 15-minute shower. Then compare pairs of showerheads, telling how many more gallons one would use than the other.

SAMPLE RESPONSE AND RUBRIC

4-Point Solution

Use the given ratios to the find the number of gallons of water used in 1 minute.

Water Miser: $\frac{6}{3} = \frac{2}{1}$ Watersaver: $\frac{5}{2} = \frac{2.5}{1}$ Waterstream: $\frac{7.5}{5} = \frac{1.5}{1}$

Let w be the gallons of water used and let m be minutes the shower runs.

Here are the functions for each showerhead.

Water Miser $w = 2m$, initial value = 0 gallons and rate of change = 2 gallons per minute

Watersaver $w = 2.5m$, initial value = 0 gallons and rate of change = 2.5 gallons per minute

Waterstream $w = 1.5m$, initial value = 0 gallons and rate of change = 1.5 gallons per minute

	1 min	6 min	8 min	10 min	12 min
Water Miser (gal)	2	12	16	20	24
Watersaver (gal)	2.5	15	20	25	30
Waterstream (gal)	1.5	9	12	15	18

The rate of change for the Waterstream brand is less than the others. That means it uses less water each minute.

For a 10-minute shower Waterstream uses only 15 gallons compared to 25 gallons that Watersaver uses. I would save 10 gallons of water for every 10-minute shower, so I would buy the Waterstream.

REFLECT ON MATHEMATICAL PRACTICES

1. Students should explain that the unit rate allows them to compare accurately because they are measuring how much water flows in 1 minute for each showerhead. **(SMP 2)**

2. Students' explanations should include a mathematical justification based on the information in their solutions, as part or all of their criteria. Accept any response that makes sense. **(SMP 3)**

SCORING RUBRIC

4 points   All parts of the problem are complete and correct. The function equations, rates of change, and initial values are correct. Students show all work and explain their purchasing decision.

3 points   The student has completed all parts of the problem, with one or two errors. Possible errors include an incorrect rate of change or amount of water used, or an incomplete explanation.

2 points   The student has attempted all parts of the problem, with a number of errors. Some rates, amounts of water used, and functions may be incorrect. Not all work is shown, and the explanation may be incomplete.

1 point   Much of the problem is incomplete, with several errors. Rates, amount of water used, functions, student's work, and explanation are incomplete, missing, or incorrect.

SOLUTION TO THE EXTENSION

Possible Solution

Water Miser: $\frac{2 \text{ gallons}}{1 \text{ minute}} = \frac{30 \text{ gallons}}{15 \text{ minutes}}$ *Watersaver:* $\frac{2.5 \text{ gallons}}{1 \text{ minute}} = \frac{37.5 \text{ gallons}}{15 \text{ minutes}}$ *Waterstream:* $\frac{1.5 \text{ gallons}}{1 \text{ minute}} = \frac{22.5 \text{ gallons}}{15 \text{ minutes}}$

Water Miser uses 7.5 gallons less than Watersaver and 7.5 gallons more than Waterstream. Watersaver uses 15 gallons more than Waterstream.

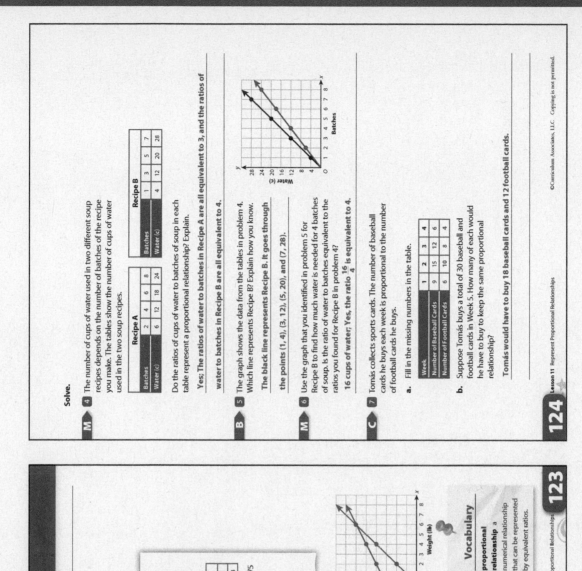

Page 123

Lesson 11

Represent Proportional Relationships

Name:

Prerequisite: Identify Proportional Relationships

Study the example showing how to tell whether a relationship is proportional. Then solve problems 1–7.

Example

Suppose you are buying grapes at a farmers' market. The cost of the grapes you buy depends on how many pounds you get. Two different stalls sell grapes at the market. Find the ratio of the cost to weight for each pair of values in both tables.

Stall A

Weight, in Pounds	2	4	6	8
Total Cost ($)	4	8	12	16

$\frac{4}{2} = 2 \quad \frac{8}{4} = 2 \quad \frac{12}{6} = 2 \quad \frac{16}{8} = 2$

Stall B

Weight, in Pounds	2	4	6	8
Total Cost ($)	8	10	12	14

$\frac{8}{2} = 4 \quad \frac{10}{4} = 2.5 \quad \frac{12}{6} = 2 \quad \frac{14}{8} = 1.75$

If a group of ratios are equivalent, they are part of a proportional relationship.

The relationship of total cost to weight in Stall A is proportional.

The relationship of total cost to weight in Stall B is not proportional.

B **1** Plot a point for each of the first three ordered pairs in each table. Connect the points for each relationship by drawing a line through the points to the y-axis.

B **2** Look at your graph in problem 1. Does the line for either the proportional relationship or the relationship that is not proportional go through the origin? If so, which relationship?

Yes; The graph of the proportional relationship connects to the origin.

B **3** Suppose the cost of 10 pounds of grapes at Stall A is $15. Would the relationship still be proportional? Explain.

No. The ratio $\frac{15}{10}$ equals 1.5, not 2, so the ratios would not be equivalent.

Vocabulary

proportional relationship a numerical relationship that can be represented by equivalent ratios.

Page 124

Solve.

M **4** The number of cups of water used in two different soup recipes depends on the number of batches of the recipe you make. The tables show the number of cups of water used in the two soup recipes.

Recipe A

Batches	2	4	6	8
Water (c)	6	12	18	24

Recipe B

Batches	1	3	5	7
Water (c)	4	12	20	28

Do the ratios of cups of water to batches of soup in each table represent a proportional relationship? Explain.

Yes; The ratios of water to batches in Recipe A are all equivalent to 3, and the ratios of water to batches in Recipe B are all equivalent to 4.

B **5** The graph shows the data from the tables in problem 4. Which line represents Recipe B? Explain how you know.

The black line represents Recipe B. It goes through the points (1, 4), (3, 12), (5, 20), and (7, 28).

M **6** Use the graph that you identified in problem 5 for Recipe B to find how much water is needed for 4 batches of soup. Is the ratio of water to batches equivalent to the ratios you found for Recipe B in problem 4?

16 cups of water; Yes; the ratio $\frac{16}{4}$ is equivalent to 4.

C **7** Tomás collects sports cards. The number of baseball cards he buys each week is proportional to the number of football cards he buys.

a. Fill in the missing numbers in the table.

Week	1	2	3	4
Number of Baseball Cards	9	15	12	6
Number of Football Cards	6	10	8	4

b. Suppose Tomás buys a total of 30 baseball and football cards in Week 5. How many of each would he have to buy to keep the same proportional relationship?

Tomás would have to buy 18 baseball cards and 12 football cards.

Key

B Basic   **M** Medium   **C** Challenge

Lesson 11

Name: _____

Use Tables, Graphs, and Equations

Study the example problem showing how to use a table and a graph to find a unit cost. Then solve problems 1–6.

Example

The table shows the costs for different numbers of tickets for the band concert. Find the unit cost.

Band Concert Tickets

Number of Tickets	2	4	6	8
Cost ($)	12	24	36	48

Use a Table

The ratios in the table are all equivalent, so you can divide the cost by the number of tickets in any of the ratios to find the unit cost.

$$\frac{\$24}{4 \text{ tickets}} = \frac{\$6}{1 \text{ ticket}}, \text{ or } \$6 \text{ for 1 ticket}$$

The unit cost is 6.

Use a Graph

The graph of the data shows that the cost of one ticket, is $6, so the unit cost is 6.

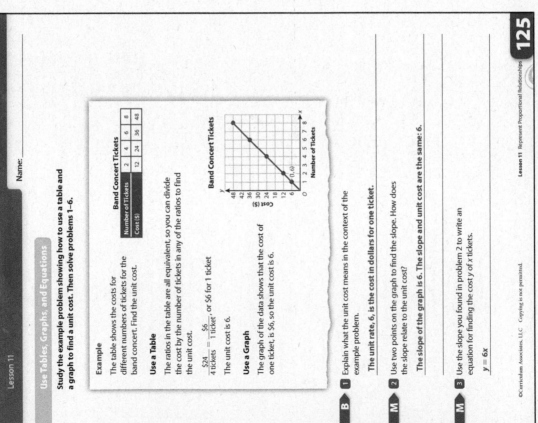

1 Explain what the unit cost means in the context of the example problem.

The unit rate, 6, is the cost in dollars for one ticket.

2 Use two points on the graph to find the slope. How does the slope relate to the unit cost?

The slope of the graph is 6. The slope and unit cost are the same: 6.

3 Use the slope you found in problem 2 to write an equation for finding the cost y of x tickets.

$y = 6x$

Solve.

4 The table shows the distance Nikki travels on her bike as a function of how many hours she rides at a constant rate. Use the information in the table to make a graph, using the coordinate plane to the right. Find the slope of the graph and explain what it means in this situation.

Number of Hours	2	4	6	8
Number of Miles	16.5	33	49.5	66

8.25; Nikki rides 8.25 miles per hour.

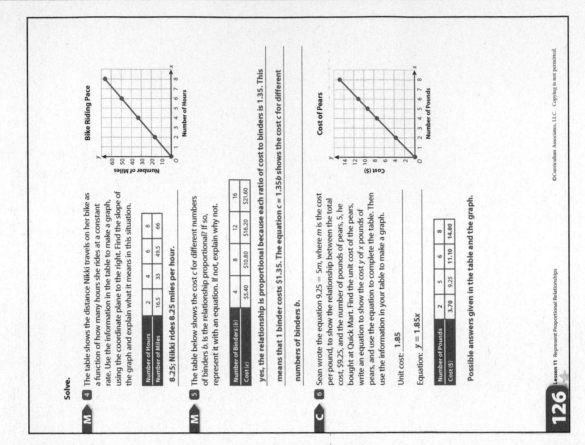

5 The table below shows the cost c for different numbers of binders b. Is the relationship proportional? If so, represent it with an equation. If not, explain why not.

Number of Binders (b)	4	8	12	16
Cost (c)	$5.40	$10.80	$16.20	$21.60

yes, the relationship is proportional because each ratio of cost to binders is 1.35. This means that 1 binder costs $1.35. The equation $c = 1.35b$ shows the cost c for different numbers of binders b.

6 Sean wrote the equation $9.25 = 5m$, where m is the cost per pound, to show the relationship between the total cost, $9.25, and the number of pounds of pears, 5, he bought at Quick Mart. Find the unit cost of the pears, write an equation to show the cost y of x pounds of pears, and use the equation to complete the table. Then use the information in your table to make a graph.

Unit cost: __1.85__

Equation: $y = 1.85x$

Number of Pounds	2	5	6	8
Cost ($)	3.70	9.25	11.10	14.80

Possible answers given in the table and the graph.

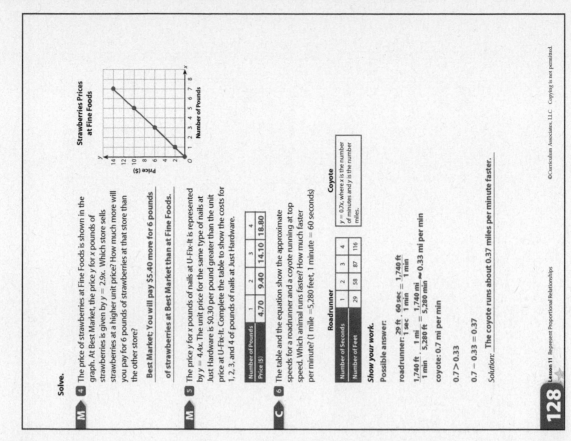

Solve.

M **4** The price of strawberries at Fine Foods is shown in the graph. At Best Market, the price y for x pounds of strawberries is given by $y = 2.9x$. Which store sells strawberries at a higher unit price? How much more will you pay for 6 pounds of strawberries at that store than the other store?

Strawberries Prices at Fine Foods

Best Market; You will pay $5.40 more for 6 pounds

of strawberries at Best Market than at Fine Foods.

M **5** The price y for x pounds of nails at U-Fix-It is represented by $y = 4.4x$. The unit price for the same type of nails at Just Hardware is $0.30 per pound greater than the unit price at U-Fix-It. Complete the table to show the costs for 1, 2, 3, and 4 of pounds of nails at Just Hardware.

Number of Pounds	1	2	3	4
Price ($)	4.70	9.40	14.10	18.80

C **6** The table and the equation show the approximate speeds for a roadrunner and a coyote running at top speed. Which animal runs faster? How much faster per minute? (1 mile = 5,280 feet, 1 minute = 60 seconds)

Roadrunner

Number of Seconds	1	2	3	4
Number of Feet	29	58	87	116

Coyote

$y = 0.7x$, where x is the number of minutes and y is the number of miles.

Show your work.
Possible answer:

roadrunner: $\dfrac{29 \text{ ft}}{1 \text{ sec}} \cdot \dfrac{60 \text{ sec}}{1 \text{ min}} = \dfrac{1{,}740 \text{ ft}}{1 \text{ min}}$

$\dfrac{1{,}740 \text{ ft}}{1 \text{ min}} \cdot \dfrac{1 \text{ mi}}{5{,}280 \text{ ft}} = \dfrac{1{,}740 \text{ mi}}{5{,}280 \text{ min}} \approx 0.33 \text{ mi per min}$

coyote: 0.7 mi per min

$0.7 > 0.33$

$0.7 - 0.33 = 0.37$

Solution: The coyote runs about 0.37 miles per minute faster.

Lesson 11

Name: _____

Compare Proportional Relationships

Study the example problem showing how to compare proportional relationships. Then solve problems 1–6.

Example

The table and the equation show the rates at which two different students read in words per minute. Which student reads faster?

Student A

Number of Minutes	1	2	3	4
Number of Words Read	150	300	450	600

Student B

$y = 158x$, where x is the number of minutes and y is the number of words read.

For Student A use the table to find the number of words read in 1 minute, and for Student B use the slope in the equation.

Student A: 150 words per minute
Student B: 158 words per minute

Compare the rates: 158 > 150.
Student B reads faster.

B **1** How much faster does Student B read than Student A?
Student B reads $158 - 150 = 8$ more words per minute than student A.

B **2** The graph shows the rate at which Student C reads. Explain how to find the reading rate for Student C from the graph.

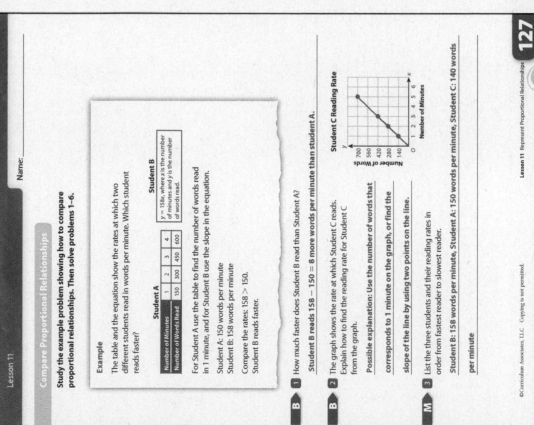

Student C Reading Rate

Possible explanation: Use the number of words that corresponds to 1 minute on the graph, or find the slope of the line by using two points on the line.

M **3** List the three students and their reading rates in order from fastest reader to slowest reader.
Student B: 158 words per minute, Student A: 150 words per minute, Student C: 140 words

per minute

Lesson 11

Name: _____

Represent Proportional Relationships

Solve the problems.

B

1 The cost y for x pounds of peanuts is represented by the equation $y = 0.23x$. The cost y for x pounds of pecans is represented by the equation $y = 0.45x$. Which statement is true? Select all that apply.

Ⓐ The cost for peanuts is $0.22 per ounce less than the cost for pecans.

B The cost for peanuts is greater than the cost for pecans.

C The cost for 8 ounces of peanuts is $3.60.

Ⓓ The cost for 8 ounces of pecans is $3.60.

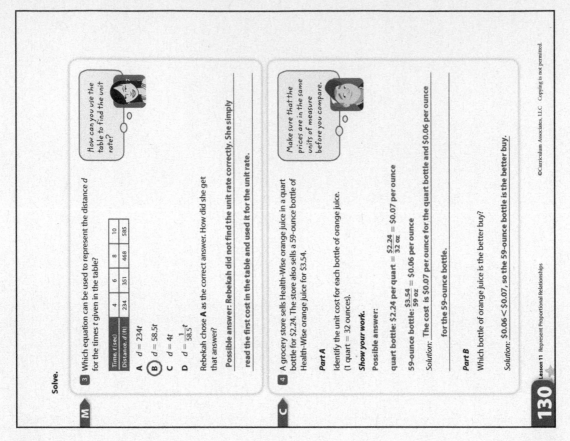

How do the equations show the unit cost?

M

2 For each table, write in the equation that represents the price per ticket.

Tickets	2	5	6	8
Price ($)	15	37.50	45	60

$y = 7.5x$

Tickets	3	4	5	6
Price ($)	27.75	37	46.25	55.50

$y = 9.25x$

Tickets	2	3	4	5
Price ($)	12	18	24	30

$y = 6x$

How can you use the tables to find the unit price?

Solve.

M

3 Which equation can be used to represent the distance d for the times t given in the table?

Time, t (sec)	4	6	8	10
Distance, d (ft)	234	351	468	585

A $d = 234t$

Ⓑ $d = 58.5t$

C $d = 4t$

D $d = \frac{1}{58.5}t$

Rebekah chose **A** as the correct answer. How did she get that answer?

Possible answer: Rebekah did not find the unit rate correctly. She simply read the first cost in the table and used it for the unit rate.

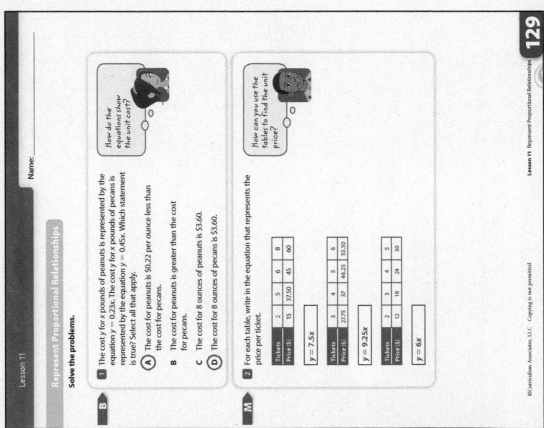

How can you use the table to find the unit rate?

C

4 A grocery store sells Health-Wise orange juice in a quart bottle for $2.24. The store also sells a 59-ounce bottle of Health-Wise orange juice for $3.54.

Part A

Identify the unit cost for each bottle of orange juice. (1 quart = 32 ounces).

Show your work.

Possible answer:

quart bottle: $2.24 per quart = $\frac{\$2.24}{32 \text{ oz}}$ = $0.07 per ounce

59-ounce bottle: $\frac{\$3.54}{59 \text{ oz}}$ = $0.06 per ounce

Solution: The cost is $0.07 per ounce for the quart bottle and $0.06 per ounce for the 59-ounce bottle.

Part B

Which bottle of orange juice is the better buy?

Solution: $0.06 < $0.07, so the 59-ounce bottle is the better buy.

Make sure that the prices are in the same units of measure before you compare.

Lesson 12
Understand the Slope-Intercept Equation for a Line

Name: _____

Prerequisite: How can you represent and interpret proportional relationships?

Study the example problem showing how to represent and interpret a proportional relationship. Then solve problems 1–5.

Example

The table shows the costs for 2, 3, 4, and 5 vegetable seed packets. What is the unit rate?

Use the data to make a graph. Find the cost of 1 seed packet.

The unit rate is the cost in dollars for 1 packet. The graph shows that the unit rate is 1.50.

Vegetable Seeds

Number of Packets	2	3	4	5
Cost ($)	3.00	4.50	6.00	7.50

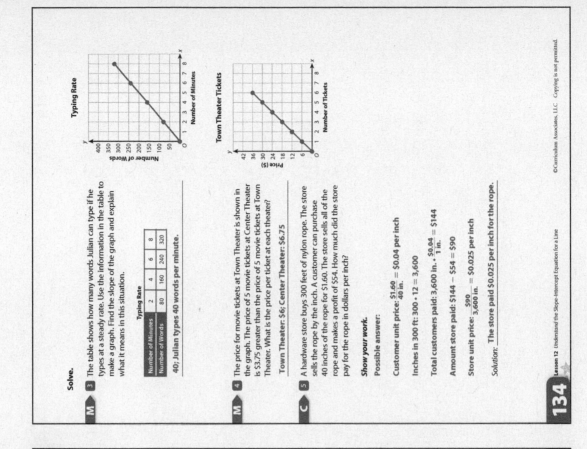

Vegetable Seeds graph — Cost ($) vs Number of Packets, point (1, 1.50)

B **1** How you can use the table to find the unit rate in the example problem?

Possible answer: You can divide the cost of any number of packets by the corresonding number of packets.

B **2** What is the constant of proportionality in the example? What is the slope of the graph? What do they represent in the context of this problem? How do the constant of proportionality and slope relate to the unit rate?

The constant of proportionality is 1.50 and the slope is 1.50. They represent that 1 packet of seeds costs $1.50. The constant of proportionality, the slope, and the unit rate are the same.

©Curriculum Associates, LLC Copying is not permitted.   Lesson 12 *Understand* the Slope-Intercept Equation for a Line **133**

Solve.

M **3** The table shows how many words Julian can type if he types at a steady rate. Use the information in the table to make a graph. Find the slope of the graph and explain what it means in this situation.

Typing Rate

Number of Minutes	2	4	6	8
Number of Words	80	160	240	320

40; Julian types 40 words per minute.

Typing Rate graph — Number of Words (50–400) vs Number of Minutes (1–8)

M **4** The price for movie tickets at Town Theater is shown in the graph. The price of 5 movie tickets at Center Theater is $3.75 greater than the price of 5 movie tickets at Town Theater. What is the price per ticket at each theater?

Town Theater: $6; Center Theater: $6.75

Town Theater Tickets graph — Price ($) vs Number of Tickets (1–8)

C **5** A hardware store buys 300 feet of nylon rope. The store sells the rope by the inch. A customer can purchase 40 inches of the rope for $1.60. The store sells all of the rope and makes a profit of $54. How much did the store pay for the rope in dollars per inch?

Show your work.

Possible answer:

Customer unit price: $\dfrac{\$1.60}{40 \text{ in.}} = \$0.04$ per inch

Inches in 300 ft: $300 \cdot 12 = 3{,}600$

Total customers paid: $3{,}600$ in. $\cdot \dfrac{\$0.04}{1 \text{ in.}} = \$144$

Amount store paid: $\$144 - \$54 = \$90$

Store unit price: $\dfrac{\$90}{3{,}600 \text{ in.}} = \$0.025$ per inch

Solution: The store paid $0.025 per inch for the rope.

134 Lesson 12 *Understand* the Slope-Intercept Equation for a Line   ©Curriculum Associates, LLC   Copying is not permitted.

Key

B Basic   **M** Medium   **C** Challenge

Lesson 12

Name: _____

Writing a Linear Equation in Slope-Intercept Form

Study the example problem showing how to write an equation in slope-intercept form. Then solve problems 1–6.

Example

Write an equation for the line shown in the diagram.

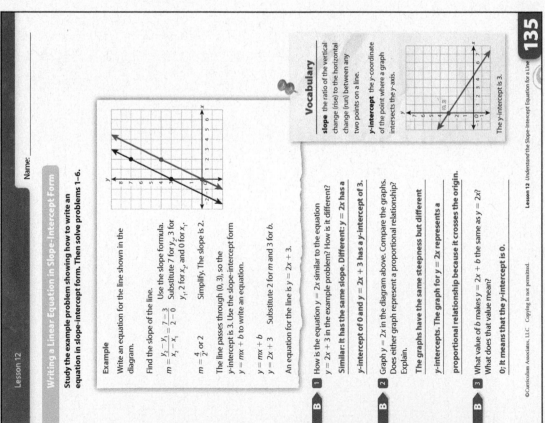

Find the slope of the line.

$m = \frac{y_2 - y_1}{x_2 - x_1} = \frac{7-3}{2-0}$ Use the slope formula. Substitute 7 for y_2, 3 for y_1, 2 for x_2, and 0 for x_1.

$m = \frac{4}{2}$ or 2   Simplify. The slope is 2.

The line passes through (0, 3), so the y-intercept is 3. Use the slope-intercept form $y = mx + b$ to write an equation.

$y = mx + b$
$y = 2x + 3$ Substitute 2 for m and 3 for b.

An equation for the line is $y = 2x + 3$.

Vocabulary

slope the ratio of the vertical change (rise) to the horizontal change (run) between any two points on a line.

y-intercept the y-coordinate of the point where a graph intersects the y-axis.

The y-intercept is 3.

1 How is the equation $y = 2x$ similar to the equation $y = 2x + 3$ in the example problem? How is it different?

Similar: It has the same slope. Different: $y = 2x$ has a y-intercept of 0 and $y = 2x + 3$ has a y-intercept of 3.

2 Graph $y = 2x$ in the diagram above. Compare the graphs. Does either graph represent a proportional relationship? Explain.

The graphs have the same steepness but different y-intercepts. The graph for $y = 2x$ represents a proportional relationship because it crosses the origin.

3 What value of b makes $y = 2x + b$ the same as $y = 2x$? What does that value mean?

0; It means that the y-intercept is 0.

Solve.

4 Andy uses the table below to write a linear equation.

x	−1	0	1	2
y	2	4	6	8

He says he can write an equation of the form $y = mx$ for the given values. Is he correct? Explain your reasoning.

No; Possible explanation: The graph of an equation in the form $y = mx$ goes through the origin, (0, 0), but the graph of this relationship would go through (0, 4).

5 Look at these equations. Write each equation in slope-intercept form. Are the equations the same or different? Explain.

$y + 1 = 2x - 3$
$y = 2x - 3 - 1$
$y = 2x - 4$

$2x - 3 = y + 1$
$2x = y + 1 + 3$
$2x = y + 4$
$2x - 4 = y$
$y = 2x - 4$

$2y + 2 = 4x - 6$
$\frac{2y}{2} + \frac{2}{2} = \frac{4x}{2} - \frac{6}{2}$
$y + 1 = 2x - 3$
$y = 2x - 3 - 1$
$y = 2x - 4$

Possible explanation: They are identical because each is $y = 2x - 4$ when written in slope-intercept form.

6 Explain how you can write an equation for a line with slope $\frac{1}{2}$ that crosses the y-axis at the point (0, –1). Graph the line for your equation.

Possible explanation: I can use the slope-intercept form $y = mx + b$. The slope is $\frac{1}{2}$. The y-coordinate of the point where the line crosses the y-axis, (0, −1), is the y-intercept, so the y-intercept is −1. The equation is $y = \frac{1}{2}x - 1$.

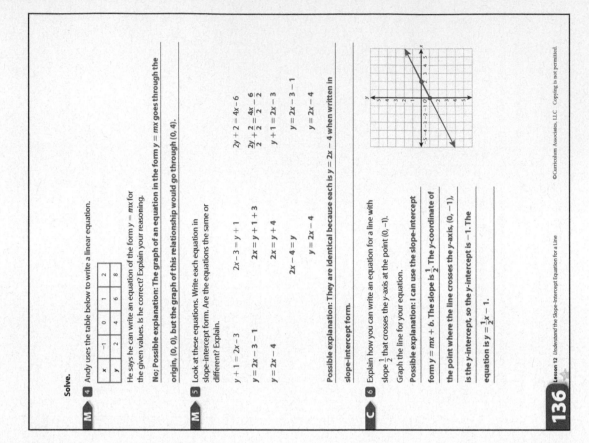

Lesson 12

Name: _____

Reason and Write

Study the example. Underline two parts that you think make it a particularly good answer and a helpful example.

Example

Draw two lines that have the same slope on the coordinate grid. Let one represent a proportional relationship and one represent a relationship that is not proportional. Label one line A and the other B.

Predict how you expect the slope-intercept equations of your lines to be similar and different. Then write the equations to check your predictions.

Show your work. Use graphs, words, and numbers to explain your answer.

> *Answers will vary. Note whether students incorporate the features they chose in their answer on the next page.*

> *Where does the example . . .*
> - *answer each part of the problem?*
> - *use a graph to explain.*
> - *use words to explain?*
> - *use numbers to explain?*

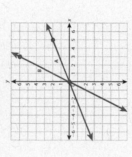

I predict that the slope-intercept equations will have the same value for m because the lines have the same slope. The equations will have different values for b, because Line A crosses the y-axis at (0, 0) and Line B crosses the y-axis at (0, 3).

To write the equations, I first find the slope and y-intercept of each line. Line A: slope $= \frac{2-0}{3-0} = \frac{2}{3}$, y-intercept $= 0$;
Line B: slope $= \frac{6-4}{3-0} = \frac{2}{3}$, y-intercept $= 4$. Equation for Line A: $y = \frac{2}{3}x$. Equation for Line B: $y = \frac{2}{3}x + 4$.

My predictions were correct. The equations have the same value for m, $\frac{2}{3}$, and different values for b, 0 and 4.

©Curriculum Associates, LLC   Copying is not permitted.
Lesson 12 *Understand* the Slope-Intercept Equation for a Line **137**

Solve the problem. Use what you learned from the model.

Draw two lines that both represent proportional relationships but have different slopes. Label one line A and the other B.

Predict how you expect the slope-intercept equations of your lines to be similar and different. Then write the equations to check your predictions.

Show your work. Use graphs, words, and numbers to explain your answer.

> *Did you . . .*
> - *answer each part of the problem?*
> - *use a graph to explain.*
> - *use words to explain?*
> - *use numbers to explain?*

Possible answer: I predict that the equations will both have 0 as the value of b because they both cross the y-axis at (0, 0). The equations will have different values for m because they have different slopes.

To write the equations, I first find the slope and y-intercept of each line.

Line A: slope $= \frac{2-0}{5-0} = \frac{2}{5}$, y-intercept $= 0$;
Line B: slope $= \frac{6-0}{3-0} = \frac{6}{3} = 2$, y-intercept $= 0$.
Equation for Line A: $y = \frac{2}{5}x$. Equation for Line B: $y = 2x$.

My predictions were correct. The slope-intercept equations have the same value for b, 0, and different values for m, $\frac{2}{5}$ and 2.

138 **Lesson 12** *Understand* the Slope-Intercept Equation for a Line
©Curriculum Associates, LLC   Copying is not permitted.

Lesson 13

Solve Linear Equations with Rational Coefficients

Prerequisite: Solve Problems with Expressions

Study the example problem showing how to write equivalent expressions. Then solve problems 1–10.

Example

The lengths of the sides of an equilateral triangle are shown. Write two different expressions for the perimeter of the triangle.

Triangle with sides labeled $d + 5$

Expression 1
Find the sum of the side lengths.
$(d + 5) + (d + 5) + (d + 5)$

Expression 2
Multiply the side length by 3.
$3(d + 5)$

B 1 Simplify Expression 1.
$(d + 5) + (d + 5) + (d + 5) = 3d + 15$

B 2 Simplify Expression 2.
$3(d + 5) = 3d + 15$

B 3 What do you notice about the simplified expressions in problems 1 and 2?
They are equivalent.

B 4 Jessica rewrites Expression 1 as $d + d + d + 5 + 5 + 5$. Why might she have done this?
Possible explanation: To gather like terms.

B 5 Is Jessica's expression equivalent to Expression 2? Explain how you know.
Yes; Possible explanation: I simplified her expression to $3d + 15$, which is the same as the simplified version of Expression 2.

141

Solve.

M 6 The lengths of the sides of a rectangle are shown. Write two equivalent expressions for the perimeter of the rectangle.

Rectangle with sides labeled t and $t + 3$

Possible answers: $2(t) + 2(t + 3)$, $t + t + (t + 3) + (t + 3)$, or $4t + 6$. Accept all other correct expressions.

M 7 Write two different expressions that are equivalent to $12 - 16x$. Use factoring to write one of the expressions.

Possible answers: $4(3 - 4x)$, $2(6 - 8x)$, $(3 - 4x) + (3 - 4x) + (3 - 4x) + (3 - 4x)$, $(6 - 8x) + (6 - 8x)$, or $12 - 16x$. Accept all other correct expressions.

M 8 Describe how to determine whether $18 - 3(2p + 4) - 3p$ is equivalent to $3(2 - 3p)$. Are the expressions equivalent?

Yes, $18 - 3(2p + 4) - 3p$ is equivalent to $3(2 - 3p)$.

Start with $18 - 3(2p + 4) - 3p$.

Use the distributive property: $18 - 6p - 12 - 3p$.

Combine like terms: $6 - 9p$. Factor: $3(2 - 3p)$.

M 9 Tran says that $-\frac{1}{4}x - 7 + \frac{9}{4}x + 2x$ is equivalent to $4x - 7$. How can substituting any value for x help you determine whether Tran is correct? Is Tran correct? Use substitution to justify your answer.

Any value of x gives the same result for equivalent expressions. For example, if $x = 4$,
$-\frac{1}{4}(4) - 7 + \frac{9}{4}(4) + 2(4) = -1 - 7 + 9 + 8 = 9$ and $4(4) - 7 = 16 - 7 = 9$. The results are the same, so Tran is correct.

C 10 The perimeter of a square can be represented by the expression $8x - 10 + 8x - 10$. Write an expression to represent the length of one side of the square.

Show your work.

$8x - 10 + 8x - 10 = 16x - 20$
$= 4(4x - 5)$

Solution: The length of one side of the square is $4x - 5$.

142

Key

B Basic   **M** Medium   **C** Challenge

Name: _____

Lesson 13

Solve Equations with Rational Coefficients

Study the example showing how to solve an equation with rational coefficients. Then solve problems 1–6.

Example

Solve the equation: $4n = \frac{1}{2}(2n - 12)$.

$4n = \frac{1}{2}(2n - 12)$

$4n = n - 6$ **Step 1:** Use the distributive property.

$4n - n = n - 6 - n$ **Step 2:** Subtract n from both sides.

$3n = -6$ **Step 3:** Simplify.

$\frac{3n}{3} = \frac{-6}{3}$ **Step 4:** Divide both sides by 3.

$n = -2$ **Step 5:** Simplify.

B **1** Check the solution to the example problem by replacing n in the original equation with -2 and evaluating both sides. What true statement do you get?

$-8 = -8$

M **2** Suppose that you first want to eliminate the fraction in the example equation. What would your first step be? Is -2 still the solution when you start by eliminating the fraction first? Explain.

Multiply both sides of the equation by 2. Yes; I get the equation $8n = 2n - 12$, which

simplifies to $n = -2$.

M **3** Trey solved the equation $\frac{1}{4}(8x + 16) = 4x$, as shown at the right. Describe the error that he made. Then solve the problem.

$\frac{1}{4}(8x + 16) = 4x$

$2x + 16 = 4x$

$\frac{16}{2} = \frac{2x}{2}$

$8 = x$

Possible answer: Trey did not multiply 16 by $\frac{1}{4}$ when he applied the distributive property.

The correct solution is $x = 2$.

Solve.

M **4** Describe the first step you would use to solve the equation $20 = 7y + 2 - y$. Is that the only possible first step?

Possible answer: I would start by combining like terms on the right side of the equation to

get $20 = 6y + 2$. No, I also could have subtracted 2 from both sides to get $18 = 7y - y$.

M **5** Solve the equation in two different ways: $6p = 0.6(5p + 15)$.

Show your work.

Possible solutions:

$6p = 0.6(5p + 15)$	$6p = 0.6(5p + 15)$
$6p = 3p + 9$	$\frac{6p}{0.6} = \frac{0.6(5p + 15)}{0.6}$
$6p - 3p = 3p + 9 - 3p$	$10p = 5p + 15$
$3p = 9$	$10p - 5p = 5p + 15 - 5p$
$\frac{3p}{3} = \frac{9}{3}$	$5p = 15$
$p = 3$	$\frac{5p}{5} = \frac{15}{5}$
	$p = 3$

Solution: $p = 3$

C **6** The two rectangles shown below have the same perimeter. Write and solve an equation to find the value of x. Then find the measures of the length and width of Rectangle B. All measurements are in inches.

Rectangle A

7

5

Rectangle B

$4x - 3$

x

Equation: Possible answer: $2(4x - 3) + 2x = 24$

$x =$ 3

Length of Rectangle B: 9 inches

Width of Rectangle B: 3 inches

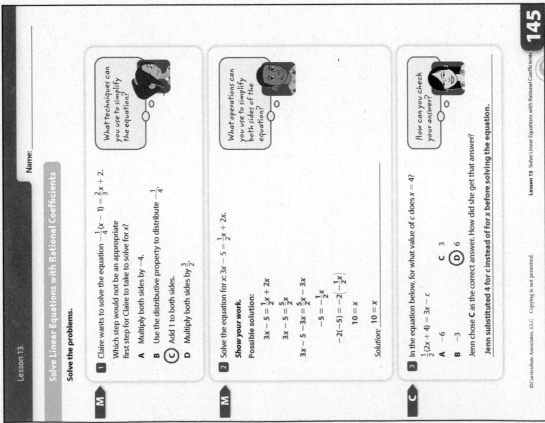

Lesson 13

Name: _____

Solve Linear Equations with Rational Coefficients

Solve the problems.

M

1 Claire wants to solve the equation $-\frac{1}{4}(x - 1) = \frac{2}{3}x + 2$.

Which step would not not be an appropriate first step for Claire to take to solve for x?

A Multiply both sides by −4.

B Use the distributive property to distribute $-\frac{1}{4}$.

C Add 1 to both sides.

D Multiply both sides by $\frac{3}{2}$.

What techniques can you use to simplify the equation?

M

2 Solve the equation for x: $3x - 5 = \frac{1}{2}x + 2x$.

Show your work.

Possible solution:

$3x - 5 = \frac{1}{2}x + 2x$

$3x - 5 = \frac{5}{2}x$

$3x - 5 - 3x = \frac{5}{2}x - 3x$

$-5 = -\frac{1}{2}x$

$-2(-5) = -2\left(-\frac{1}{2}x\right)$

$10 = x$

Solution: __10 = x__

What operations can you use to simplify both sides of the equation?

C

3 In the equation below, for what value of c does x = 4?

$\frac{1}{2}(2x + 4) = 3x - c$

A −6   **C** 3

B −3   **(D)** 6

Jenn chose **C** as the correct answer. How did she get that answer?

__Jenn substituted 4 for c instead of for x before solving the equation.__

How can you check your answer?

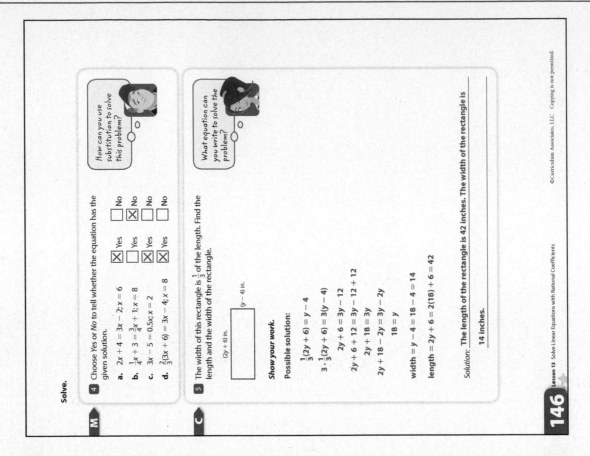

Solve.

M

4 Choose Yes or No to tell whether the equation has the given solution.

a. $2x + 4 = 3x - 2; x = 6$ ☒ Yes   ☐ No

b. $\frac{1}{4}x + 3 = \frac{3}{4}x + 1; x = 8$ ☐ Yes   ☒ No

c. $3x - 5 = 0.5x; x = 2$ ☒ Yes   ☐ No

d. $\frac{2}{3}(3x + 6) = 3x - 4; x = 8$ ☒ Yes   ☐ No

How can you use substitution to solve this problem?

C

5 The width of this rectangle is $\frac{1}{3}$ of the length. Find the length and the width of the rectangle.

(2y + 6) in.
(y − 4) in.

Show your work.

Possible solution:

$\frac{1}{3}(2y + 6) = y - 4$

$3 \cdot \frac{1}{3}(2y + 6) = 3(y - 4)$

$2y + 6 = 3y - 12$

$2y + 6 + 12 = 3y - 12 + 12$

$2y + 18 = 3y$

$2y + 18 - 2y = 3y - 2y$

$18 = y$

width = $y - 4 = 18 - 4 = 14$

length = $2y + 6 = 2(18) + 6 = 42$

Solution: __The length of the rectangle is 42 inches. The width of the rectangle is 14 inches.__

What equation can you write to solve the problem?

Lesson 14

Solutions of Linear Equations

Name: _____

Prerequisite: Solve Equations with Rational Coefficients

Study the example problem showing how to solve an equation with rational coefficients. Then solve problems 1–6.

Example

Solve the equation: $6p = \frac{1}{2}(4p + 8)$.

Here is one way you can solve the given equation.

$6p = \frac{1}{2}(4p + 8)$	**Step 1:** Apply the distributive property.
$6p = 2p + 4$	**Step 2:** Subtract $2p$ from both sides.
$6p - 2p = 2p + 4 - 2p$	**Step 3:** Simplify.
$4p = 4$	**Step 4:** Divide both sides by 4.
$\frac{4p}{4} = \frac{4}{4}$	**Step 5:** Simplify.
$p = 1$	

Vocabulary

rational number a number that can be expressed as the quotient of two integers.

$3 = \frac{3}{1}$ $0.5 = \frac{5}{10}$

coefficient the number multiplied by the variable in a variable term.

10 is the coefficient in the term 10x.

B **1** Explain how the distributive property was applied in Step 1.

Each of the terms inside the parentheses, 4p and 8, was multiplied by $\frac{1}{2}$.

M **2** A different Step 1 for the example is shown below.

$6p = \frac{1}{2}(4p + 8)$

$2 \cdot 6p = 2 \cdot \frac{1}{2}(4p + 8)$ **Step 1:** Multiply both sides by 2.

Explain why both sides of the equation were multiplied by 2. What is the resulting equation?

Possible explanation: Both sides were multiplied by 2 to eliminate the fraction. The resulting equation is 12p = 4p + 8.

B **3** What are the coefficients of p in the equation you wrote in problem 2? Are they rational numbers?

12 and 4; yes

Lesson 14 Solutions of Linear Equations **149**

Solve.

M **4** Show two different ways to solve $\frac{2}{3}(3x + 6) = 4x + 3$.

Show your work. Possible answers:

$$\frac{2}{3}(3x + 6) = 4x + 3$$
$$3 \cdot \frac{2}{3}(3x + 6) = 3 \cdot (4x + 3)$$
$$2(3x + 6) = 12x + 9$$
$$6x + 12 = 12x + 9$$
$$6x + 12 - 6x = 12x + 9 - 6x$$
$$12 = 6x + 9$$
$$12 - 9 = 6x + 9 - 9$$
$$3 = 6x$$
$$\frac{3}{6} = \frac{6x}{6}$$
$$\frac{1}{2} = x$$

$$\frac{2}{3}(3x + 6) = 4x + 3$$
$$2x + 4 = 4x + 3$$
$$2x + 4 - 2x = 4x + 3 - 2x$$
$$4 = 2x + 3$$
$$4 - 3 = 2x + 3 - 3$$
$$1 = 2x$$
$$\frac{1}{2} = \frac{2x}{2}$$
$$\frac{1}{2} = x$$

Solution: $x = \frac{1}{2}$

M **5** Koby's solution for $4(x - 3) = \frac{1}{2}x + 2$ is shown at the right. Did he solve the equation correctly? Explain why or why not.

$$4(x - 3) = \frac{1}{2}x + 2$$
$$4x - 12 = \frac{1}{2}x + 2$$
$$2 \cdot (4x - 12) = 2 \cdot \left(\frac{1}{2}x + 2\right)$$
$$8x - 12 = x + 2$$
$$8x = x + 14$$
$$\frac{7x}{7} = \frac{14}{7}$$
$$x = 2$$

No; Possible explanation: He did not apply the distributive property correctly when he multiplied each side of the equation by 2. The result should be 8x − 24 = x + 4, not 8x − 12 = x + 2, and the solution should be x = 4.

C **6** In the equation $3(x - 1) = 2x + c$, for what value of c will x = 3? Explain your reasoning.

When c = 0, then x = 3. Possible explanation: I can simplify the equation to x − 3 = c.

If x = 3, then c = 3 − 3, or 0.

150 Lesson 14 Solutions of Linear Equations

Key

B Basic   **M** Medium   **C** Challenge

Page 151

Lesson 14

Name: _____

Determining the Number of Solutions of an Equation

Study the example showing how to identify the number of solutions an equation has. Then solve problems 1–7.

Example

How many solutions does the equation
$2(x + 2) + 1 = 2x − 3 + 6$ have?

Simplify the equation.

$2(x + 2) + 1 = 2x − 3 + 6$
$2x + 4 + 1 = 2x + 3$
$2x + 5 = 2x + 3$

The variable terms on each side of the simplified equation are the same but the constants are different, so the equation has no solution.

Number of Solutions

- An equation has *infinitely many solutions* when you simplify and the variable terms and constants are the same on each side, as in $2x + 5 = 2x + 5$ or $4 = 4$.
- An equation has *no solution* when you simplify and the variable terms on each side are the same but the constants are different, as in $2x + 5 = 2x + 3$ or $4 = 2$.
- An equation has *one solution* when the variable terms on each side are different, as in $3x + 1 = 2x − 5$.

B 1 Suppose the right side of the equation in the example problem is $2x − 3 + 8$. How many solutions would the equation have? Explain.

infinitely many solutions; Possible explanation: The two sides would simplify to the true sentence $2x + 5 = 2x + 5$.

B 2 Suppose the right side of the equation in the example problem is $3x − 3 + 6$. How many solutions would the equation have? Explain.

one solution; Possible explanation: The two sides would simplify to $2x + 5 = 3x + 3$. The variable terms on each side are different, so there is one solution.

M 3 Look at the model at the right. Does it represent an equation that has one solution, no solutions, or infinitely many solutions? Explain how you know.

one solution; Possible explanation: The model shows $2x + 2 = x + 3$. The variable terms are different, so there is one solution.

Page 152

Solve.

C 4 Consider the equation $cx − d = 2x + 4$.

a. Replace c in the equation with 2. For what value of d would the equation have infinitely many solutions? Explain.

$d = −4$; Possible explanation: For the equation $2x − d = 2x + 4$ to have infinitely many solutions, the variable terms and the constants on each side must be the same. If $d = −4$, $2x − (−4) = 2x + 4$, which simplifies to $2x + 4 = 2x + 4$.

b. Replace d in the equation with 2. For what value of c would the equation have no solution? Explain.

$c = 2$; Possible explanation: For the equation $cx − 2 = 2x + 4$ to have no solutions, the variable terms on each side must be the same and the constants must be different. If $c = 2$, then there would be no solution.

M 5 Evelyn says that the equation $3(x − 3) + 5 = 3x + 1 + 4$ has infinitely many solutions because the variable terms on each side are the same. Do you agree with Evelyn? Explain why or why not.

I do not agree with Evelyn. Possible explanation: When you simplify both sides of the equation $3(x − 3) + 5 = 3x + 1 + 4$, you get $3x − 4 = 3x + 5$. The variable terms are the same, but the constants are different. The equation will have no solution.

M 6 Explain why the equation $5(2x + 1) − 2 = 6x + 5$ has only one solution. Then find the solution.

Possible explanation: When you simplify both sides of the equation, you get $10x + 3 = 6x + 5$. The variable terms are different, so there is only one solution. The solution is $x = \frac{1}{2}$.

C 7 Write an equation that has one solution, an equation that has no solution, and an equation that has infinitely many solutions. Each equation should have one variable term on each side and a total of four terms.

Possible equations are given.

One solution: $3x − 2 = 2x + 2$ (Variable terms are different.)

No solution: $4x + 1 = 4x + 3$ (Variable terms are equal; constants are different.)

Infinitely many solutions: $3x + 2 = 3x + 2$ (Variable terms are equal; constants are equal.)

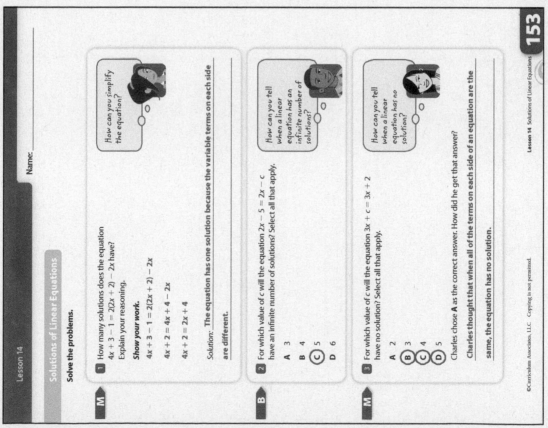

Lesson 14

Solutions of Linear Equations

Name: _____

Solve the problems.

1 How many solutions does the equation
$4x + 3 - 1 = 2(2x + 2) - 2x$ have?
Explain your reasoning.

[How can you simplify the equation?]

Show your work.

$4x + 3 - 1 = 2(2x + 2) - 2x$

$4x + 2 = 4x + 4 - 2x$

$4x + 2 = 2x + 4$

Solution: The equation has one solution because the variable terms on each side are different.

2 For which value of c will the equation $2x - 5 = 2x - c$ have an infinite number of solutions? Select all that apply.

A 3
B 4
Ⓒ 5
D 6

[How can you tell when a linear equation has an infinite number of solutions?]

3 For which value of c will the equation $3x + c = 3x + 2$ have no solution? Select all that apply.

A 2
Ⓑ 3
Ⓒ 4
Ⓓ 5

[How can you tell when a linear equation has no solution?]

Charles chose **A** as the correct answer. How did he get that answer?

Charles thought that when all of the terms on each side of an equation are the same, the equation has no solution.

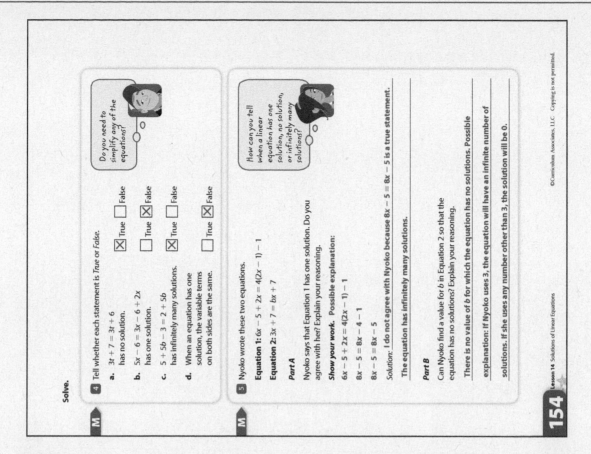

Solve.

4 Tell whether each statement is *True* or *False*.

a. $3t + 7 = 3t + 6$ has no solution. [X] True [ ] False

b. $5x - 6 = 3x - 6 + 2x$ has one solution. [ ] True [X] False

c. $5 + 5b - 3 = 2 + 5b$ has infinitely many solutions. [X] True [ ] False

d. When an equation has one solution, the variable terms on both sides are the same. [ ] True [X] False

[Do you need to simplify any of the equations?]

5 Nyoko wrote these two equations.

Equation 1: $6x - 5 + 2x = 4(2x - 1) - 1$

Equation 2: $3x + 7 = bx + 7$

[How can you tell when a linear equation has one solution, no solution, or infinitely many solutions?]

Part A

Nyoko says that Equation 1 has one solution. Do you agree with her? Explain your reasoning.

Show your work. Possible explanation:

$6x - 5 + 2x = 4(2x - 1) - 1$

$8x - 5 = 8x - 4 - 1$

$8x - 5 = 8x - 5$

Solution: I do not agree with Nyoko because $8x - 5 = 8x - 5$ is a true statement. The equation has infinitely many solutions.

Part B

Can Nyoko find a value for b in Equation 2 so that the equation has no solutions? Explain your reasoning.

There is no value of b for which the equation has no solutions. Possible explanation: If Nyoko uses 3, the equation will have an infinite number of solutions. If she uses any number other than 3, the solution will be 0.

Lesson 15

Understand Systems of Equations

> **Prerequisite: How can you find out whether an equation has infinitely many solutions?**

Study the example showing how to tell if an equation has infinitely many solutions. Then solve problems 1–8.

Example

Does the equation $3(x + 5) - 10 = 3 + 3x + 2$ have infinitely many solutions?

When you solve a linear equation and the equation simplifies to have the same variable terms and constants on both sides, the linear equation has infinitely many solutions.

$$3(x + 5) - 10 = 3 + 3x + 2$$
$$3x + 15 - 10 = 5 + 3x$$
$$3x + 5 = 5 + 3x$$

You can see from $3x + 5 = 5 + 3x$ that both sides of the equation are equal, or you can further simplify to get $5 = 5$. Either way, the equation $3(x + 5) - 10 = 3 + 3x + 2$ has infinitely many solutions.

B **1** Substitute 4 for x in the equation in the example and evaluate both sides of the equation. What is the result? Is it a true statement?

$17 = 17$; Yes, it is a true statement.

B **2** Choose any value for x and substitute it in the equation in the example. Evaluate both sides of the equation. Is the result a true statement?

Values of x will vary. Yes, the result is a true statement.

M **3** How many solutions does the equation $3(x + 2) = 2x + 14 - x$ have? Explain.

one solution; Possible explanation: Simplifying both sides of the equation gives $3x + 6 = x + 14$. The variable terms are different, so there is only one solution, $x = 4$.

> **Vocabulary**
>
> **infinitely many** an unlimited amount; for example, a linear equation has infinitely many solutions when the equation is true no matter what value is substituted for the variable.

©Curriculum Associates, LLC Copying is not permitted.

Lesson 15 *Understand Systems of Equations* **157**

Name: _____

Solve.

Use the equations to solve problems 4–5.

Equation 1: $-4x - 5 = 4x + 11$

Equation 2: $4x - 4 + x = 5x - 4$

Equation 3: $x + 3 + 2x = 3x + 2$

M **4** Which equation has infinitely many solutions? Explain.

Equation 2; Possible explanation: The equation simplifies to $5x - 4 = 5x - 4$, so the variable terms and constants are the same on each side. The equation has infinitely many solutions.

M **5** Which equation has no solution? Explain.

Equation 3; Possible explanation: The equation simplifies to $3x + 3 = 3x + 2$, so the variable terms on each side are the same but the constants are different.

The equation has no solution.

M **6** Chelsea wrote the equation $cx + d = 4(0.5x - 5)$. What values can she use for c and d so that the equation has infinitely many solutions? Explain your reasoning.

$c = 2$ and $d = -20$; Possible explanation: To make the variable terms equal and the constants equal, c must be 2 and d must be -20 because $4(0.5x - 5) = 2x - 20$.

M **7** Suppose that you use 3 for c and -20 for d in problem 6. How many solutions would the equation have? Explain.

one solution; Possible explanation: The equation would be $3x - 20 = 2x - 20$. The variable terms are different, so there is only one solution, $x = 0$.

C **8** The equation $3(x + 2) + 4x = 6x + 8 + x$ has no solution. Ricco correctly says that he can change one number in the equation to make an equation that has infinitely many solutions. What number should he change? What number should he use instead? Explain.

Possible answer: He should change the 8 on the right side of the equation to a 6. The constant on the left side of the equation is now 6, and the constant on the right side is 8.

For the equation to have infinitely many solutions, the constants must be the same.

158 Lesson 15 *Understand Systems of Equations*

©Curriculum Associates, LLC Copying is not permitted.

Key

| **B** Basic | **M** Medium | **C** Challenge |

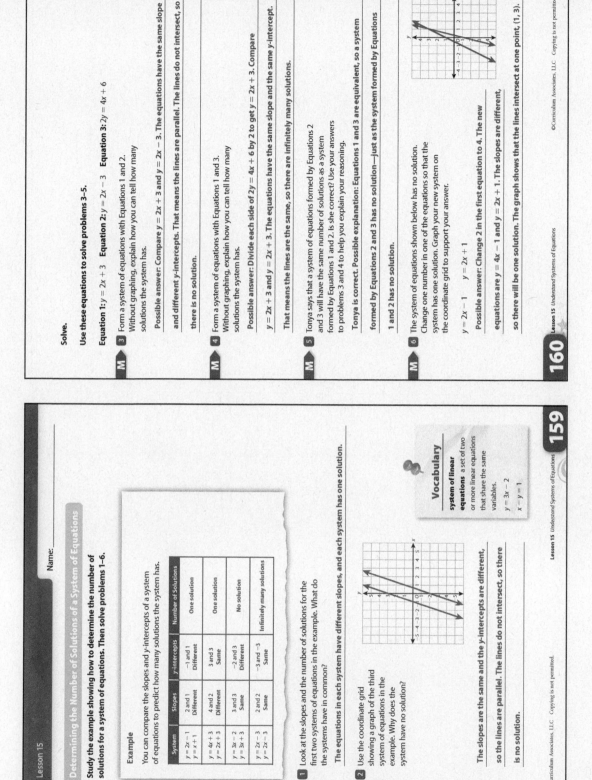

Name: _____

Lesson 15

Determining the Number of Solutions of a System of Equations

Study the example showing how to determine the number of solutions for a system of equations. Then solve problems 1–6.

Example
You can compare the slopes and y-intercepts of a system of equations to predict how many solutions the system has.

System	Slopes	y-intercepts	Number of Solutions
$y = 2x - 1$ $y = x + 1$	2 and 1 Different	-1 and 1 Different	One solution
$y = 4x + 3$ $y = 2x + 3$	4 and 2 Different	3 and 3 Same	One solution
$y = 3x - 2$ $y = 3x + 3$	3 and 3 Same	-2 and 3 Different	No solution
$y = 2x - 3$ $y = 2x - 3$	2 and 2 Same	-3 and -3 Same	Infinitely many solutions

B **1** Look at the slopes and the number of solutions for the first two systems of equations in the example. What do the systems have in common?

The equations in each system have different slopes, and each system has one solution.

M **2** Use the coordinate grid showing a graph of the third system of equations in the example. Why does the system have no solution?

The slopes are the same and the y-intercepts are different, so the lines are parallel. The lines do not intersect, so there is no solution.

Vocabulary

system of linear equations a set of two or more linear equations that share the same variables.
$y = 3x - 2$
$x - y = 1$

Solve.

Use these equations to solve problems 3–5.

Equation 1: $y = 2x + 3$ **Equation 2:** $y = 2x - 3$ **Equation 3:** $2y = 4x + 6$

M **3** Form a system of equations with Equations 1 and 2. Without graphing, explain how you can tell how many solutions the system has.

Possible answer: Compare $y = 2x + 3$ and $y = 2x - 3$. The equations have the same slope and different y-intercepts. That means the lines are parallel. The lines do not intersect, so there is no solution.

M **4** Form a system of equations with Equations 1 and 3. Without graphing, explain how you can tell how many solutions the system has.

Possible answer: Divide each side of $2y = 4x + 6$ by 2 to get $y = 2x + 3$. Compare $y = 2x + 3$ and $y = 2x + 3$. The equations have the same slope and the same y-intercept. That means the lines are the same, so there are infinitely many solutions.

M **5** Tonya says that a system of equations formed by Equations 2 and 3 will have the same number of solutions as a system formed by Equations 1 and 2. Is she correct? Use your answers to problems 3 and 4 to help you explain your reasoning.

Tonya is correct. Possible explanation: Equations 1 and 3 are equivalent, so a system formed by Equations 2 and 3 has no solution—just as the system formed by Equations 1 and 2 has no solution.

M **6** The system of equations shown below has no solution. Change one number in one of the equations so that the system has one solution. Graph your new system on the coordinate grid to support your answer.

$y = 2x - 1$ $y = 2x + 1$

Possible answer: Change 2 in the first equation to 4. The new equations are $y = 4x - 1$ and $y = 2x + 1$. The slopes are different, so there will be one solution. The graph shows that the lines intersect at one point, (1, 3).

Page 162

Solve the problem. Use what you learned from the model.

Consider the equation $3y - 6x = 9$.

Write another equation that forms a system of equations with the equation above that has either one solution or infinitely many solutions.

Without graphing, explain how you know that your system has one solution or infinitely many solutions.

Justify your equation by graphing the system of equations. Explain how your graph supports your choice of equation.

Show your work. Use words, models, and numbers to explain your answer.

Possible answers:

(one solution)

First I solved the given equation for y to get $y = 2x + 3$. For the system to have one solution, the slopes must be different. So $y = x + 3$ will form a system with one solution.

My graph of the system supports my equation. The lines intersect at one point, $(0, 3)$, so there is one solution.

(infinitely many solutions)

For the system to have infinitely many solutions, the equations in the system must simplify to be the same equation. So $-12x + 6y = 18$ will form a system with infinitely many solutions because it simplifies to be the same as the given equation.

My graph of the system supports my equation because both equations form the same line, so there are infinitely many solutions. (The graph will show only one line: $y = 2x + 3$.)

> Where did you . . .
> • answer all parts of the problem?
> • use words to explain?
> • use a graph to explain?
> • use numbers to explain?

Page 161

Lesson 15   Name: _____

Reason and Write

Study the example problem. Underline two parts that you think make it a particularly good answer and a helpful example.

Answers will vary. Note whether students incorporate the features they chose in their answer on the next page.

Example

Look at the three systems of equations shown below.

System 1	System 2	System 3
$y = 2x + 5$	$y = 4x - 1$	$y - 3x = 2$
$y = \frac{1}{2}(4x + 10)$	$3y = 3x + 6$	$y = 3x - 5$

Choose one of the systems. Without graphing, explain how you can use the slopes and y-intercepts of the equations to predict how many solutions the system of equations has. Then predict the number of solutions.

Justify your prediction by graphing the system of equations. Explain how your graph supports your prediction.

Show your work. Use words, graphs, and numbers to explain your answer.

I chose System 3. I solved for y in the first equation, $y - 3x = 2$, to get $y = 3x + 2$. The equations have the same slope, 3, and different y-intercepts, 2 and -5. When the equations in a system have the same slopes and different y-intercepts, there is no solution. I predict that the system of equations has no solution.

My graph of the system supports my prediction. The lines are parallel and do not intersect, so there is no solution.

> Where does the example . . .
> • answer all parts of the problem?
> • use words to explain?
> • use a graph to explain?
> • use numbers to explain?

Lesson 16
Solve Systems of Equations Algebraically

Prerequisite: Find the Number of Solutions of a System

Study the example showing a system of linear equations with no solution. Then solve problems 1–6.

Example

Graph of the system of equations below to show that it has no solutions.

$y = 2x + 4$
$y = 2x - 1$

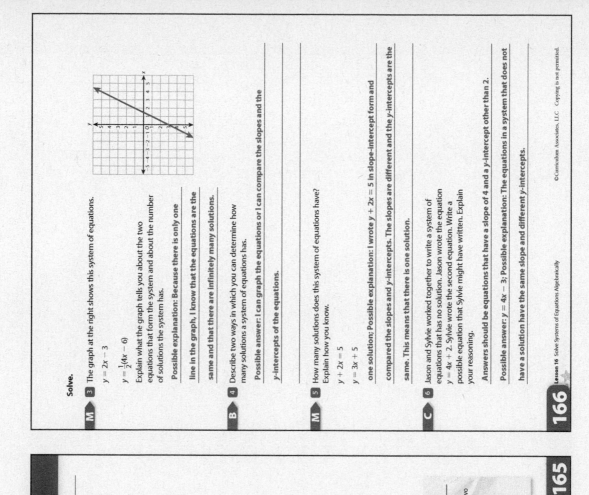

The lines do not intersect, so there is no ordered pair that will satisfy both equations.
The system of equations has no solution.

Vocabulary

system of linear equations a set of two or more related linear equations that share the same variables.
$y = 3x - 2$
$y = x + 1$

B 1 What type of lines are shown in the graph of the system of equations in the example?
parallel lines

M 2 The graph at the right shows this system of equations.
$y = x - 3$
$y = -3x + 1$

What is the solution? Explain how you can verify that it is a solution to both equations.

$(1, -2)$; Possible explanation:
I can substitute $(1, -2)$ into both equations to see if they result in true statements.

$y = x - 3: -2 = 1 - 3, -2 = -2;$
$y = -3x + 1: -2 = -3(1) + 1,$
$-2 = -3 + 1, -2 = -2$

Lesson 16 Solve Systems of Equations Algebraically **165**

Solve.

M 3 The graph at the right shows this system of equations.
$y = 2x - 3$
$y = \frac{1}{2}(4x - 6)$

Explain what the graph tells you about the two equations that form the system and about the number of solutions the system has.

Possible explanation: Because there is only one line in the graph, I know that the equations are the same and that there are infinitely many solutions.

B 4 Describe two ways in which you can determine how many solutions a system of equations has.

Possible answer: I can graph the equations or I can compare the slopes and the y-intercepts of the equations.

M 5 How many solutions does this system of equations have? Explain how you know.
$y + 2x = 5$
$y = 3x + 5$

one solution; Possible explanation: I wrote $y + 2x = 5$ in slope-intercept form and compared the slopes and y-intercepts. The slopes are different and the y-intercepts are the same. This means that there is one solution.

C 6 Jason and Sylvie worked together to write a system of equations that has no solution. Jason wrote the equation $y = 4x + 2$. Sylvie wrote the second equation. Write a possible equation that Sylvie might have written. Explain your reasoning.

Possible answer: $y = 4x - 3$; Possible explanation: The equations in a system that does not have a solution have the same slope and different y-intercepts.

Answers should be equations that have a slope of 4 and a y-intercept other than 2.

166 Lesson 16 Solve Systems of Equations Algebraically

Key

B Basic   **M** Medium   **C** Challenge

Name: _____

Use Substitution to Solve Systems of Equations

Study the example showing how to use substitution to solve a system of equations. Then solve problems 1–6.

Example

Solve the system of equations.

$y = x - 3$ $y + 2x = 3$

Notice that the first equation tells you that $y = x - 3$, so substitute $x - 3$ for y in the second equation and solve for x.

$y + 2x = 3$
$(x - 3) + 2x = 3$
$3x - 3 = 3$
$3x = 6$
$x = 2$

Now that you know the value of x, you can find the value of y. Substitute 2 for x in either equation and solve for y.

$y = x - 3$
$y = 2 - 3$
$y = -1$

The solution is $(2, -1)$.

B 1 Substitute the value of x in the example into the second equation, $y + 2x = 3$. What value do you get for y? Is it the same solution as in the example problem?

−1; yes

B 2 The solution in the example is $(2, -1)$. Explain what the graph of the system looks like.

Possible answer: It means that the system of equations has one solution and that a graph of the system will be two lines that intersect at the point $(2, -1)$.

M 3 Look at the system of equations below. Describe how you can use substitution to find the solution. Then find the solution.

$y - 3x = 4$ $y = x - 4$

Possible answer: I can substitute $x - 4$ for y in $y - 3x = 4$ and solve to find the value of x.

Then I can substitute that value for x into either equation to find the value of y. Those

values of x and y are the coordinates of the solution of the system.

$(x - 4) - 3x = 4, -2x - 4 = 4, -2x = 8, x = -4; y = -4 - 4, y = -8; (-4, -8)$

Solve.

M 4 Use substitution to solve the system of equations.

$y + x = 3$

$y = 1.5x + 1$

Show your work.

Possible answer:
$y + x = 3$
$(1.5x + 1) + x = 3$
$2.5x + 1 = 3$
$2.5x = 2$
$x = 0.8$

$y = 1.5x + 1$
$y = 1.5(0.8) + 1$
$y = 1.2 + 1$
$y = 2.2$

Solution: (0.8, 2.2)

M 5 The system of equations at the right shows x by itself on the left side of one equation. Solve the system by substituting for x instead of for y.

$x = -y - 2$
$0.5x + y = 1$

Show your work.

Possible answer:
$0.5x + y = 1$
$0.5(-y - 2) + y = 1$
$-0.5y - 1 + y = 1$
$0.5y + 2 = 2$
$y = 4$

$x = -y - 2$
$x = -4 - 2$
$x = -6$

Solution: (−6, 4)

C 6 Fina wants to use substitution to solve the system of equations at the right. Explain what she needs to do first before using substitution. Then solve the system of equations.

$2x - y = 3$
$-1.5x + 3y = -18$

Possible explanation: Fina needs to write one of the equations so that it has one of the

variables by itself on one side. The easiest change is to write $2x - y = 3$ as $y = 2x - 3$.

The solution of the system is $(-2, -7)$.

Lesson 16

Name: _____

Use Elimination to Solve Systems of Equations

Study the example problem showing how to use elimination to solve a system of equations. Then solve problems 1–7.

Example

Solve the system of equations.

$-x + 3y = 1$　　　$2x - 5y = -3$

Look for a way for one of the variables to have opposite coefficients in the system. You can multiply the first equation by 2 so that the coefficients of x in the system are 2 and -2.

Multiply $-x + 3y = 1$ by 2 to get $-2x + 6y = 2$. Then rewrite the system and add the like terms.

$$-2x + 6y = 2$$
$$\underline{2x - 5y = -3}$$
$$y = -1$$

Now find the value of x by substituting the value of y into either equation. For example, you can substitute -1 for y in the first equation and solve for x.

$$-x + 3y = 1$$
$$-x + 3(-1) = 1$$
$$-x - 3 = 1$$
$$-x = 4$$
$$x = -4$$

The solution is $(-4, -1)$.

B 1 Substitute -1 for y into the second equation from the example. Do you still get $x = -4$?

Yes; $2x - 5y = -3$, $2x - 5(-1) = -3$, $2x + 5 = -3$, $2x = -8$; $x = -4$

B 2 One student began to solve the example problem by multiplying the second equation by 0.5. Would that work? Explain.

Yes; Possible explanation: To eliminate one of the variables, you need opposite terms in the two equations. The first equation has $-x$, so you need x in the second equation. Multiplying the second equation by 0.5 gives x because $0.5 \times 2x = x$.

M 3 Which equation would you multiply to get opposite coefficients for one of the variables in this system? What number would you multiply that equation by? What would the new equation be?

$3x + 5y = 1$
$-2x + y = 2$

Possible answer: I'd multiply the second equation by -5; $10x - 5y = -10$

Solve.

M 4 Use elimination to solve the system of equations. Check your solution.

$4x + 3y = 6$

$2x - y = -2$

Show your work.
Possible answer:
$3(2x - y = -2)$
$6x - 3y = -6$

$$4x + 3y = 6$$
$$\underline{6x - 3y = -6}$$
$$10x = 0$$
$$x = 0$$

$2(0) - y = -2$
$0 - y = -2$
$y = 2$

Check:
$4(0) + 3(2) = 6$
$0 + 6 = 6$
$6 = 6$

Solution: $(0, 2)$

M 5 Becca says that she can use elimination to solve the system of equations at the right if she multiplies either of the equations by -1. Do you agree with Becca? Explain.

$3x + 2y = -1$
$3x + 4y = -5$

Yes; If she multiplies the first equation by -1, she will have $-3x$ in the first equation and $3x$ in the second. If she multiplies the second equation by -1, she will have $3x$ in the first equation and $-3x$ in the second.

M 6 Use elimination to find the solution of the system in problem 5.

$(1, -2)$

C 7 The value of x in the system of equations at the right is -2. What is the value of a? Use elimination to help you find the value.

$ax + 4y = 6$
$2x - 4y = -16$

Show your work.
Possible answer:
$$ax + 4y = 6$$
$$\underline{2x - 4y = -16}$$
$$ax + 2x = -10$$

Substitute -2 for x.
$a(-2) + 2(-2) = -10$
$-2a - 4 = -10$
$-2a = -6$
$a = 3$

Solution: $a = 3$

Lesson 16

Solve Systems of Equations Algebraically

Solve the problems.

1 Solve the system of equations.

$2y = 6x + 10$ $y = 2x + 4$

Show your work.

Possible answer using substitution:

$2(2x + 4) = 6x + 10$ $y = 2(-1) + 4 = 2$
$4x + 8 = 6x + 10$
$-2x = 2$
$x = -1$

(students may also use elimination to solve)

Solution: __The solution is (-1, 2).__

> You can use substitution or elimination to solve the system of equations.

2 Which ordered pair is the solution to this system of equations?

$y = x - 4$ $x - 3y = 10$

A (1, 3)   C (-3, 1)
B (1, -3)   D (-3, -1)

Zara chose **C** as the correct answer. How did she get that answer?

Possible answer: Zara reversed the values for x and y.

> How do you know when an ordered pair is a solution to a system of equations?

3 Blaine is trying to solve the following system of equations.

$5x + y = -2$ $-10x - 2y = 4$

Which method would not help Blaine solve the system?

(A) Multiply the first equation by 0.5 and solve by elimination.
B Multiply the second equation by 0.5 and solve by elimination.
C Solve the first equation for y and solve by substitution.
D Solve the second equation for y and solve by substitution.

> Remember, you're looking for the method that won't work.

Solve.

4 Consider this system of equations:

$2x - 3y = 1$
$9y = 6x - 3$

Tell whether each statement is *True* or *False*.

a. The system has infinitely many solutions.   [X] True   [ ] False
b. The system has exactly one solution.   [ ] True   [X] False
c. (5, 3) is a solution of the system.   [X] True   [ ] False
d. The equations in the system have the same slope and the same y-intercept.   [X] True   [ ] False

> Try writing the equations in the same form first.

5 Consider this system of equations:

$5x + y = -2$
$2x - 2y = 4$

Part A

Solve the system of equations algebraically.

Show your work.

Possible answer:

$2(5x + y = -2)$
$10x + 2y = -4$

$10x + 2y = -4$
$2x - 2y = 4$
$\overline{12x = 0}$
$x = 0$

$5(0) + y = -2$
$0 + y = -2$
$y = -2$

Solution: __(0, -2)__

Part B

Graph the system of equations to check your solution.

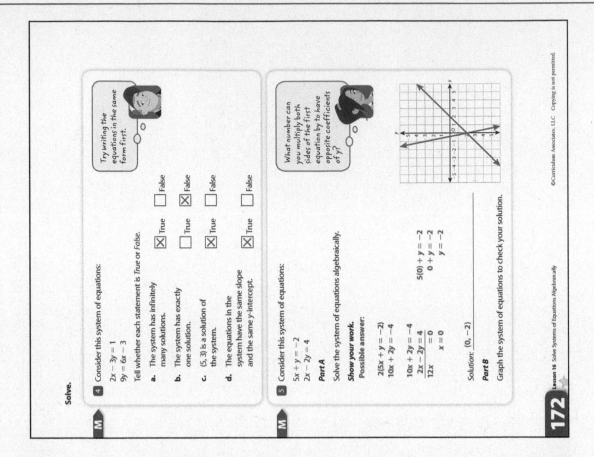

> What number can you multiply both sides of the first equation by to have opposite coefficients of y?

Lesson 17
Solve Problems Using Systems of Equations

Name: _____

Prerequisite: Use Substitution to Solve Systems of Equations

Study the example problem showing how to use substitution to solve a system of equations. Then solve problems 1–7.

Example

Use substitution to solve this system of equations.

$y + 3x = -4$
$y = x + 4$

The second equation tells you that $y = x + 4$, so you can substitute $x + 4$ for y in the first equation and solve for x.

$y + 3x = -4$
$(x + 4) + 3x = -4$
$4x + 4 = -4$
$4x = -8$
$x = -2$

Now you can find the value of y. You can substitute -2 for x into either equation and solve for y. Try using the second equation.

$y = x + 4$
$y = -2 + 4$
$y = 2$

The solution is $(-2, 2)$.

1 Explain why you substitute $x + 4$ for y in the first equation of the system in the example.

You substitute $x + 4$ for y to make an equation with just x in it.

2 Once you know the value of one variable in a system of equations, how can you find the value of the second variable?

You substitute that value into one of the equations and solve for the second variable.

3 Look at the system of equations at the right. Which variable would you find the value of first? Explain your reasoning and solve for that variable.

$4y + x = 12$
$x = 2y$

Possible answer: y; I know that $x = 2y$, so I can substitute $2y$ for x in the first equation and solve for y. $4y + 2y = 12$; $6y = 12$; $y = 2$

©Curriculum Associates, LLC Copying is not permitted.
Lesson 17 Solve Problems Using Systems of Equations **175**

Solve.

4 Use substitution to solve the system of equations.

$2y - x = -9$
$y = 2x - 3$

Show your work.

$2y - x = -9$ $y = 2x - 3$
$2(2x - 3) - x = -9$ $y = 2(-1) - 3$
$4x - 6 - x = -9$ $y = -2 - 3$
$3x - 6 = -9$ $y = -5$
$3x = -3$
$x = -1$

Solution: $(-1, -5)$

Use the system of equations at the right for problems 5–6. $y = 2x - 4$
$y = -x + 2$

5 Graph the system of equations. What ordered pair appears to be the solution?

$(2, 0)$

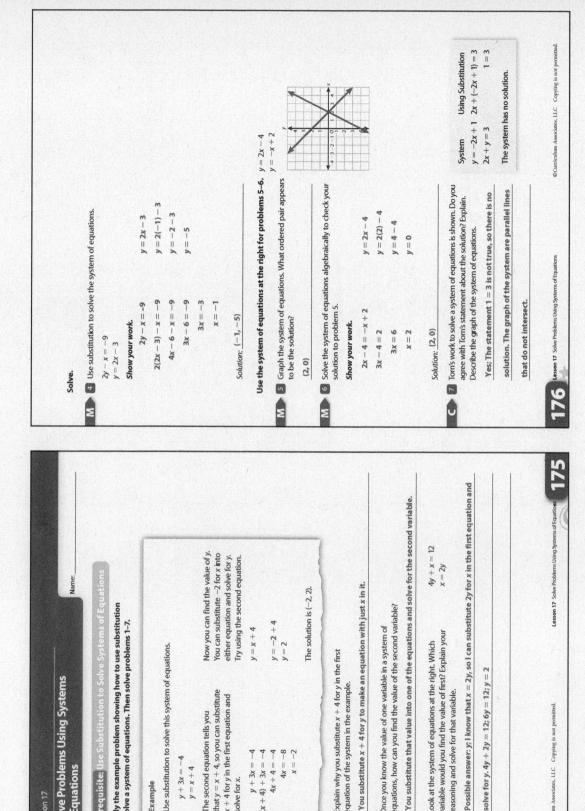

6 Solve the system of equations algebraically to check your solution to problem 5.

Show your work.

$2x - 4 = -x + 2$ $y = 2x - 4$
$3x - 4 = 2$ $y = 2(2) - 4$
$3x = 6$ $y = 4 - 4$
$x = 2$ $y = 0$

Solution: $(2, 0)$

7 Tom's work to solve a system of equations is shown. Do you agree with Tom's statement about the solution? Explain. Describe the graph of the system of equations.

System	Using Substitution
$y = -2x + 1$	$2x + (-2x + 1) = 3$
$2x + y = 3$	$1 = 3$
	The system has no solution.

Yes; The statement $1 = 3$ is not true, so there is no solution. The graph of the system are parallel lines that do not intersect.

©Curriculum Associates, LLC Copying is not permitted.
Lesson 17 Solve Problems Using Systems of Equations **176**

Key

B Basic   **M** Medium   **C** Challenge

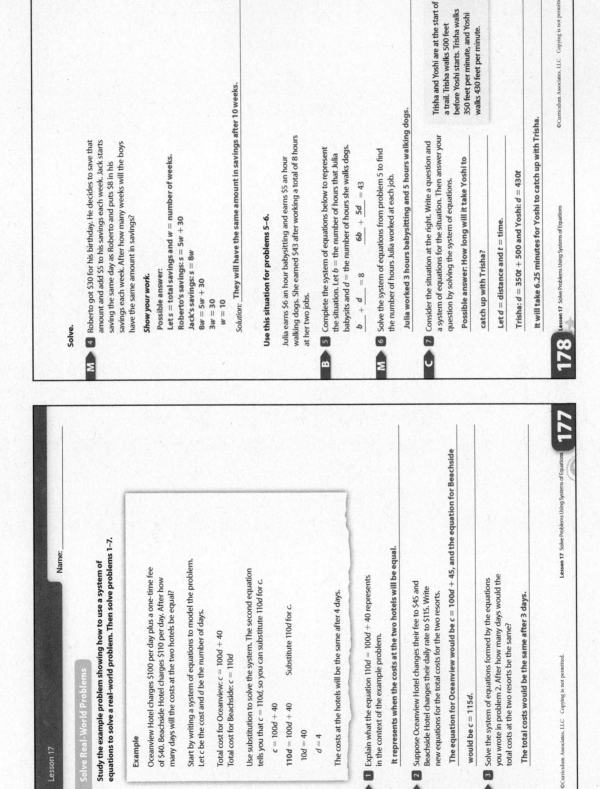

Name: _____

Lesson 17

Solve Real-World Problems

Study the example problem showing how to use a system of equations to solve a real-world problem. Then solve problems 1–7.

Example

Oceanview Hotel charges $100 per day plus a one-time fee of $40. Beachside Hotel charges $110 per day. After how many days will the costs be equal?

Start by writing a system of equations to model the problem. Let c be the cost and d be the number of days.

Total cost for Oceanview: $c = 100d + 40$
Total cost for Beachside: $c = 110d$

Use substitution to solve the system. The second equation tells you that $c = 110d$, so you can substitute $110d$ for c.

$$c = 100d + 40$$
$$110d = 100d + 40 \qquad \text{Substitute } 110d \text{ for } c.$$
$$10d = 40$$
$$d = 4$$

The costs at the hotels will be the same after 4 days.

1 Explain what the equation $110d = 100d + 40$ represents in the context of the example problem.

It represents when the costs at the two hotels will be equal.

2 Suppose Oceanview Hotel changes their fee to $45 and Beachside Hotel changes their daily rate to $115. Write new equations for the total costs for the two resorts.

The equation for Oceanview would be $c = 100d + 45$, and the equation for Beachside

would be $c = 115d$.

3 Solve the system of equations formed by the equations you wrote in problem 2. After how many days would the total costs at the two resorts be the same?

The total costs would be the same after 3 days.

Solve.

4 Roberto got $30 for his birthday. He decides to save that amount and add $5 to his savings each week. Jack starts saving the same day as Roberto and puts $8 in his savings each week. After how many weeks will the boys have the same amount in savings?

Show your work.
Possible answer:
Let s = total savings and w = number of weeks.
Roberto's savings: $s = 5w + 30$
Jack's savings: $s = 8w$
$8w = 5w + 30$
$3w = 30$
$w = 10$

Solution: They will have the same amount in savings after 10 weeks.

Use this situation for problems 5–6.

Julia earns $6 an hour babysitting and earns $5 an hour walking dogs. She earned $43 after working a total of 8 hours at her two jobs.

5 Complete the system of equations below to represent the situation. Let b = the number of hours that Julia babysits and d = the number of hours she walks dogs.

$$b + d = 8 \qquad 6b + 5d = 43$$

6 Solve the system of equations from problem 5 to find the number of hours Julia worked at each job.

Julia worked 3 hours babysitting and 5 hours walking dogs.

7 Consider the situation at the right. Write a question and a system of equations for the situation. Then answer your question by solving the system of equations.

Trisha and Yoshi are at the start of a trail. Trisha walks 500 feet before Yoshi starts. Trisha walks 350 feet per minute, and Yoshi walks 430 feet per minute.

Possible answer: How long will it take Yoshi to catch up with Trisha?

Let d = distance and t = time.

Trisha: $d = 350t + 500$ and Yoshi: $d = 430t$

It will take 6.25 minutes for Yoshi to catch up with Trisha.

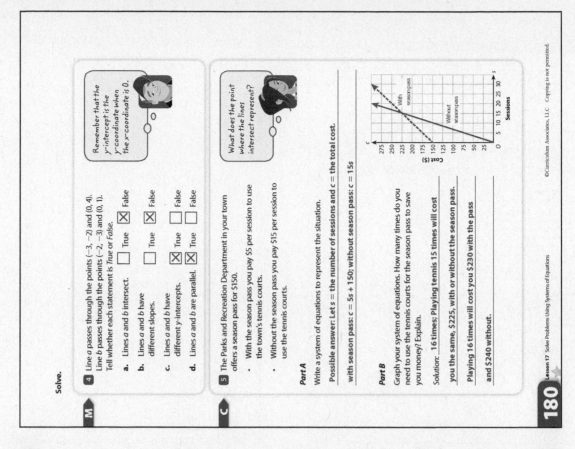

Solve.

4. Line a passes through the points $(-3, -2)$ and $(0, 4)$. Line b passes through the points $(-2, -3)$ and $(0, 1)$. Tell whether each statement is *True* or *False*.

   a. Lines a and b intersect.   True ☐   False ☒

   b. Lines a and b have different slopes.   True ☐   False ☒

   c. Lines a and b have different y-intercepts.   True ☒   False ☐

   d. Lines a and b are parallel.   True ☒   False ☐

Remember that the y-intercept is the y-coordinate when the x-coordinate is 0.

5. The Parks and Recreation Department in your town offers a season pass for $150.
   - With the season pass you pay $5 per session to use the town's tennis courts.
   - Without the season pass you pay $15 per session to use the tennis courts.

Part A

Write a system of equations to represent the situation.

Possible answer: Let s = the number of sessions and c = the total cost.

with season pass: $c = 5s + 150$; without season pass: $c = 15s$

Part B

Graph your system of equations. How many times do you need to use the tennis courts for the season pass to save you money? Explain.

Solution: 16 times; Playing tennis 15 times will cost you the same, $225, with or without the season pass. Playing 16 times will cost you $230 with the pass and $240 without.

What does the point where the lines intersect represent?

180   Lesson 17   Solve Problems Using Systems of Equations

Lesson 17   Name: _____

Solve Problems Using Systems of Equations

Solve the problems.

1. The sum of two numbers is 27. One number is 3 more than the other number. Write and solve a system of equations to find the two numbers.

Show your work.

Possible answer:
Let x = one number and y = the other number.
$$x + y = 27$$
$$x = y + 3$$
$$(y + 3) + y = 27 \qquad x + 12 = 27$$
$$2y + 3 = 27 \qquad x = 15$$
$$2y = 24$$
$$y = 12$$

Solution: The numbers are 12 and 15.

Write one equation for the sum. What will the other equation be?

2. Roberta has $4.00 in dimes and quarters. She has 5 more dimes than quarters. Write a system of equations that you could use to find how many dimes and quarters she has.

Possible answer: Let d = the number of dimes and q = the number of quarters.

$d = q + 5$ and $10d + 25q = 400$

Choose a variable for the number of dimes and a variable for the number of quarters.

3. Use the system of equations you wrote in problem 2 to find how many dimes and quarters Roberta has.

   A   10 dimes and 15 quarters

   B   10 dimes and 35 quarters

   C   15 dimes and 10 quarters *(circled)*

   D   15 dimes and 35 quarters

   Dennis chose **A** as the correct answer. How did he get that answer?

   Dennis switched the number of dimes and the number of quarters.

Check your solution in the equation that shows the total amount of money.

Lesson 17   Solve Problems Using Systems of Equations   179

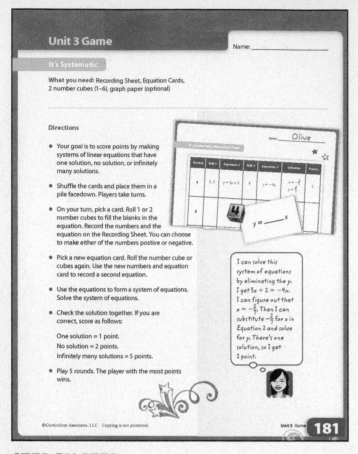

STEP BY STEP

CCSS Focus - 8.EE.C.8a, 8.EE.C.8b *Embedded SMPs* - 1, 2, 5, 6, 7	**Materials** For each pair: Recording Sheets (1 for each player)

Objectives

- Solve a system of two linear equations.
- Given a system of equations, identify how many solutions it has.

Materials For each pair: Recording Sheets (1 for each player) (TR 5), Equation Cards (TR 6), 2 number cubes (1–6), graph paper (optional)

- Your goal is to score points by making systems of linear equations that have one solution, no solution, or infinitely many solutions.

- Shuffle the cards and place them in a pile facedown. Players take turns.

- On your turn, pick a card. Roll 1 or 2 number cubes to fill the blanks in the equation. Record the numbers and the equation on the Recording Sheet. You can choose to make either of the numbers postive or negative.

- Pick a new equation card. Roll the number cube or cubes again. Use the new numbers and equation card to record a second equation.

- Use the equations to form a system of equations. Solve the system of equations.

- Check the solution together. If you are correct, score as follows:

  One solution = 1 point.

  No solution = 2 points.

  Infinitely many solutions = 5 points.

- Play 5 rounds. The player with the most points wins.

- Model one round for students before they play. Discuss strategies for creating systems of equations with 0, 1, or infinitely many solutions.

Vary the Game On any turn, re-roll up to 2 number cubes.

Extra Support Have students graph the equations to help them see the solution(s).

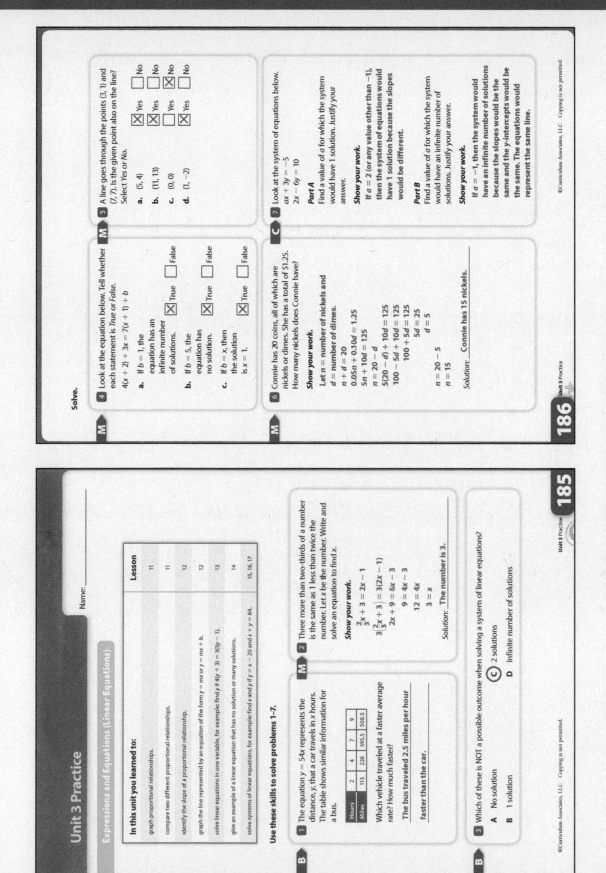

Unit 3 Practice

Name: _____

Expressions and Equations (Linear Equations)

In this unit you learned to:

	Lesson
graph proportional relationships.	11
compare two different proportional relationships.	11
identify the slope of a proportional relationship.	12
graph the line represented by an equation of the form $y = mx$ or $y = mx + b$.	12
solve linear equations in one variable, for example: find y if $4(y + 3) = 3(3y - 1)$.	13
give an example of a linear equation that has no solution or many solutions.	14
solve systems of linear equations, for example find x and y if $y = x - 20$ and $x + y = 84$.	15, 16, 17

Use these skills to solve problems 1–7.

B 1. The equation $y = 54x$ represents the distance, y, that a car travels in x hours. The table shows similar information for a bus.

Hours	2	4	7	9
Miles	113	226	395.5	508.5

Which vehicle traveled at a faster average rate? How much faster?

The bus traveled 2.5 miles per hour faster than the car.

M 2. Three more than two-thirds of a number is the same as 1 less than twice the number. Let x be the number. Write and solve an equation to find x.

Show your work.

$$\frac{2}{3}x + 3 = 2x - 1$$
$$3\left(\frac{2}{3}x + 3\right) = 3(2x - 1)$$
$$2x + 9 = 6x - 3$$
$$9 = 4x - 3$$
$$12 = 4x$$
$$3 = x$$

Solution: _The number is 3._

B 3. Which of these is NOT a possible outcome when solving a system of linear equations?

A No solution

B 1 solution

(C) 2 solutions

D Infinite number of solutions

Solve.

M 4. Look at the equation below. Tell whether each statement is *True* or *False*.

$$4(x + 2) + 3x = 7(x + 1) + b$$

a. If $b = 1$, the equation has an infinite number of solutions. [X] True [ ] False

b. If $b = 5$, the equation has no solution. [X] True [ ] False

c. If $b = x$, then the solution is $x = 1$. [X] True [ ] False

M 5. A line goes through the points (3, 1) and (7, 7). Is the given point also on the line? Select *Yes* or *No*.

a. (5, 4) [X] Yes [ ] No

b. (11, 13) [X] Yes [ ] No

c. (0, 0) [ ] Yes [X] No

d. (1, −2) [X] Yes [ ] No

M 6. Connie has 20 coins, all of which are nickels or dimes. She has a total of $1.25. How many nickels does Connie have?

Show your work.

Let n = number of nickels and d = number of dimes.

$$n + d = 20$$
$$0.05n + 0.10d = 1.25$$
$$5n + 10d = 125$$
$$n = 20 - d$$
$$5(20 - d) + 10d = 125$$
$$100 - 5d + 10d = 125$$
$$100 + 5d = 125$$
$$5d = 25$$
$$d = 5$$
$$n = 20 - 5$$
$$n = 15$$

Solution: _Connie has 15 nickels._

C 7. Look at the system of equations below.

$$ax + 3y = -5$$
$$2x - 6y = 10$$

Part A

Find a value of a for which the system would have 1 solution. Justify your answer.

Show your work.

If $a = 2$ (or any value other than −1), then the system of equations would have 1 solution because the slopes would be different.

Part B

Find a value of a for which the system would have an infinite number of solutions. Justify your answer.

Show your work.

If $a = -1$, then the system would have an infinite number of solutions because the slopes would be the same and the y-intercepts would be the same. The equations would represent the same line.

185 Unit 3 Practice

186 Unit 3 Practice

Key

B Basic   **M** Medium   **C** Challenge

TEACHER NOTES

Common Core Standards: 8.EE.C.7a, 8.EE.C.7b
Standards for Mathematical Practice: 1, 3, 6, 7
DOK: 3
Materials: None

About the Task

To complete this task, students solve a multi-step problem that involves creating equations that have no solutions, one solution, and many solutions. The task requires that students apply their knowledge of solving equations to develop equations that they can manipulate to get specific results.

Getting Started

Read the problem out loud with students. Go over the checklist and the rules of the game. Have students give examples of constants and a variable with a coefficient. Have students describe strategies for writing equations that have infinitely many, one, or no solutions. *(SMP 1)*

Completing the Task

The idea of writing an equation to meet certain criteria may be new to students. Often, students are more comfortable when they are given an equation and asked to identify its characteristics. If students struggle with this task, encourage them to begin by writing a simple equation. Once they have the basic structure of terms, operations, and an equal sign, they can make changes to bring the equation closer to meeting the stated criteria. Other students may begin with confidence, building the required terms, varying the operations used, and monitoring their progress to ascertain when they have an equation that has the needed number of solutions. *(SMP 7)*

Remind students to check their work. Have them check solutions and explanations to be sure that everything is clear and meets the criteria. *(SMP 6)*

When students are finished, break them into small groups to share their equations and discuss their strategies and results for each type of solution. *(SMP 3)*

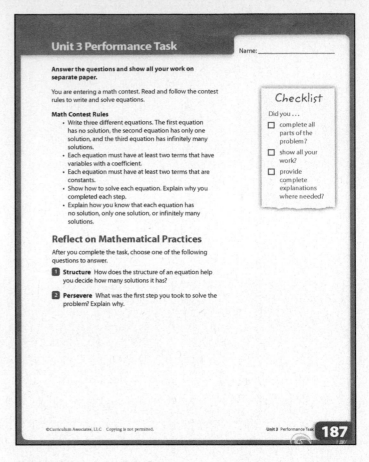

Extension

If students have more time to spend on this problem, you can have them solve this extension:

For your second contest entry, change each of your equations so that it has a different number of solutions than it had before. Keep track of how many changes you make, and try to make as few changes as possible. Swap with a partner and see whether your partner gets the same results that you did.

SAMPLE RESPONSE AND RUBRIC

4-Point Solution

$3x - 8 = 3x + 50$ has no solution. There is no value of x that can make this equation true because variable terms are the same on each side but the constants are different. If you subtract $3x$ from both sides you get $-8 = 50$, which is never true.

$2x + 9 = 18 - 2x$ has one solution.

$2x + 2x + 9 = 18$	I added $2x$ to both sides to get all of the variable terms on one side.
$4x + 9 = 18$	I combined the variable terms on the left side.
$4x = 18 - 9$	I subtracted 9 from both sides to get all of the constants on one side.
$4x = 9$	I combined the constants on the right side.
$x = \frac{9}{4}$	I divided both sides by 4 to isolate x and find the solution.

$5x + 6 = 5x + 0 + 6$ has infinitely many solution because both sides simplify to $5x + 6$. If you subtract $5x$ from both sides and subtract 6 from both sides, you get $0 = 0$, which is always true. No matter what quantity I substitute for x, the value on both sides will be the same.

REFLECT ON MATHEMATICAL PRACTICES

1. Perceptive students will look at the variable terms to determine the number of solutions. Students should also recognize the importance of simplifying expressions in order to work efficiently. **(SMP 3)**

2. First steps might involve writing equivalent expressions or writing the same variable with two different constants. **(SMP 1)**

SCORING RUBRIC

4 points All parts of the problem are complete and correct. The three equations have the required terms and types of solutions and students correctly explain how they know. Solutions are complete and correct and students correctly explain each step.

3 points The student has completed all parts of the problem, with one or two errors. Possible errors might include incorrectly solving an equation, not using the required terms, skipping a solution step, or not explaining the solution steps or the types of equations.

2 points The student has attempted all parts of the problem, with a number of errors. The equations may not have the required terms or the required types of solutions. Students' explanations may be incomplete.

1 point Much of the problem is incomplete, with several errors. The equations do not meet the criteria. Solutions may be incorrect or missing. Explanations are incorrect or missing.

SOLUTION TO THE EXTENSION

Possible Solution

I changed $3x - 8 = 3x + 50$ to $3x - 8 = 5x + 50$. Now this equation has one solution. I made one change.
$3x - 8 = 5x + 50$, $3x - 5x = 58$, $-2x = 58$, $x = \frac{58}{-2}$, or -29.

I changed $2x + 9 = 18 - 2x$ to $2x + 9 = 9 + 2x$. Now it has infinitely many solutions because both sides have the same terms. I made two changes.

I changed $5x + 6 = 5x + 0 + 6$ to $5x + 6 = 5x + 30 + 6$. Now it has no solution because the variables on each side are the same but the constants are different. I made one change.

Lesson 18
Understand Properties of Transformations

Name: _____

Prerequisite: **What properties can you use to compare shapes?**

Study the example problem showing how to compare the properties of two shapes. Then solve problems 1–6.

Example

Compare the properties of quadrilaterals *A* and *B*.

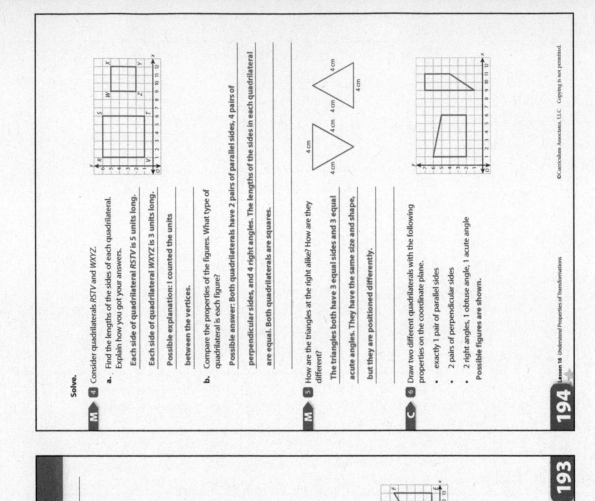

You can use a table to show the comparison.

	Parallel Sides	Perpendicular Sides	Lengths of Opposite Sides	Angles
A	2 pairs	4 pairs	equal	4 right
B	2 pairs	4 pairs	equal	4 right

B **1** What types of quadrilaterals are figures *A* and *B* in the example problem? Explain how you know.

They are both rectangles. They both have 2 pairs of parallel sides and 4 right angles.

Use △ABC and △DEF to answer problems 2–3.

M **2** In △ABC the measure of angle A is 30°. In △DEF the measure of angle F is 60°. Find the rest of the angle measures in each triangle and compare them.

$m\angle B = 90°$, $m\angle C = 60°$, $m\angle D = 30°$, $m\angle E = 90°$;

∠A and ∠D have the same measure and so do ∠B and ∠E as well as ∠C and ∠F.

B **3** What types of triangles are △ABC and △DEF?

They are both right triangles.

©Curriculum Associates, LLC Copying is not permitted.
Lesson 18 *Understand* Properties of Transformations 193

Solve.

M **4** Consider quadrilaterals *RSTV* and *WXYZ*.

a. Find the lengths of the sides of each quadrilateral. Explain how you got your answers.

Each side of quadrilateral *RSTV* is 5 units long.

Each side of quadrilateral *WXYZ* is 3 units long.

Possible explanation: I counted the units

between the vertices.

b. Compare the properties of the figures. What type of quadrilateral is each figure?

Possible answer: Both quadrilaterals have 2 pairs of parallel sides, 4 pairs of perpendicular sides, and 4 right angles. The lengths of the sides in each quadrilateral are equal. Both quadrilaterals are squares.

M **5** How are the triangles at the right alike? How are they different?

The triangles both have 3 equal sides and 3 equal acute angles. They have the same size and shape, but they are positioned differently.

C **6** Draw two different quadrilaterals with the following properties on the coordinate plane.

- exactly 1 pair of parallel sides
- 2 pairs of perpendicular sides
- 2 right angles, 1 obtuse angle, 1 acute angle
Possible figures are shown.

194 Lesson 18 *Understand* Properties of Transformations
©Curriculum Associates, LLC Copying is not permitted.

Key

B Basic   **M** Medium   **C** Challenge

©Curriculum Associates, LLC   Copying is not permitted.

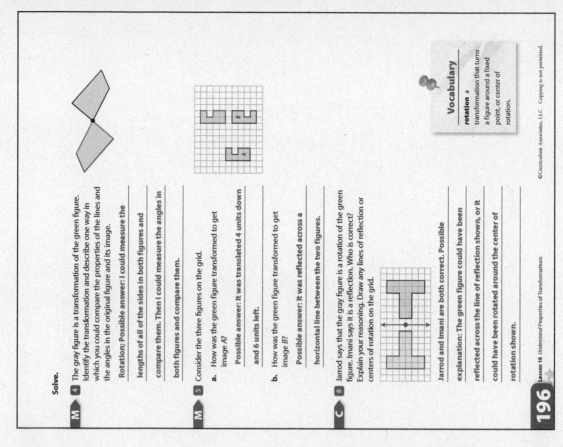

Solve.

4 The gray figure is a transformation of the green figure. Identify the transformation and describe one way in which you could compare the properties of the lines and the angles in the original figure and its image.

Rotation; Possible answer: I could measure the lengths of all of the sides in both figures and compare them. Then I could measure the angles in both figures and compare them.

5 Consider the three figures on the grid.

a. How was the green figure transformed to get image A?

Possible answer: It was translated 4 units down and 6 units left.

b. How was the green figure transformed to get image B?

Possible answer: It was reflected across a horizontal line between the two figures.

6 Jarrod says that the gray figure is a rotation of the green figure. Imani says it is a reflection. Who is correct? Explain your reasoning. Draw any lines of reflection or centers of rotation on the grid.

Jarrod and Imani are both correct. Possible explanation: The green figure could have been reflected across the line of reflection shown, or it could have been rotated around the center of rotation shown.

Vocabulary
rotation a transformation that turns a figure around a fixed point, or center of rotation.

Lesson 18

Name: _____

Explore Properties of Transformations

Study the example problem showing how to analyze a figure and its image after a transformation. Then solve problems 1–6.

Example

The gray figure is a transformation of the green figure. Compare the figures. Tell what is the same and what is different about the original figure and its image. Identify the transformation.

Same: The figures have the same shape and size. Parallel lines are still parallel and perpendicular lines are still perpendicular. The lengths of the sides are the same, and the measures of the angles are the same.

Different: The image is in a different location than the original figure.

The transformation is a translation.

Vocabulary
transformation a change in position or size of a figure.
translation a transformation that moves each point of a figure the same distance and in the same direction.
reflection a transformation that flips a figure over a line of reflection.

1 Describe how the original figure in the example problem was moved to get the image.

The original figure was moved 7 units right and 2 units down.

2 A figure and a line of reflection are shown. Draw the image of the figure after it is reflected across the line.

3 Look at the image you drew in problem 2. Are the properties of the sides and angles in the image the same as the properties of the sides and angles in the original figure? Explain.

Yes; the lengths of the sides and the measures of the angles are the same. Parallel lines are still parallel, and perpendicular lines are still perpendicular.

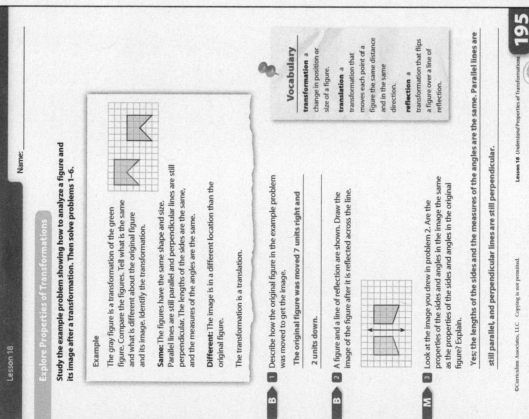

Page 198

Solve the problem. Use what you learned from the model.

Draw a scalene right triangle in the middle of the grid below. Label it J. Then draw the following transformations of your triangle.

- a translation 3 units down and 9 units left. Label it K.
- a reflection over a vertical line of reflection. Label it L. Draw the line of reflection.
- a 90° clockwise rotation around a center of rotation. Label it M. Draw the point that is the center of rotation.

Explain how the properties of the lines and angles in your transformations are the same as the properties of the lines and angles in your original figure.

Show your work. Use words and drawings to explain your answer. Possible drawings shown.

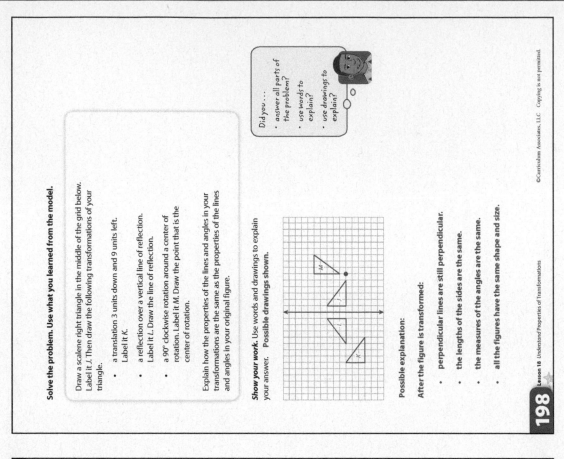

Possible explanation:

After the figure is transformed:

- perpendicular lines are still perpendicular.
- the lengths of the sides are the same.
- the measures of the angles are the same.
- all the figures have the same shape and size.

Did you . . .
- *answer all parts of the problem?*
- *use words to explain?*
- *use drawings to explain?*

Page 197

Lesson 18

Name: _____

Reason and Write

Study the example. Underline two parts that you think make it a particularly good answer and a helpful example.

Example

Draw a trapezoid in the middle of the grid below. Label it A. Then draw the following transformations of your trapezoid.

- a translation 2 units up and 8 units right. Label this figure B.
- a reflection over a horizontal line of reflection. Label this figure C. Draw the line of reflection.
- a 180° counterclockwise rotation around a center of rotation. Label this figure D. Draw the point that is the center of rotation.

Explain how the properties of the lines and angles in your transformations are the same as the properties of the lines and angles in your original figure.

Show your work. Use words and drawings to explain your answer.

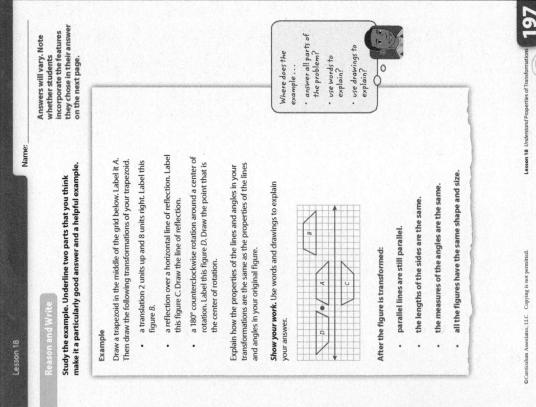

After the figure is transformed:

- parallel lines are still parallel.
- the lengths of the sides are the same.
- the measures of the angles are the same.
- all the figures have the same shape and size.

Where does the example . . .
- *answer all parts of the problem?*
- *use words to explain?*
- *use drawings to explain?*

Answers will vary. Note whether students incorporate the features they chose in their answer on the next page.

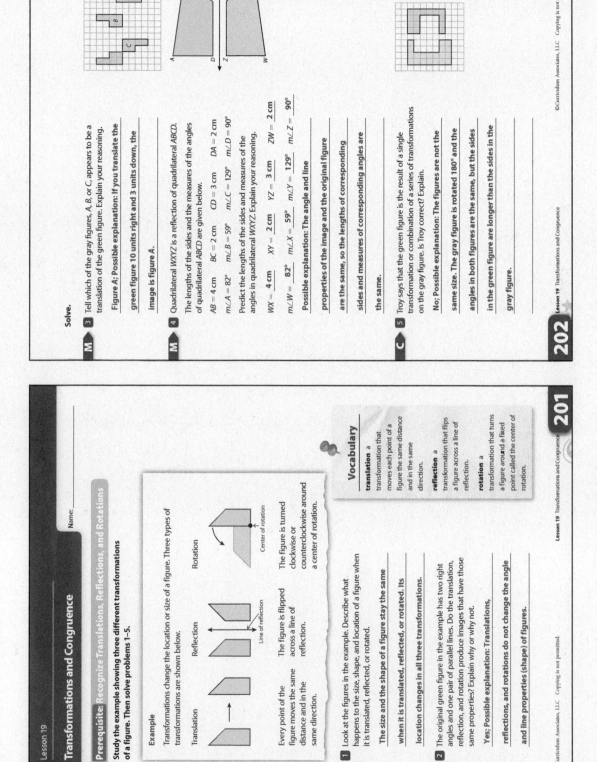

Page 201

Lesson 19

Transformations and Congruence

Name: _____

Prerequisite: Recognize Translations, Reflections, and Rotations

Study the example showing three different transformations of a figure. Then solve problems 1–5.

Example

Transformations change the location or size of a figure. Three types of transformations are shown below.

Translation   Reflection   Rotation

Center of rotation

Every point of the figure moves the same distance and in the same direction.

The figure is flipped across a line of reflection.

The figure is turned clockwise or counterclockwise around a center of rotation.

B 1 Look at the figures in the example. Describe what happens to the size, shape, and location of a figure when it is translated, reflected, or rotated.

The size and the shape of a figure stay the same

when it is translated, reflected, or rotated. Its

location changes in all three transformations.

B 2 The original green figure in the example has two right angles and one pair of parallel lines. Do the translation, reflection, and rotation produce images that have those same properties? Explain why or why not.

Yes; Possible explanation: Translations,

reflections, and rotations do not change the angle

and line properties (shape) of figures.

Vocabulary

translation a transformation that moves each point of a figure the same distance and in the same direction.

reflection a transformation that flips a figure across a line of reflection.

rotation a transformation that turns a figure around a fixed point called the center of rotation.

Page 202

Solve.

M 3 Tell which of the gray figures, A, B, or C, appears to be a translation of the green figure. Explain your reasoning.

Figure A; Possible explanation: If you translate the

green figure 10 units right and 3 units down, the

image is figure A.

M 4 Quadrilateral *WXYZ* is a reflection of quadrilateral *ABCD*. The lengths of the sides and the measures of the angles of quadrilateral *ABCD* are given below.

$AB = 4\,cm$ $BC = 2\,cm$ $CD = 3\,cm$ $DA = 2\,cm$
$m\angle A = 82°$ $m\angle B = 59°$ $m\angle C = 129°$ $m\angle D = 90°$

Predict the lengths of the sides and measures of the angles in quadrilateral *WXYZ*. Explain your reasoning.

$WX =$ __4 cm__ $XY =$ __2 cm__ $YZ =$ __3 cm__ $ZW =$ __2 cm__
$m\angle W =$ __82°__ $m\angle X =$ __59°__ $m\angle Y =$ __129°__ $m\angle Z =$ __90°__

Possible explanation: The angle and line

properties of the image and the original figure

are the same, so the lengths of corresponding

sides and measures of corresponding angles are

the same.

C 5 Troy says that the green figure is the result of a single transformation or combination of a series of transformations on the gray figure. Is Troy correct? Explain.

No; Possible explanation: The figures are not the

same size. The gray figure is rotated 180° and the

angles in both figures are the same, but the sides

in the green figure are longer than the sides in the

gray figure.

Key

B Basic   **M** Medium   **C** Challenge

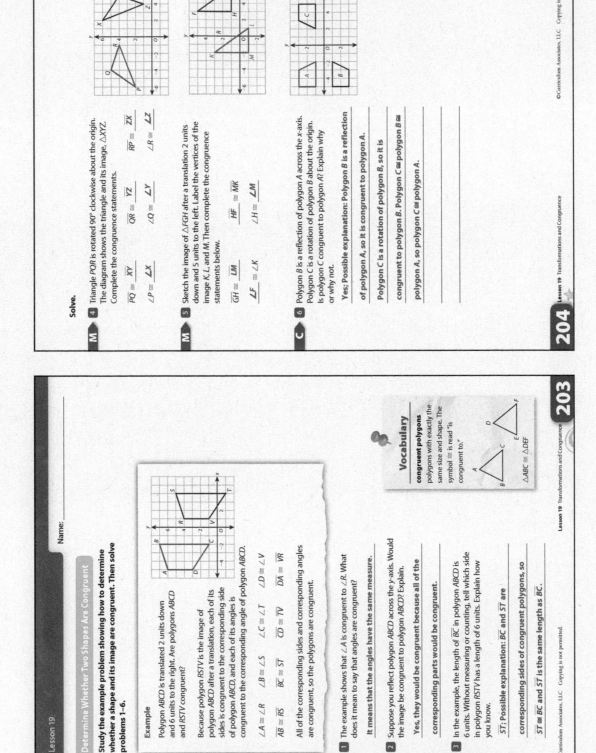

Lesson 19

Name: _____

Determine Whether Two Shapes Are Congruent

Study the example problem showing how to determine whether a shape and its image are congruent. Then solve problems 1–6.

Example

Polygon ABCD is translated 2 units down and 6 units to the right. Are polygons ABCD and RSTV congruent?

Because polygon RSTV is the image of polygon ABCD after a translation, each of its sides is congruent to the corresponding side of polygon ABCD, and each of its angles is congruent to the corresponding angle of polygon ABCD.

$\angle A \cong \angle R$ $\angle B \cong \angle S$ $\angle C \cong \angle T$ $\angle D \cong \angle V$

$\overline{AB} \cong \overline{RS}$ $\overline{BC} \cong \overline{ST}$ $\overline{CD} \cong \overline{TV}$ $\overline{DA} \cong \overline{VR}$

All of the corresponding sides and corresponding angles are congruent, so the polygons are congruent.

1 The example shows that $\angle A$ is congruent to $\angle R$. What does it mean to say that angles are congruent?

It means that the angles have the same measure.

2 Suppose you reflect polygon ABCD across the y-axis. Would the image be congruent to polygon ABCD? Explain.

Yes, they would be congruent because all of the corresponding parts would be congruent.

3 In the example, the length of $\overline{BC}$ in polygon ABCD is 6 units. Without measuring or counting, tell which side in polygon RSTV has a length of 6 units. Explain how you know.

$\overline{ST}$; Possible explanation: $\overline{BC}$ and $\overline{ST}$ are corresponding sides of congruent polygons, so $\overline{ST} \cong \overline{BC}$ and $\overline{ST}$ is the same length as $\overline{BC}$.

Vocabulary

congruent polygons polygons with exactly the same size and shape. The symbol $\cong$ is read "is congruent to."

$\triangle ABC \cong \triangle DEF$

Solve.

4 Triangle PQR is rotated 90° clockwise about the origin. The diagram shows the triangle and its image, $\triangle XYZ$. Complete the congruence statements.

$\overline{PQ} \cong \underline{\overline{XY}}$ $\overline{QR} \cong \underline{\overline{YZ}}$ $\overline{RP} \cong \underline{\overline{ZX}}$

$\angle P \cong \underline{\angle X}$ $\angle Q \cong \underline{\angle Y}$ $\angle R \cong \underline{\angle Z}$

5 Sketch the image of $\triangle FGH$ after a translation 2 units down and 5 units to the left. Label the vertices of the image K, L, and M. Then complete the congruence statements below.

$\overline{GH} \cong \underline{\overline{LM}}$ $\overline{HF} \cong \underline{\overline{MK}}$

$\angle F \cong \underline{\angle K}$ $\angle H \cong \underline{\angle M}$

6 Polygon B is a reflection of polygon A across the x-axis. Polygon C is a rotation of polygon B about the origin. Is polygon C congruent to polygon A? Explain why or why not.

Yes; Possible explanation: Polygon B is a reflection of polygon A, so it is congruent to polygon A.

Polygon C is a rotation of polygon B, so it is congruent to polygon B. Polygon C ≅ polygon B ≅ polygon A, so polygon C ≅ polygon A.

Lesson 19

Compare Coordinates

Study the example problem showing how to describe a transformation. Then solve problems 1–7.

Example

△ABC was transformed to produce a congruent triangle, △A'B'C'. What transformation produced △A'B'C'?

Compare the corresponding vertices in △ABC and △A'B'C'.

△ABC (Original)	△A'B'C' (Image)
A(−5, 4)	A'(4, 5)
B(−1, 4)	B'(4, 1)
C(−5, 1)	C'(1, 5)

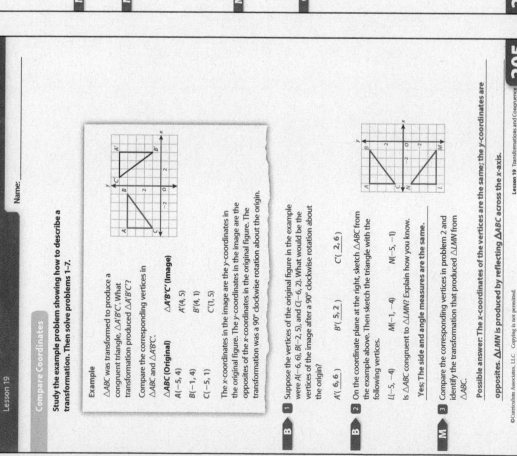

The x-coordinates in the image are the y-coordinates in the original figure. They y-coordinates in the image are the opposites of the x-coordinates in the original figure. The transformation was a 90° clockwise rotation about the origin.

B **1** Suppose the vertices of the original figure in the example were A(−6, 6), B(−2, 5), and C(−6, 2). What would be the vertices of the image after a 90° clockwise rotation about the origin?

A'(6, 6)   B'(5, 2)   C'(2, 6)

B **2** On the coordinate plane at the right, sketch △ABC from the example above. Then sketch the triangle with the following vertices.

L(−5, −4)   M(−1, −4)   N(−5, −1)

Is △ABC congruent to △LMN? Explain how you know.

Yes; The side and angle measures are the same.

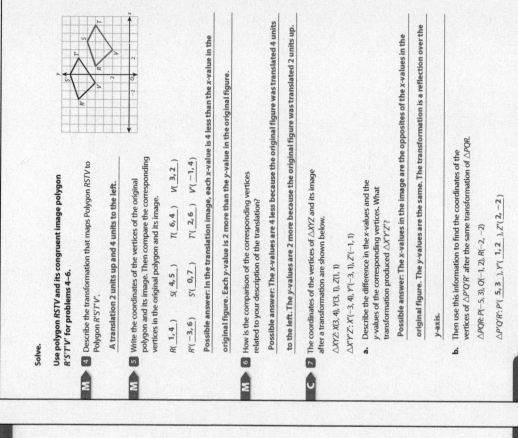

M **3** Compare the corresponding vertices in problem 2 and identify the transformation that produced △LMN from △ABC.

Possible answer: The x-coordinates of the vertices are the same; the y-coordinates are opposites. △LMN is produced by reflecting △ABC across the x-axis.

Lesson 19 Transformations and Congruence   **205**

Solve.

Use polygon RSTV and its congruent image polygon R'S'T'V' for problems 4–6.

M **4** Describe the transformation that maps Polygon RSTV to Polygon R'S'T'V'.

A translation 2 units up and 4 units to the left.

M **5** Write the coordinates of the vertices of the original polygon and its image. Then compare the corresponding vertices in the original polygon and its image.

R(1, 4)	S(4, 5)	T(6, 4)	V(3, 2)
R'(−3, 6)	S(0, 7)	T'(2, 6)	V'(−1, 4)

Possible answer: In the translation image, each x-value is 4 less than the x-value in the original figure. Each y-value is 2 more than the y-value in the original figure.

M **6** How is the comparison of the corresponding vertices related to your description of the translation?

Possible answer: The x-values are 4 less because the original figure was translated 4 units to the left. The y-values are 2 more because the original figure was translated 2 units up.

C **7** The coordinates of the vertices of △XYZ and its image after a transformation are shown below.

△XYZ: X(3, 4), Y(3, 1), Z(1, 1)
△X'Y'Z': X'(−3, 4), Y'(−3, 1), Z'(−1, 1)

a. Describe the difference in the x-values and the y-values of the corresponding vertices. What transformation produced △X'Y'Z'?

Possible answer: The x-values in the image are the opposites of the x-values in the original figure. The y-values are the same. The transformation is a reflection over the y-axis.

b. Then use this information to find the coordinates of the vertices of △P'Q'R' after the same transformation of △PQR.

△PQR: P(−5, 3), Q(−1, 2), R(−2, −2)

△P'Q'R': P'(5, 3), Y'(1, 2), Z'(2, −2)

206 Lesson 19 Transformations and Congruence

Lesson 19

Name: _____

Transformations and Congruence

Solve the problems.

1 Triangle A transforms to Triangle W.

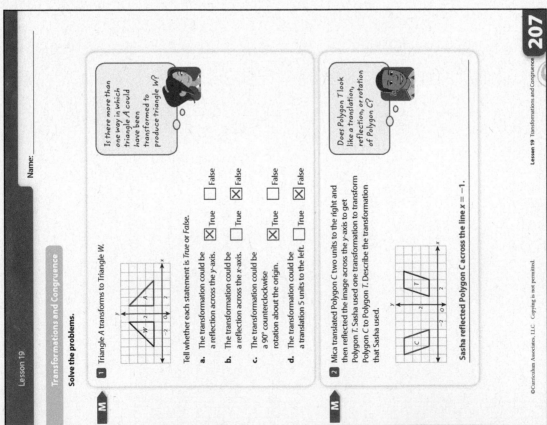

Is there more than one way in which triangle A could have been transformed to produce triangle W?

Tell whether each statement is *True* or *False*.

a. The transformation could be a reflection across the y-axis. [X] True [ ] False

b. The transformation could be a reflection across the x-axis. [ ] True [X] False

c. The transformation could be a 90° counterclockwise rotation about the origin. [X] True [ ] False

d. The transformation could be a translation 5 units to the left. [ ] True [X] False

2 Mica translated Polygon C two units to the right and then reflected the image across the y-axis to get Polygon T. Sasha used one transformation to transform Polygon C to Polygon T. Describe the transformation that Sasha used.

Does Polygon T look like a translation, reflection, or rotation of Polygon C?

Sasha reflected Polygon C across the line x = −1.

Solve.

3 Which graph shows the image of △ABC after the following series of transformations?

A translation 6 units left and 2 units down, followed by a reflection over the line x = −2.

Make a sketch of the transformations before you choose.

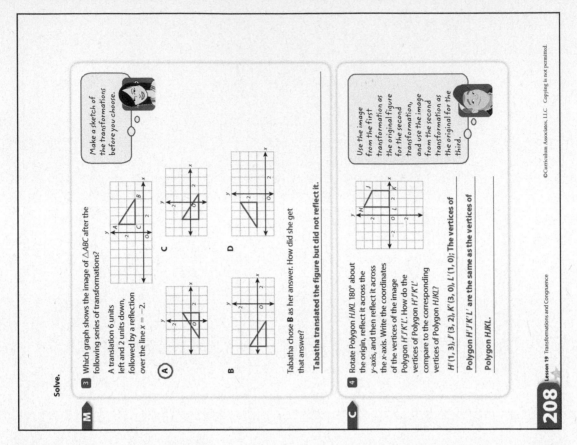

(A)

Tabatha chose **B** as her answer. How did she get that answer?

Tabatha translated the figure but did not reflect it.

4 Rotate Polygon HJKL 180° about the origin, reflect it across the y-axis, and then reflect it across the x-axis of the vertices of the image Polygon H'J'K'L'. How do the vertices of Polygon H'J'K'L' compare to the corresponding vertices of Polygon HJKL?

Use the image from the first transformation as the original figure for the second transformation, and use the image from the second transformation as the original for the third.

H'(1, 3), J'(3, 2), K'(3, 0), L'(1, 0); The vertices of Polygon H'J'K'L' are the same as the vertices of Polygon HJKL.

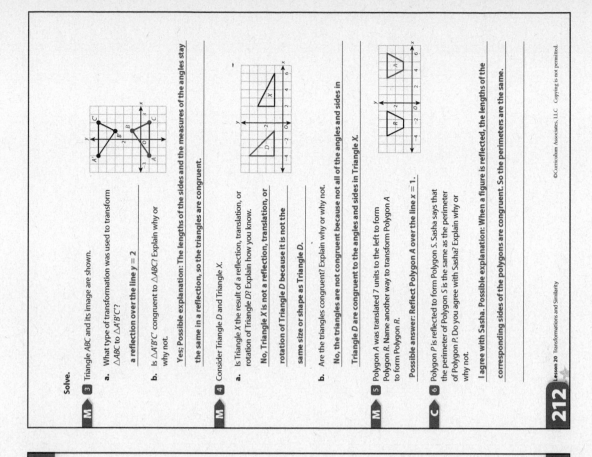

Lesson 20

Transformations and Similarity

Prerequisite: Use Transformations to Identify Congruent Figures

Study the example problem showing how to use transformations to identify two congruent figures. Then solve problems 1–6.

Example

Polygon *KLMN* is translated 3 units down and 5 units to the left. Polygon *K'L'M'N'* is its image. Are Polygon *KLMN* and its image congruent?

Because Polygon *K'L'M'N'* is the image of Polygon *KLMN* after a translation, each of its sides is congruent to the corresponding side of Polygon *KLMN*, and each of its angles is congruent to the corresponding angle of Polygon *KLMN*.

$\angle K \cong \angle K'$ $\angle L \cong \angle L'$ $\angle M \cong \angle M'$ $\angle N \cong \angle N'$

$\overline{KL} \cong \overline{K'L'}$ $\overline{LM} \cong \overline{L'M'}$ $\overline{MN} \cong \overline{M'N'}$ $\overline{NK} \cong \overline{N'K'}$

All of the corresponding parts are congruent, so the polygons are congruent.

B 1 When Polygon *KLMN* in the example was translated, how did the angle and line properties change? Explain.

They did not change. Possible explanation: The

lengths of the sides and the measures of the

angles stay the same in a translation.

B 2 If you rotate Polygon *KLMN* 180° about the origin, how would the measures of the angles in the image compare to the measures of the corresponding angles in the original figure?

The measures would be the same.

Vocabulary

congruent polygons
polygons with exactly the same size and shape. The symbol $\cong$ is read "is congruent to."

$\triangle ABC \cong \triangle DEF$

Solve.

M 3 Triangle *ABC* and its image are shown.

a. What type of transformation was used to transform △*ABC* to △*A'B'C'*?

a reflection over the line *y* = 2

b. Is △*A'B'C'* congruent to △*ABC*? Explain why or why not.

Yes; Possible explanation: The lengths of the sides and the measures of the angles stay

the same in a reflection, so the triangles are congruent.

M 4 Consider Triangle *D* and Triangle *X*.

a. Is Triangle *X* the result of a reflection, translation, or rotation of Triangle *D*? Explain how you know.

No, Triangle *X* is not a reflection, translation, or

rotation of Triangle *D* because it is not the

same size or shape as Triangle *D*.

b. Are the triangles congruent? Explain why or why not.

No, the triangles are not congruent because not all of the angles and sides in

Triangle *D* are congruent to the angles and sides in Triangle *X*.

M 5 Polygon *A* was translated 7 units to the left to form Polygon *R*. Name another way to transform Polygon *A* to form Polygon *R*.

Possible answer: Reflect Polygon *A* over the line *x* = 1.

C 6 Polygon *P* is reflected to form Polygon *S*. Sasha says that the perimeter of Polygon *S* is the same as the perimeter of Polygon *P*. Do you agree with Sasha? Explain why or why not.

I agree with Sasha. Possible explanation: When a figure is reflected, the lengths of the

corresponding sides of the polygons are congruent. So the perimeters are the same.

Key

B Basic   **M** Medium   **C** Challenge

Solve.

M **3** The coordinates of the vertices of Polygon RSTV are R(2, 4), S(6, 4), T(6, 0), and V(2, 0). The Polygon is dilated with scale factor of $\frac{3}{2}$ and center (0, 0). Explain how you can find the coordinates of the vertices of Polygon R'S'T'V' from the coordinates of the vertices of the Polygon RSTV.

Possible explanation: I can multiply the x-coordinate and the y-coordinate of each vertex by $\frac{3}{2}$. R'(3, 6), S'(9, 6), T'(9, 0), V'(3, 0)

M **4** Triangle PQR is shown at the right.

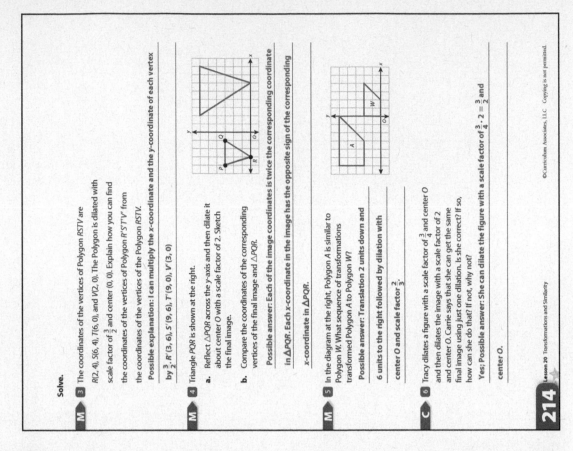

a. Reflect △PQR across the y-axis and then dilate it about center O with a scale factor of 2. Sketch the final image.

b. Compare the coordinates of the corresponding vertices of the final image and △PQR.

Possible answer: Each of the image coordinates is twice the corresponding coordinate in △PQR. Each x-coordinate in the image has the opposite sign of the corresponding x-coordinate in △PQR.

M **5** In the diagram at the right, Polygon A is similar to Polygon W. What sequence of transformations transformed Polygon A to Polygon W?

Possible answer: Translation 2 units down and 6 units to the right followed by dilation with center O and scale factor $\frac{2}{3}$.

C **6** Tracy dilates a figure with a scale factor of $\frac{3}{4}$ and center O and then dilates the image with a scale factor of 2 and center O. Carrie says that she can get the same final image using just one dilation. Is she correct? If so, how can she do that? If not, why not?

Yes; Possible answer: She can dilate the figure with a scale factor of $\frac{3}{4} \cdot 2 = \frac{3}{2}$ and center O.

Name: _____

Lesson 20

Combine Dilations and Other Transformations

Study the example problem showing how to combine a dilation with other transformations. Then solve problems 1–6.

Example

In the diagram, △ABC is similar to △HJK. A sequence of transformations was used to transform △ABC to △HJK.

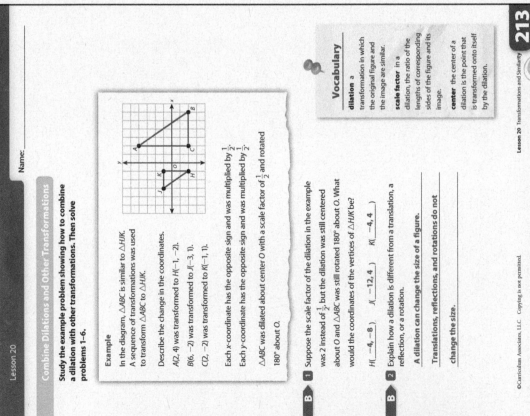

Describe the change in the coordinates.

A(2, 4) was transformed to H(-1, -2).
B(6, -2) was transformed to J(-3, 1).
C(2, -2) was transformed to K(-1, 1).

Each x-coordinate has the opposite sign and was multiplied by $\frac{1}{2}$.
Each y-coordinate has the opposite sign and was multiplied by $\frac{1}{2}$.

△ABC was dilated about center O with a scale factor of $\frac{1}{2}$ and rotated 180° about O.

B **1** Suppose the scale factor of the dilation in the example was 2 instead of $\frac{1}{2}$, but the dilation was still centered about O and △ABC was still rotated 180° about O. What would the coordinates of the vertices of △HJK be?

H(-4, -8)   J(-12, 4)   K(-4, 4)

B **2** Explain how a dilation is different from a translation, a reflection, or a rotation.

A dilation can change the size of a figure.

Translations, reflections, and rotations do not change the size.

Vocabulary

dilation a transformation in which the original figure and the image are similar.

scale factor in a dilation, the ratio of the lengths of corresponding sides of the figure and its image.

center the center of a dilation is the point that is transformed onto itself by the dilation.

Lesson 20

Transformations and Similarity

Name: _____

Solve the problems.

M 1 Polygon ABCD is shown on the coordinate plane. Sketch the image after it is rotated 90° clockwise about O and then dilated with scale factor 2 and center O.

> Make sure you rotate the polygon clockwise.

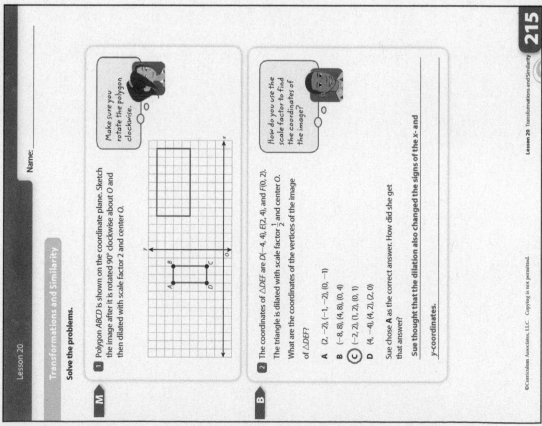

B 2 The coordinates of △DEF are D(−4, 4), E(2, 4), and F(0, 2). The triangle is dilated with scale factor $\frac{1}{2}$ and center O. What are the coordinates of the vertices of the image of △DEF?

A (2, −2), (−1, −2), (0, −1)

B (−8, 8), (4, 8), (0, 4)

C (−2, 2), (1, 2), (0, 1)

D (4, −4), (4, 2), (2, 0)

> How do you use the scale factor to find the coordinates of the image?

Sue chose **A** as the correct answer. How did she get that answer?

Sue thought that the dilation also changed the signs of the x- and y-coordinates.

Solve.

M 3 Tell whether each statement is *True* or *False*.

> What types of transformations keep the size and shape of the original figure?

a. A dilation image is always congruent to the original figure. ☐ True ☒ False

b. A rotation image is always congruent to the original figure. ☒ True ☐ False

c. A reflection image is never congruent to the original figure. ☐ True ☒ False

d. A translation image is always congruent to the original figure. ☒ True ☐ False

C 4 Polygon LMNP was transformed to Polygon WXYZ.

> What type of transformation can change the size of a figure?

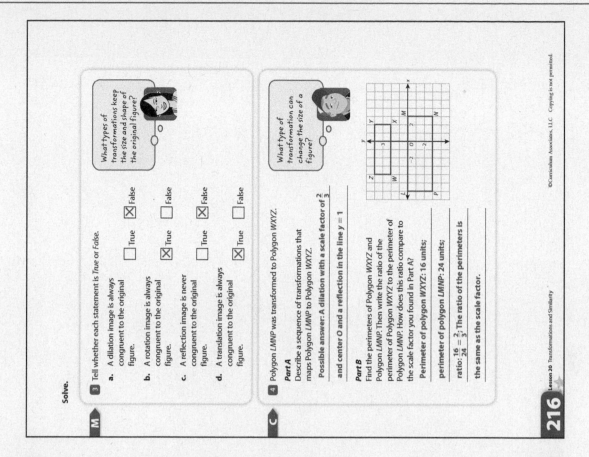

Part A

Describe a sequence of transformations that maps Polygon LMNP to Polygon WXYZ.

Possible answer: A dilation with a scale factor of $\frac{2}{3}$ and center O and a reflection in the line $y = 1$

Part B

Find the perimeters of Polygon WXYZ and Polygon LMNP. Then write the ratio of the perimeter of Polygon WXYZ to the perimeter of Polygon LMNP. How does this ratio compare to the scale factor you found in Part A?

Perimeter of polygon WXYZ: 16 units;

perimeter of polygon LMNP: 24 units;

ratio: $\frac{16}{24} = \frac{2}{3}$; The ratio of the perimeters is the same as the scale factor.

Lesson 21
Understand
Angle Relationships

Name: _____

Prerequisite: How can you use facts about angles to help you find a missing angle measure?

Study the example showing how to find the measure of a missing angle. Then solve problems 1–6.

Example
Triangle ABC is a right triangle whose right angle is $\angle ABC$. Find the measure of $\angle EBF$.

$\angle ABC$ and $\angle DBF$ are vertical angles, so they have the same measure. Because $m\angle ABC$ is 90°, the sum of $m\angle DBE$ and $m\angle EBF$ must also be 90°.

Solve for x in this equation.

$x + (x - 12) = 90$
$2x - 12 = 90$
$2x = 102$
$x = 51$

$m\angle EBF = 51°$

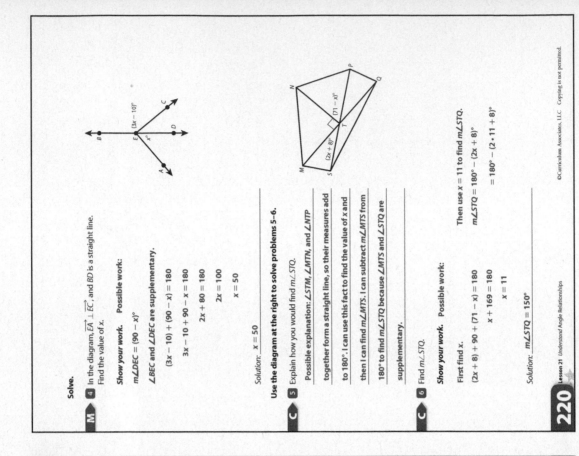

> **Vocabulary**
> **complementary angles**
> two angles whose measures add to 90°.
> **supplementary angles**
> two angles whose measures add to 180°.
> **vertical angles**
> the non-adjacent angles formed by intersecting lines. Vertical angles have the same measure.

B **1** What is $m\angle DBE$? Explain.
39°; $x = 51$, so $x - 12 = 51 - 12 = 39$.

B **2** What is $m\angle GBC$? Explain.
39°; $\angle GBC$ and $\angle DBE$ are vertical angles, so they have the same measure.

M **3** Explain how to find $m\angle ABD$.
Possible explanation: $\angle ABD$ and $\angle DBF$ are supplementary angles, and $\angle DBF$ is a right angle.
$180 - 90 = 90$, so $m\angle ABD = 90°$.

Solve.

M **4** In the diagram, $\overrightarrow{EA} \perp \overrightarrow{EC}$, and BD is a straight line. Find the value of x.

Show your work.   Possible work:

$m\angle DEC = (90 - x)°$
$\angle BEC$ and $\angle DEC$ are supplementary.
$(3x - 10) + (90 - x) = 180$
$3x - 10 + 90 - x = 180$
$2x + 80 = 180$
$2x = 100$
$x = 50$

Solution: $x = 50$

Use the diagram at the right to solve problems 5–6.

C **5** Explain how you would find $m\angle STQ$.
Possible explanation: $\angle STM$, $\angle MTN$, and $\angle NTP$ together form a straight line, so their measures add to 180°. I can use this fact to find the value of x and then I can find $m\angle MTS$. I can subtract $m\angle MTS$ from 180° to find $m\angle STQ$ because $\angle MTS$ and $\angle STQ$ are supplementary.

C **6** Find $m\angle STQ$.

Show your work.   Possible work:

First find x.
$(2x + 8) + 90 + (71 - x) = 180$
$x + 169 = 180$
$x = 11$

Then use $x = 11$ to find $m\angle STQ$.
$m\angle STQ = 180° - (2x + 8)$
$= 180° - (2 \cdot 11 + 8)°$
$m\angle STQ = 150°$

Solution: $m\angle STQ = 150°$

Key
B Basic   **M** Medium   **C** Challenge

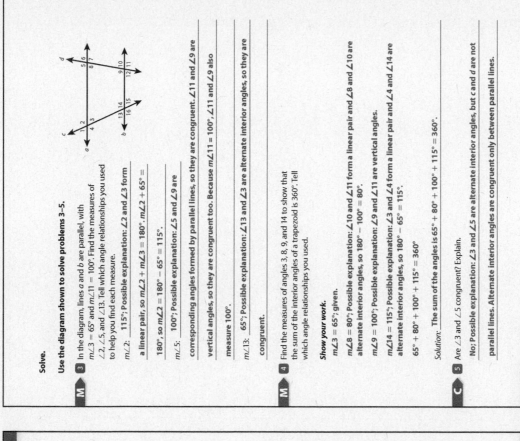

Lesson 21

Name: _____

Identify Angle Pairs

Study the example showing how to use angle pair relationships to find measures of angles. Then solve problems 1–5.

Example
In the diagram, lines w, x, and y are parallel. Use the terms *corresponding angles*, *alternate interior angles*, and *linear pair* to describe some of the angle relationships in the diagram.

∠1 and ∠9 are corresponding angles.
Corresponding angles formed by a transversal crossing parallel lines are congruent, so ∠1 ≅ ∠9.

∠4 and ∠5 are alternate interior angles. Alternate interior angles between parallel lines are congruent, so ∠4 ≅ ∠5.

∠1 and ∠3 form a linear pair. Linear pairs are supplementary, so $m∠1 + m∠3 = 180°$.

B 1 Use the diagram in the example. Name a different pair of corresponding angles, a different pair of alternate interior angles, and a different linear pair.

corresponding angles: Possible answer: ∠6 and ∠10
alternate interior angles: Possible answer: ∠8 and ∠9
linear pair: Possible answer: ∠2 and ∠4

M 2 Use the diagram in the example. If $m∠7 = 108°$, what is $m∠12$? Explain how you found the measure.

72°; Possible explanation:
∠7 and ∠11 are corresponding angles,
so ∠7 ≅ ∠11 and $m∠11 = 108°$.
∠11 and ∠12 are a linear pair, so $m∠11 + m∠12 = 180°$ and $m∠12 = 180° − 108° = 72°$.

Vocabulary

transversal a line that crosses two lines.

corresponding angles angles in the same position in the intersections of a transversal and two or more parallel lines.

alternate interior angles angles between two parallel lines and on opposite sides of a transversal.

linear pair adjacent supplementary angles.

Lesson 21 *Understand Angle Relationships*
221

Solve.

Use the diagram shown to solve problems 3–5.

M 3 In the diagram, lines a and b are parallel, with $m∠3 = 65°$ and $m∠11 = 100°$. Find the measures of ∠2, ∠5, and ∠13. Tell which angle relationships you used to help you find each measure.

$m∠2$: 115°; Possible explanation: ∠2 and ∠3 form a linear pair, so $m∠2 + m∠3 = 180°$. $m∠2 + 65° = 180°$, so $m∠2 = 180° − 65° = 115°$.

$m∠5$: 100°; Possible explanation: ∠5 and ∠9 are corresponding angles formed by parallel lines, so they are congruent. ∠9 and ∠11 are vertical angles, so they are congruent too. Because $m∠11 = 100°$, ∠11 and ∠9 also measure 100°.

$m∠13$: 65°; Possible explanation: ∠13 and ∠3 are alternate interior angles, so they are congruent.

M 4 Find the measures of angles 3, 8, 9, and 14 to show that the sum of the interior angles of a trapezoid is 360°. Tell which angle relationships you used.

Show your work.
$m∠3 = 65°$; given.
$m∠8 = 80°$; Possible explanation: ∠10 and ∠11 form a linear pair and ∠8 and ∠10 are alternate interior angles, so $180° − 100° = 80°$.
$m∠9 = 100°$; Possible explanation: ∠9 and ∠11 are vertical angles.
$m∠14 = 115°$; Possible explanation: ∠3 and ∠4 form a linear pair and ∠4 and ∠14 are alternate interior angles, so $180° − 65° = 115°$.
$65° + 80° + 100° + 115° = 360°$

Solution: The sum of the angles is $65° + 80° + 100° + 115° = 360°$.

C 5 Are ∠3 and ∠5 congruent? Explain.
No; Possible explanation: ∠3 and ∠5 are alternate interior angles, but c and d are not parallel lines. Alternate interior angles are congruent only between parallel lines.

222 Lesson 21 *Understand Angle Relationships*

Lesson 21

Reason and Write

Study the example. Underline two parts that you think make it a particularly good answer and a helpful example.

Example

Elena drew a map of a neighborhood park. She says that the park has three straight sidewalks, two of which are parallel. Her map shows vertical angles, corresponding angles, alternate interior angles, and linear pairs of angles that are formed by the three straight sidewalks in the park.

Draw a map of a park that matches Elena's description. Label the sidewalks m, n, and p, and label the angles formed by the sidewalks 1, 2, 3, 4, and so on.

Describe how the lines for the sidewalks are related. Name one pair of angles in your map to illustrate each angle relationship mentioned in Elena's description. Tell how you know that the angles illustrate the relationship.

Show your work. Use a diagram, words, and angle relationships to explain your answer.

Possible answer:

Lines m and n are parallel, and line p is a transversal that intersects the two parallel lines.

$\angle 1$ and $\angle 3$ are vertical angles because they are non-adjacent angles formed by intersecting lines.

$\angle 1$ and $\angle 5$ are corresponding angles because they are in the same position in the intersections of the transversal and the parallel lines.

$\angle 2$ and $\angle 8$ are alternate interior angles because they are between two parallel lines and on opposite sides of the transversal.

$\angle 1$ and $\angle 2$ form a linear pair because they are adjacent supplementary angles.

> Where does the example . . .
> • answer each part of the problem?
> • use a diagram to illustrate?
> • use words to explain?
> • use angle relationships to explain?

Name: _____

Answers will vary. Note whether students incorporate the features they chose in their answer on the next page.

©Curriculum Associates, LLC   Copying is not permitted.

Lesson 21 *Understand* Angle Relationships

223

Solve the problem. Use what you learned from the model.

Von makes a design with four lines. At least two of them are parallel. He says that his design shows vertical angles, corresponding angles, alternate interior angles, and linear pairs of angles.

Draw a diagram of Von's design. Label the lines a, b, c, and d, and label the angles formed by the lines 1, 2, 3, 4, and so on.

Describe how the lines are related. List all of the angles that are congruent to $\angle 1$ in your diagram. Then list all of the angles that are congruent to $\angle 2$.

Name one pair of angles in your diagram to illustrate each angle relationship mentioned in Von's description. Tell how you know that the angles illustrate the relationship.

Show your work. Use a diagram, words, and angle relationships to explain your answer.

Answers will vary depending on the diagram drawn by the student.

Possible answer:

Lines a, b, and c are parallel, and line d is a transversal that intersects the three parallel lines.

The angles that are congruent to $\angle 1$ are $\angle 3$, $\angle 5$, $\angle 7$, $\angle 9$, and $\angle 11$.

The angles that are congruent to $\angle 2$ are $\angle 4$, $\angle 6$, $\angle 8$, $\angle 10$, and $\angle 12$.

$\angle 1$ and $\angle 3$ are vertical angles because they are non-adjacent angles formed by intersecting lines.

$\angle 1$ and $\angle 5$ are corresponding angles because they are in the same position in the intersections of the transversal and two of the parallel lines.

$\angle 2$ and $\angle 8$ are alternate interior angles because they are between two parallel lines and on opposite sides of the transversal.

$\angle 1$ and $\angle 2$ form a linear pair because they are adjacent supplementary angles.

> Did you . . .
> • answer each part of the problem?
> • use a diagram to illustrate?
> • use words to explain?
> • use angle relationships to explain?

224   Lesson 21 *Understand* Angle Relationships

©Curriculum Associates, LLC   Copying is not permitted.

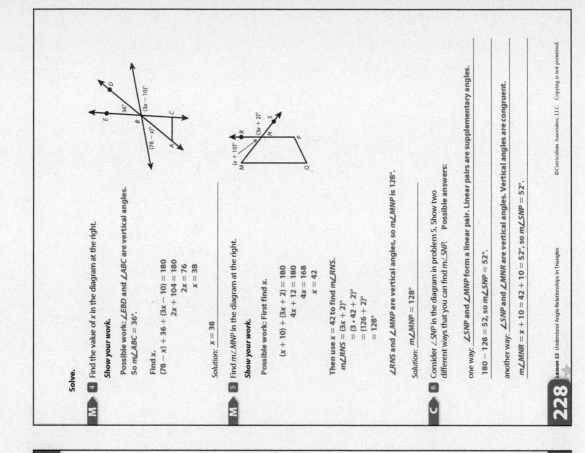

Lesson 22
Understand
Angle Relationships in Triangles

Name: _____

Prerequisite: How can you use what you know about angle relationships to solve problems?

Study the example showing how to find the measure of a missing angle. Then solve problems 1–6.

Example

$\overline{AB}$ and $\overline{AD}$ of parallelogram *ABCD* are extended as shown. Find the measure of ∠*FAB*.

∠*FAB* and ∠*FAE* are supplementary angles, so the sum of the measures of ∠*FAB* and ∠*FAE* is 180°.

$$(x + 7) + (2x - 1) = 180$$
$$x + 7 + 2x - 1 = 180$$
$$3x + 6 = 180$$
$$3x = 174$$
$$x = 58$$

This means the measure of ∠*FAB* is $(2x - 1)° = (2(58) - 1)° = 115°$.

B **1** What is *m*∠*FAE*? Explain your reasoning.
65°; Possible explanation: *x* = 58, so *x* + 7 = 58 + 7 = 65.

B **2** What is *m*∠*BAD*? Explain your reasoning.
65°; Possible explanation: ∠*FAE* and ∠*BAD* are vertical angles, so they have the same measure.

M **3** Explain a way to find *m*∠*ABC*. Then find *m*∠*ABC*.
Possible explanation: $\overline{AD}$ and $\overline{BC}$ are parallel sides of the parallelogram. ∠*FAB* and ∠*ABC* are alternate interior angles, so they are congruent: *m*∠*ABC* = 115°.

Solve.

M **4** Find the value of *x* in the diagram at the right.
Show your work.
Possible work: ∠*EBD* and ∠*ABC* are vertical angles.
So *m*∠*ABC* = 36°.
Find *x*.
$$(78 - x) + 36 + (3x - 10) = 180$$
$$2x + 104 = 180$$
$$2x = 76$$
$$x = 38$$

Solution: **x = 38**

M **5** Find *m*∠*MNP* in the diagram at the right.
Show your work.
Possible work: First find *x*.
$$(x + 10) + (3x + 2) = 180$$
$$4x + 12 = 180$$
$$4x = 168$$
$$x = 42$$

Then use *x* = 42 to find *m*∠*RNS*.
$$m∠RNS = (3x + 2)°$$
$$= (3 \cdot 42 + 2)°$$
$$= (126 + 2)°$$
$$= 128°$$

∠*RNS* and ∠*MNP* are vertical angles, so *m*∠*MNP* is 128°.

Solution: *m*∠*MNP* = **128°**

C **6** Consider ∠*SNP* in the diagram in problem 5. Show two different ways that you can find *m*∠*SNP*.   Possible answers:
one way: ∠*SNP* and ∠*MNP* form a linear pair. Linear pairs are supplementary angles.
180 − 128 = 52, so *m*∠*SNP* = 52°.

another way: ∠*SNP* and ∠*MNR* are vertical angles. Vertical angles are congruent.
m∠*MNR* = *x* + 10 = 42 + 10 = 52°, so *m*∠*SNP* = 52°.

Key

B Basic   **M** Medium   **C** Challenge

Lesson 22

Name: _____

Angles in a Triangle

Study the example showing how to use facts about angles and triangles to find a missing angle measure. Then solve problems 1–6.

Example

In the diagram at the right, show that △ABC and △EDC are similar triangles. Then find m∠CED.

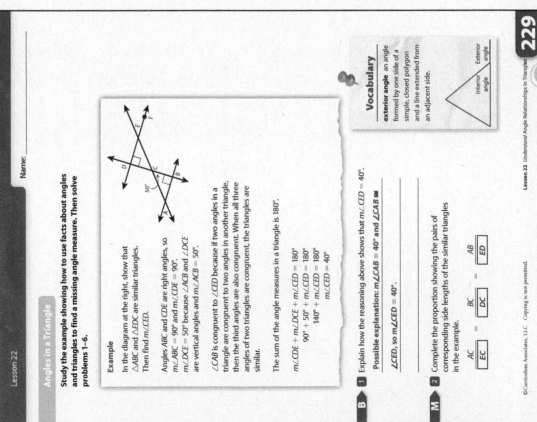

Angles ABC and CDE are right angles, so m∠ABC = 90° and m∠CDE = 90°; m∠DCE = 50° because ∠ACB and ∠DCE are vertical angles and m∠ACB = 50°.

∠CAB is congruent to ∠CED because if two angles in a triangle are congruent to two angles in another triangle, then the third angles are also congruent. When all three angles of two triangles are congruent, the triangles are similar.

The sum of the angle measures in a triangle is 180°.

$$m\angle CDE + m\angle DCE + m\angle CED = 180°$$
$$90° + 50° + m\angle CED = 180°$$
$$140° + m\angle CED = 180°$$
$$m\angle CED = 40°$$

Vocabulary
exterior angle an angle formed by one side of a simple, closed polygon and a line extended from an adjacent side.

B 1 Explain how the reasoning above shows that m∠CED = 40°.
Possible explanation: m∠CAB = 40° and ∠CAB ≅ ∠CED, so m∠CED = 40°.

M 2 Complete the proportion showing the pairs of corresponding side lengths of the similar triangles in the example.

$$\frac{AC}{EC} = \frac{BC}{DC} = \frac{AB}{ED}$$

Solve.

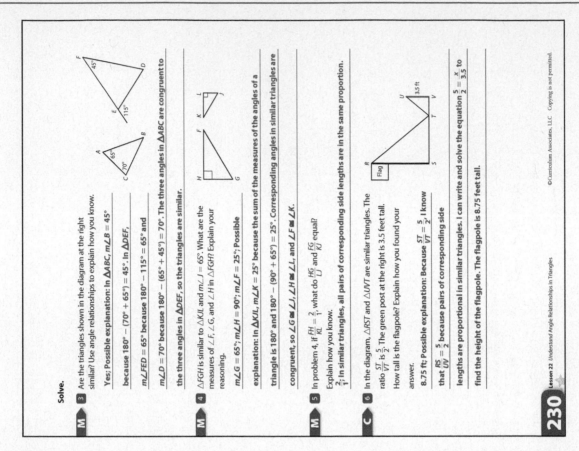

M 3 Are the triangles shown in the diagram at the right similar? Use angle relationships to explain how you know.
Yes; Possible explanation: In △ABC, m∠B = 45°
because 180° − (70° + 65°) = 45°. In △DEF,
m∠FED = 65° because 180° − 115° = 65° and
m∠D = 70° because 180° − (65° + 45°) = 70°. The three angles in △ABC are congruent to
the three angles in △DEF, so the triangles are similar.

M 4 △FGH is similar to △KJL and m∠J = 65°. What are the measures of ∠F, ∠G, and ∠H in △FGH? Explain your reasoning.
m∠G = 65°; m∠H = 90°; m∠F = 25°; Possible
explanation: In △KJL, m∠K = 25° because the sum of the measures of the angles of a
triangle is 180° and 180° − (90° + 65°) = 25°. Corresponding angles in similar triangles are
congruent, so ∠G ≅ ∠J, ∠H ≅ ∠L, and ∠F ≅ ∠K.

M 5 In problem 4, if $\frac{FH}{KL} = \frac{2}{1}$, what do $\frac{HG}{LJ}$ and $\frac{FG}{KJ}$ equal?
Explain how you know.
$\frac{2}{1}$; In similar triangles, all pairs of corresponding side lengths are in the same proportion.

C 6 In the diagram, △RST and △UVT are similar triangles. The ratio $\frac{ST}{VT}$ is $\frac{5}{2}$. The green post at the right is 3.5 feet tall. How tall is the flagpole? Explain how you found your answer.
8.75 ft; Possible explanation: Because $\frac{ST}{VT} = \frac{5}{2}$, I know
that $\frac{RS}{UV} = \frac{5}{2}$ because pairs of corresponding side
lengths are proportional in similar triangles. I can write and solve the equation $\frac{5}{2} = \frac{x}{3.5}$ to
find the height of the flagpole. The flagpole is 8.75 feet tall.

Page 232 content

Solve the problem. **Use what you learned from the model.**

Tara is making a quilt. She will use blue triangles represented by △*GHJ* shown below. She will also use red triangles that are similar to △*GHJ*. The ratio of the side lengths of the red triangles to the side lengths of the blue triangles is $\frac{4}{3}$.

Draw △*KLM* to represent a red triangle. Explain how you found the side lengths of △*KLM*.

Find the length of the longest leg of the red triangle if the length of the longest leg of the blue triangle is 4.5 inches.

Show your work. Use a diagram, words, and numbers to explain your answer.

Possible answer:

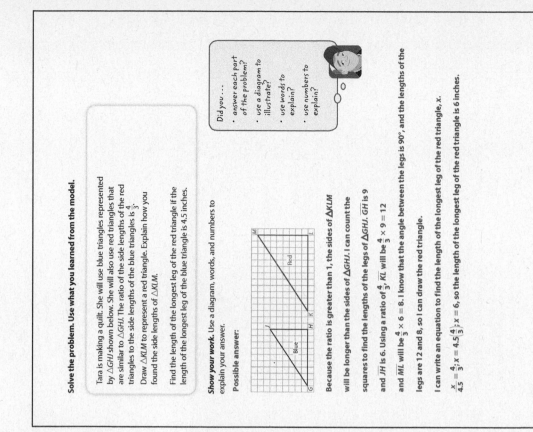

Because the ratio is greater than 1, the sides of △*KLM* will be longer than the sides of △*GHJ*. I can count the squares to find the lengths of the legs of △*GHJ*. $\overline{GH}$ is 9 and *JH* is 6. Using a ratio of $\frac{4}{3}$, *KL* will be $\frac{4}{3} \times 9 = 12$ and $\overline{ML}$ will be $\frac{4}{3} \times 6 = 8$. I know that the angle between the legs is 90°, so I can draw the red triangle.

legs are 12 and 8, so I can draw the red triangle.

I can write an equation to find the length of the longest leg of the red triangle, *x*.

$\frac{x}{4.5} = \frac{4}{3}$; $x = 4.5\left(\frac{4}{3}\right)$; $x = 6$, so the length of the longest leg of the red triangle is 6 inches.

Lesson 22 *Understand* Angle Relationships in Triangles

232

Thought bubble (page 232)

Did you . . .
- answer each part of the problem?
- use a diagram to illustrate?
- use words to explain?
- use numbers to explain?

Page 231 content

Lesson 22

Name:

Reason and Write

Study the example. Underline two parts that you think make it a particularly good answer and a helpful example.

Example

In the diagram below, △*ABC* represents Paulo's triangular vegetable garden. Rosanne wants to plant a garden that is similar to Paulo's garden. The ratio of the side lengths of Rosanne's garden to the side lengths of Paulo's garden should be $\frac{2}{3}$.

Draw △*DEF* to represent Rosanne's garden. Explain how you found the side lengths of △*DEF*.

Find the length of the shortest side of Rosanne's garden if the shortest side of Paulo's garden is 16 feet.

Show your work. Use a diagram, words, and numbers to explain your answer.

Possible answer:

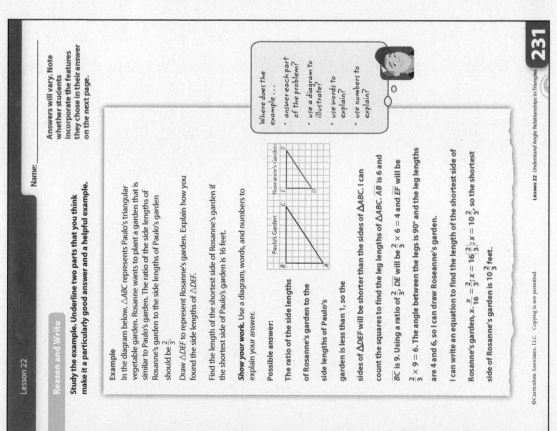

The ratio of the side lengths of Rosanne's garden to the side lengths of Paulo's garden is less than 1, so the sides of △*DEF* will be shorter than the sides of △*ABC*. I can count the squares to find the leg lengths of △*ABC*. $\overline{AB}$ is 6 and $\overline{BC}$ is 9. Using a ratio of $\frac{2}{3}$, $\overline{DE}$ will be $\frac{2}{3} \times 6 = 4$ and $\overline{EF}$ will be $\frac{2}{3} \times 9 = 6$. The angle between the legs is 90° and the leg lengths are 4 and 6, so I can draw Rosanne's garden.

I can write an equation to find the length of the shortest side of Rosanne's garden, x. $\frac{x}{16} = \frac{2}{3}$; $x = 16\left(\frac{2}{3}\right)$; $x = 10\frac{2}{3}$, so the shortest side of Rosanne's garden is $10\frac{2}{3}$ feet.

Side note (page 231)

Answers will vary. Note whether students incorporate the features they chose in their answer on the next page.

Thought bubble (page 231)

Where does the example . . .
- answer each part of the problem?
- use a diagram to illustrate?
- use words to explain?
- use numbers to explain?

Lesson 22 *Understand* Angle Relationships in Triangles

231

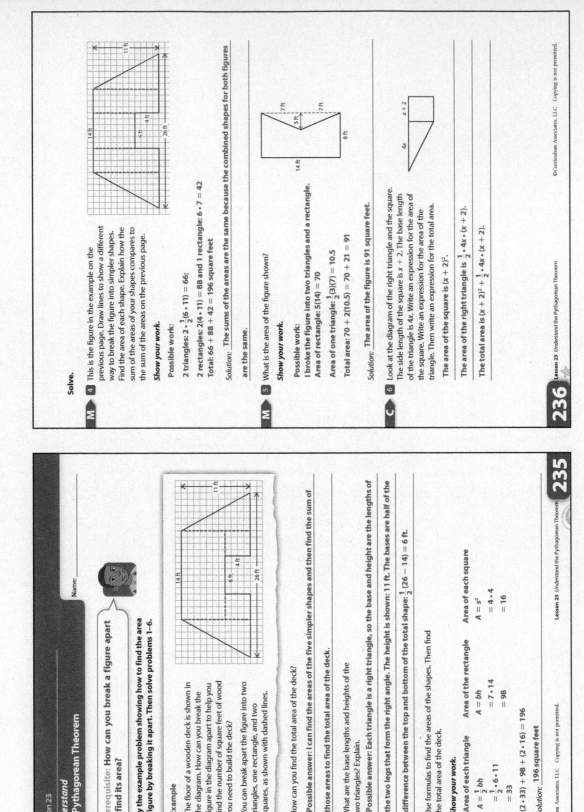

Lesson 23
Understand
the Pythagorean Theorem

Name: _____

Prerequisite: How can you break a figure apart to find its area?

Study the example problem showing how to find the area of a figure by breaking it apart. Then solve problems 1–6.

Example

The floor of a wooden deck is shown in the diagram. How can you break the figure in the diagram apart to help you find the number of square feet of wood you need to build the deck?

You can break apart the figure into two triangles, one rectangle, and two squares, as shown with dashed lines.

B **1** How can you find the total area of the deck?

Possible answer: I can find the areas of the five simpler shapes and then find the sum of those areas to find the total area of the deck.

M **2** What are the base lengths and heights of the two triangles? Explain.

Possible answer: Each triangle is a right triangle, so the base and height are the lengths of the two legs that form the right angle. The height is shown: 11 ft. The bases are half of the difference between the top and bottom of the total shape: $\frac{1}{2}(26 - 14) = 6$ ft.

M **3** Use formulas to find the areas of the shapes. Then find the total area of the deck.

Show your work.

Area of each triangle	Area of the rectangle	Area of each square
$A = \frac{1}{2}bh$	$A = bh$	$A = s^2$
$= \frac{1}{2} \cdot 6 \cdot 11$	$= 7 \cdot 14$	$= 4 \cdot 4$
$= 33$	$= 98$	$= 16$

$(2 \cdot 33) + 98 + (2 \cdot 16) = 196$

Solution: __196 square feet__

Solve.

M **4** This is the figure in the example on the previous page. Draw lines to show a different way to break the figure into simpler shapes. Find the area of each shape. Explain how the sum of the areas of your shapes compares to the sum of the areas on the previous page.

Show your work.

Possible work:

2 triangles: $2 \cdot \frac{1}{2}(6 \cdot 11) = 66$;

2 rectangles: $2(4 \cdot 11) = 88$ and 1 rectangle: $6 \cdot 7 = 42$

Total: $66 + 88 + 42 = 196$ square feet

Solution: The sums of the areas are the same because the combined shapes for both figures are the same.

M **5** What is the area of the figure shown?

Show your work.

Possible work:

I broke the figure into two triangles and a rectangle.

Area of rectangle: $5(14) = 70$

Area of one triangle: $\frac{1}{2}(3)(7) = 10.5$

Total area: $70 + 2(10.5) = 70 + 21 = 91$

Solution: The area of the figure is 91 square feet.

C **6** Look at the diagram of the right triangle and the square. The side length of the square is $x + 2$. The base length of the triangle is $4x$. Write an expression for the area of the square. Write an expression for the area of the triangle. Then write an expression for the total area.

The area of the square is $(x + 2)^2$.

The area of the right triangle is $\frac{1}{2} \cdot 4x \cdot (x + 2)$.

The total area is $(x + 2)^2 + \frac{1}{2} \cdot 4x \cdot (x + 2)$.

Lesson 23 *Understand the Pythagorean Theorem*   **236**

Lesson 23 *Understand the Pythagorean Theorem*   **235**

Key
B Basic   **M** Medium   **C** Challenge

Lesson 23

Name: _____

Pythagorean Theorem Proof

Study the example showing how to prove the Pythagorean Theorem. Then solve problems 1–9.

Example

The Pythagorean Theorem states that in a right triangle the sum of the squares of the lengths of the legs is equal to the square of the length of the hypotenuse: $a^2 + b^2 = c^2$.

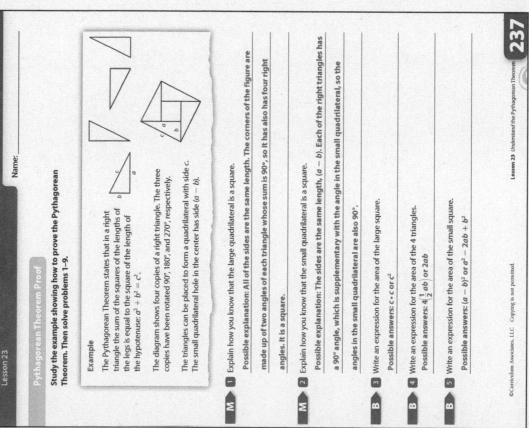

The diagram shows four copies of a right triangle. The three copies have been rotated 90°, 180°, and 270°, respectively.

The triangles can be placed to form a quadrilateral with side c. The small quadrilateral hole in the center has side $(a - b)$.

M 1 Explain how you know that the large quadrilateral is a square.
Possible explanation: All of the sides are the same length. The corners of the figure are made up of two angles of each triangle whose sum is 90°, so it has also has four right angles. It is a square.

M 2 Explain how you know that the small quadrilateral is a square.
Possible explanation: The sides are the same length, $(a - b)$. Each of the right triangles has a 90° angle, which is supplementary with the angle in the small quadrilateral, so the angles in the small quadrilateral are also 90°.

B 3 Write an expression for the area of the large square.
Possible answers: $c \cdot c$ or c^2

B 4 Write an expression for the area of the 4 triangles.
Possible answers: $4\left(\frac{1}{2}ab\right)$ or $2ab$

B 5 Write an expression for the area of the small square.
Possible answers: $(a - b)^2$ or $a^2 - 2ab + b^2$

Solve.

M 6 This diagram from the example on the previous page shows that the area of the large square is equal to the sum of the areas of the four triangles and the small square.

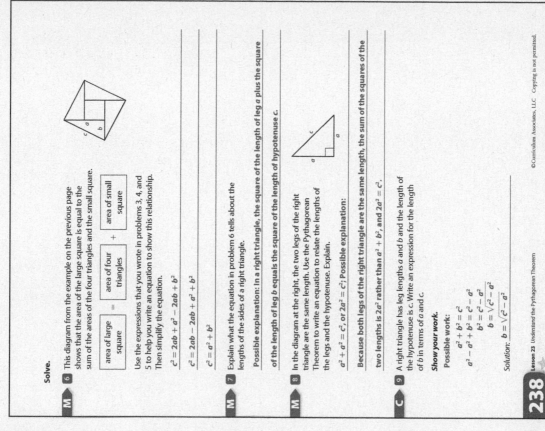

area of large square	=	area of four triangles	+	area of small square

Use the expressions that you wrote in problems 3, 4, and 5 to help you write an equation to show this relationship. Then simplify the equation.

$c^2 = 2ab + a^2 - 2ab + b^2$

$c^2 = 2ab - 2ab + a^2 + b^2$

$c^2 = a^2 + b^2$

M 7 Explain what the equation in problem 6 tells about the lengths of the sides of a right triangle.
Possible explanation: In a right triangle, the square of the length of leg a plus the square of the length of leg b equals the square of the length of hypotenuse c.

M 8 In the diagram at the right, the two legs of the right triangle are the same length. Use the Pythagorean Theorem to write an equation to relate the lengths of the legs and the hypotenuse. Explain.
$a^2 + a^2 = c^2$, or $2a^2 = c^2$; Possible explanation:

Because both legs of the right triangle are the same length, the sum of the squares of the two lengths is $2a^2$ rather than $a^2 + b^2$, and $2a^2 = c^2$.

C 9 A right triangle has leg lengths a and b and the length of the hypotenuse is c. Write an expression for the length of b in terms of a and c.
Show your work.
Possible work:
$$a^2 + b^2 = c^2$$
$$a^2 - a^2 + b^2 = c^2 - a^2$$
$$b^2 = c^2 - a^2$$
$$b = \sqrt{c^2 - a^2}$$

Solution: $b = \sqrt{c^2 - a^2}$

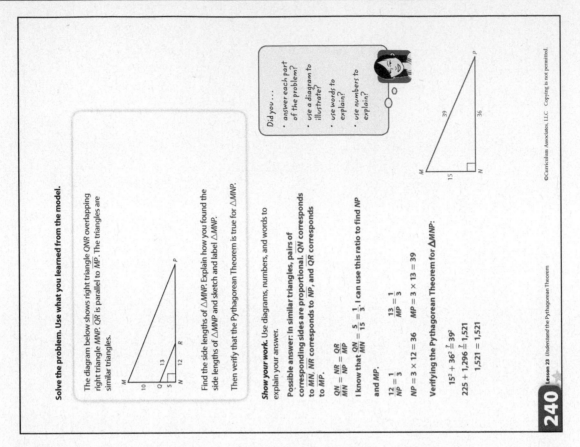

Page 240

Solve the problem. Use what you learned from the model.

The diagram below shows right triangle *QNR* overlapping right triangle *MNP*. *QR* is parallel to *MP*. The triangles are similar triangles.

Find the side lengths of △*MNP*. Explain how you found the side lengths of △*MNP* and sketch and label △*MNP*.

Then verify that the Pythagorean Theorem is true for △*MNP*.

Show your work. Use diagrams, numbers, and words to explain your answer.

Possible answer: In similar triangles, pairs of corresponding sides are proportional. *QN* corresponds to *MN*, *NR* corresponds to *NP*, and *QR* corresponds to *MP*.

$$\frac{QN}{MN} = \frac{NR}{NP} = \frac{QR}{MP}$$

I know that $\frac{QN}{MN} = \frac{5}{15} = \frac{1}{3}$. I can use this ratio to find *NP* and *MP*.

$$\frac{12}{NP} = \frac{1}{3} \qquad\qquad \frac{13}{MP} = \frac{1}{3}$$

$NP = 3 \times 12 = 36 \qquad MP = 3 \times 13 = 39$

Verifying the Pythagorean Theorem for △*MNP*:

$$15^2 + 36^2 \overset{?}{=} 39^2$$
$$225 + 1{,}296 \overset{?}{=} 1{,}521$$
$$1{,}521 = 1{,}521$$

Did you . . .
• answer each part of the problem?
• use a diagram to illustrate?
• use words to explain?
• use numbers to explain?

240 Lesson 23 *Understand* the Pythagorean Theorem

Page 239

Name: _____

Lesson 23

Reason and Write

Study the example. Underline two parts that you think make it a particularly good answer and a helpful example.

Answers will vary. Note whether students incorporate the features they chose in their answer on the next page.

Example

Right triangle *ABC* has legs with lengths 3 and 4 and a hypotenuse with length 5. Sketch △*ABC*. Label the vertices of the triangle and the side lengths.

Now sketch a triangle similar to △*ABC*. Label the vertices of the similar triangle *D*, *E*, and *F*. Use what you know about the relationship of corresponding sides in similar triangles to label the lengths of the sides in △*DEF*.

Determine the leg lengths of △*DEF* and explain how you found the lengths. Verify that the Pythagorean Theorem is true for △*DEF*.

Show your work. Use diagrams, numbers, and words to explain your answer.

Possible answer:

I multiplied each side length of △*ABC* by two, so each side length of △*DEF* is two times the corresponding side length in △*ABC*. I let *DE* correspond to *AB*, *EF* correspond to *BC*, and *DF* correspond to *AC*.

$$\frac{DE}{AB} = \frac{EF}{BC} = \frac{DF}{AC} = \frac{2}{1}$$

$DE = 2 \times 3 = 6$

$EF = 2 \times 4 = 8$

$DF = 2 \times 5 = 10$

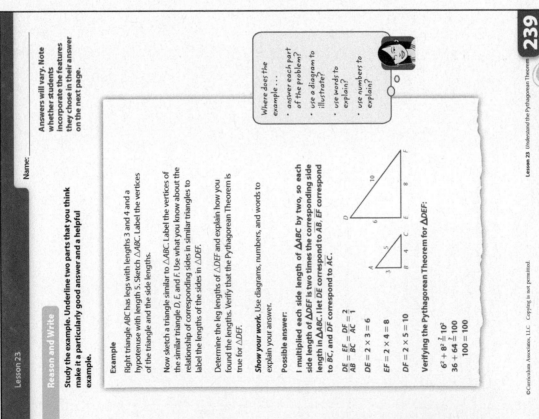

Verifying the Pythagorean Theorem for △*DEF*:

$$6^2 + 8^2 \overset{?}{=} 10^2$$
$$36 + 64 \overset{?}{=} 100$$
$$100 = 100$$

Where does the example . . .
• answer each part of the problem?
• use a diagram to illustrate?
• use words to explain?
• use numbers to explain?

239 Lesson 23 *Understand* the Pythagorean Theorem

Lesson 24
Solve Problems Using the Pythagorean Theorem

Prerequisite: Finding Square Roots

Study the example showing how to solve a problem that involves square roots. Then solve problems 1–7.

Example

Leroy's backyard is a rectangle that is three times as long as it is wide. What is the perimeter and the area of the yard?

First draw a diagram to help you solve the problem. Let a be the width of Leroy's yard.

Leroy's Backyard

a · $3a$

The perimeter is $a + 3a + a + 3a$, or $8a$. The area of a rectangle is $\ell \cdot w$, so the area of the backyard is $a \cdot 3a$, or $3a^2$.

B 1 Suppose you know the area of the yard is 7,500 square feet. How can you find the value of a?

The area of the backyard is $3a^2$, so I can solve the equation $3a^2 = 7,500$.

M 2 Use your answer to problem 1 to find the value of a.
Show your work.

$3a^2 = 7,500$
$a^2 = 2,500$
$a = \sqrt{2,500}$
$a = 50$

Solution: __The value of a is 50 feet.__

M 3 What is the perimeter of the backyard?

$8a = 8 \cdot 50 = 400$. The perimeter is 400 feet.

Vocabulary

square root a factor of a number that when multiplied by itself results in the number. For example, 9 is a square root of 81 because $9 \times 9 = 81$.

©Curriculum Associates, LLC   Copying is not permitted.   Lesson 24 Solve Problems Using the Pythagorean Theorem   **243**

Solve.

M 4 The area of the floor of a square room is 144 square feet. What is the perimeter of the room? Include a diagram in your solution.

Show your work.

The area of the floor is s^2.
$s^2 = 144$
$s = \sqrt{144} = \sqrt{12^2} = 12$
The perimeter of the floor is $4 \cdot s$.
$4 \cdot s = 4 \cdot 12 = 48$

Area 144 ft²

s

s

Solution: __The perimeter of the room is 48 feet.__

M 5 Which two numbers in the box are perfect squares? Explain how you know they are perfect squares.

20	125	196	500	625

$14 \cdot 14 = 196$ and $25 \cdot 25 = 625$, so 196 and 625 are perfect squares. Possible explanation: You cannot multiply an integer by itself to get 20, 125, or 500, so they are not perfect squares.

M 6 What is the side length of a square whose area is $\frac{1}{64}$ square mile? Explain your answer.

$\frac{1}{8}$ mile; Possible explanation: To find the side length, I can take the square root of $\frac{1}{64}$, which is $\frac{1}{8}$.

C 7 Natasha says that if the area of a square is a, then the length of a side of the square is $\sqrt{a}$. Do you agree? Explain.

Yes; Possible explanation: If $\sqrt{a}$ is the length of a side of a square, then $(\sqrt{a})^2$ is the area. $(\sqrt{a})^2 = a$, so if the area of a square is a, then the length of a side is $\sqrt{a}$.

244 Lesson 24 Solve Problems Using the Pythagorean Theorem   ©Curriculum Associates, LLC   Copying is not permitted.

Key

B Basic	M Medium	C Challenge

Lesson 24

Name: _____

Solve Problems Using Right Triangles

Study the example showing how to solve a problem that involves distance. Then solve problems 1–5.

Example

Mr. Nichols followed the road from the entrance of a park to his campsite. He drove 6 miles south, then 5 miles east, 3 miles south, and finally 7 miles east to the campsite. In all, how far did Mr. Nichols drive? Suppose Mr. Nichols had been able to drive straight from the entrance of the park to the campsite. How could you find that distance?

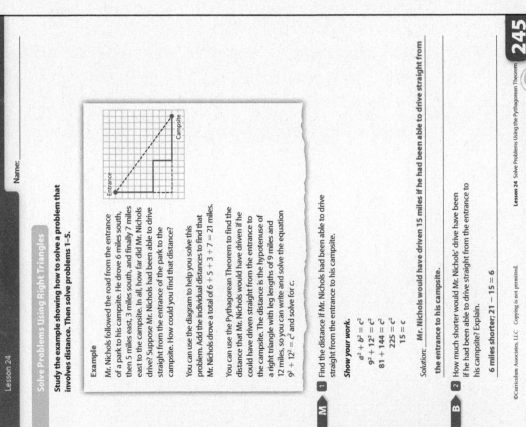

You can use the diagram to help you solve this problem. Add the individual distances to find that Mr. Nichols drove a total of 6 + 5 + 3 + 7 = 21 miles.

You can use the Pythagorean Theorem to find the distance that Mr. Nichols would have driven if he could have driven straight from the entrance to the campsite. The distance is the hypotenuse of a right triangle with leg lengths of 9 miles and 12 miles, so you can write and solve the equation $9^2 + 12^2 = c^2$ and solve for c.

Show your work.

$a^2 + b^2 = c^2$
$9^2 + 12^2 = c^2$
$81 + 144 = c^2$
$225 = c^2$
$15 = c$

Solution: Mr. Nichols would have driven 15 miles if he had been able to drive straight from the entrance to his campsite.

M 1 Find the distance if Mr. Nichols had been able to drive straight from the entrance to his campsite.

B 2 How much shorter would Mr. Nichols' drive have been if he had been able to drive straight from the entrance to his campsite? Explain.

6 miles shorter; 21 − 15 = 6

Solve.

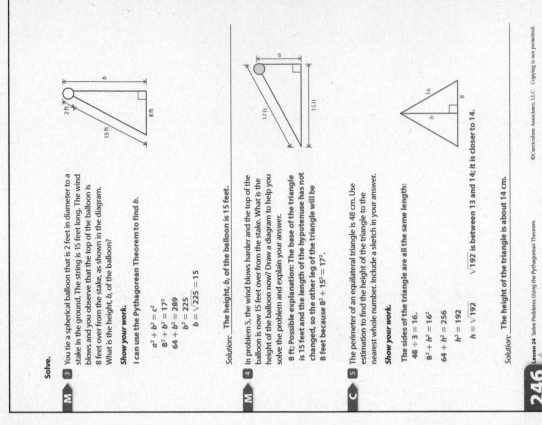

M 3 You tie a spherical balloon that is 2 feet in diameter to a stake in the ground. The string is 15 feet long. The wind blows and you observe that the top of the balloon is 8 feet over from the stake, as shown in the diagram. What is the height, b, of the balloon?

Show your work.

I can use the Pythagorean Theorem to find b.

$a^2 + b^2 = c^2$
$8^2 + b^2 = 17^2$
$64 + b^2 = 289$
$b^2 = 225$
$b = \sqrt{225} = 15$

Solution: The height, b, of the balloon is 15 feet.

M 4 In problem 5, the wind blows harder and the top of the balloon is now 15 feet over from the stake. What is the height of the balloon now? Draw a diagram to help you solve the problem and explain your answer.

8 ft; Possible explanation: The base of the triangle is 15 feet and the length of the hypotenuse has not changed, so the other leg of the triangle will be 8 feet because $8^2 + 15^2 = 17^2$.

C 5 The perimeter of an equilateral triangle is 48 cm. Use estimation to find the height of the triangle to the nearest whole number. Include a sketch in your answer.

Show your work.

The sides of the triangle are all the same length:
$48 \div 3 = 16$.
$8^2 + h^2 = 16^2$
$64 + h^2 = 256$
$h^2 = 192$
$h = \sqrt{192}$ $\sqrt{192}$ is between 13 and 14; it is closer to 14.

Solution: The height of the triangle is about 14 cm.

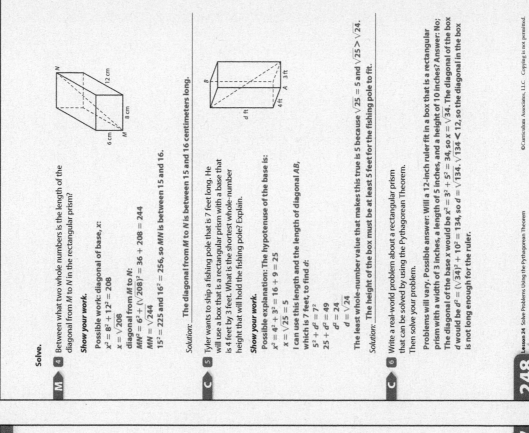

Lesson 24

The Pythagorean Theorem and Three-Dimensional Figures

Study the example showing how to apply the Pythagorean Theorem. Then solve problems 1–6.

Example

The diagram shows a diagonal drawn from point A to point B in a rectangular prism. How can you find the length of this diagonal?

You can use what you know about right triangles that are related to the diagonal.

The triangle on the base of the prism with side lengths 6, 8, and c is a right triangle. The triangle that includes the diagonal from point A to point B with side lengths c, 24, and d is a right triangle.

Use the Pythagorean Theorem to solve for c. Then use c to solve for d.

B 1 How do you know that the triangle with side lengths 6, 8, and c is a right triangle?

The three-dimensional figure is a rectangular prism, so all of the faces are rectangles. Rectangles have square corners. The triangle with side lengths 6, 8, and c is on the base of the prism, so the angle between the sides labeled 6 and 8 is a right angle.

M 2 How do you know that the triangle with side lengths c, 24, and d is a right triangle?

The three-dimensional figure is a rectangular prism, so all of the faces are perpendicular. In the triangle with side lengths c, 24, and d, lengths c and 24 are on adjacent faces, so they are perpendicular and the angle between them is a right angle.

M 3 Use the Pythagorean Theorem to write equations to find the values of c and d. Find the value of c and then find the value of d.

$$6^2 + 8^2 = c^2 \qquad c^2 + 24^2 = d^2$$
$$36 + 64 = c^2 \qquad 100 + 576 = d^2$$
$$100 = c^2 \qquad 676 = d^2$$
$$\sqrt{100} = \sqrt{c^2} \qquad \sqrt{676} = \sqrt{d^2}$$
$$10 = c \qquad 26 = d$$

Solve.

M 4 Between what two whole numbers is the length of the diagonal from M to N in the rectangular prism?

Show your work.

Possible work: diagonal of base, x:
$$x^2 = 8^2 + 12^2 = 208$$
$$x = \sqrt{208}$$
diagonal from M to N:
$$MN^2 = 6^2 + (\sqrt{208})^2 = 36 + 208 = 244$$
$$MN = \sqrt{244}$$
$15^2 = 225$ and $16^2 = 256$, so MN is between 15 and 16.

Solution: **The diagonal from M to N is between 15 and 16 centimeters long.**

C 5 Tyler wants to ship a fishing pole that is 7 feet long. He will use a box that is a rectangular prism with a base that is 4 feet by 3 feet. What is the shortest whole-number height that will hold the fishing pole? Explain.

Show your work.

Possible explanation: The hypotenuse of the base is:
$$x^2 = 4^2 + 3^2 = 16 + 9 = 25$$
$$x = \sqrt{25} = 5$$
I can use this length and the length of diagonal AB, which is 7 feet, to find d:
$$5^2 + d^2 = 7^2$$
$$25 + d^2 = 49$$
$$d^2 = 24$$
$$d = \sqrt{24}$$
The least whole-number value that makes this true is 5 because $\sqrt{25} = 5$ and $\sqrt{25} > \sqrt{24}$.

Solution: **The height of the box must be at least 5 feet for the fishing pole to fit.**

C 6 Write a real-world problem about a rectangular prism that can be solved by using the Pythagorean Theorem. Then solve your problem.

Problems will vary. Possible answer: Will a 12-inch ruler fit in a box that is a rectangular prism with a width of 3 inches, a length of 5 inches, and a height of 10 inches? Answer: No; The diagonal of the base x would be $x^2 = 3^2 + 5^2 = 34$, so $x = \sqrt{34}$. The diagonal of the box d would be $d^2 = (\sqrt{34})^2 + 10^2 = 134$, so $d = \sqrt{134}$. $\sqrt{134} < 12$, so the diagonal in the box is not long enough for the ruler.

Lesson 24

Name: _____

Solve Problems Using the Pythagorean Theorem

Solve the problems.

B **1** Elsa is flying a kite. She let out 25 meters of string. The kite is directly above a spot that is 7 meters away. How high above the ground is the kite?

What lengths of the right triangle are you given: both legs or one leg and the hypotenuse?

Show your work.

$7^2 + b^2 = 25^2$
$49 + b^2 = 625$
$b^2 = 576$
$b = \sqrt{576} = 24$

Solution: ___24 meters___

M **2** The dimensions of a box that is a rectangular prism are 3 inches, 4 inches, and 6 inches. What is the length of the diagonal from point R to point S, to the nearest tenth of an inch?

What is the length of the hypotenuse of the base? How can this length help you solve the problem?

A 5 inches **C** 7.8 inches

B 6.7 inches **D** 61 inches

Rodney chose **B** as the correct answer. How did he get that answer?

___He thought the diagonal of the base was the same as the diagonal of the prism.___

M **3** Margo drew a diagram of a square wooden deck, with side length c feet, that she wants to build in her square yard. Explain how to find the perimeter of the deck. Then find the perimeter.

How is the length, c related to the lengths 9 and 12?

Show your work.

Possible explanation: The length of one side of the deck is the hypotenuse of a right triangle with legs that are 9 and 12 feet long.
$c^2 = 9^2 + 12^2 = 81 + 144 = 225$, so $c = \sqrt{225} = 15$.
The perimeter of the deck is: $4c = 4 \times 15 = 60$.

Solution: ___60 feet___

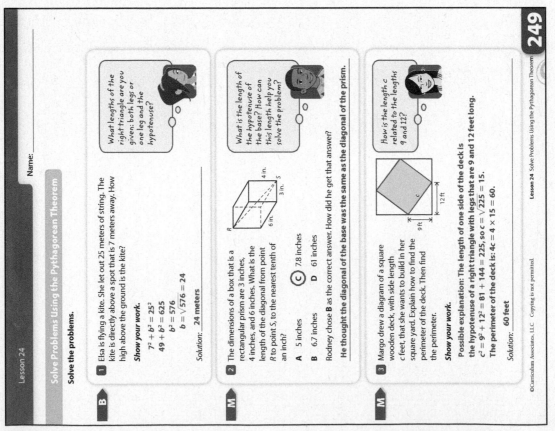

Solve.

M **4** Tell whether each statement is *True* or *False* about the right triangle shown.

What does the Pythagorean Theorem tell you about the side lengths of a right triangle?

a. The square of b is always equal to the square of c minus the square of a.   ☒ True ☐ False

b. The square of c equals the square of b plus the square of a.   ☒ True ☐ False

c. The value of c is equal to the square of the sum of b and c.   ☐ True ☒ False

C **5** An isosceles right triangle has a hypotenuse of 12. Between which two whole numbers are the lengths of the legs of the triangle?

What do you know about the sides of an isosceles triangle?

Show your work.

Let a be the length of one of the legs of the triangle.
$a^2 + a^2 = 12^2$
$2a^2 = 144$
$a^2 = 72$
$a = \sqrt{72} \approx 8.5$

Solution: ___The lengths of the legs are between 8 and 9.___

C **6** The length of the base of a rectangular prism is 3 feet and its width is 2 feet. The length of the diagonal of the prism is 6 feet. What is the height of the prism to the nearest tenth of a foot?

You can draw a diagram to help you visualize the problem.

A 3.3 ft   **C** 13 ft

(B) 4.8 ft   **D** 23 ft

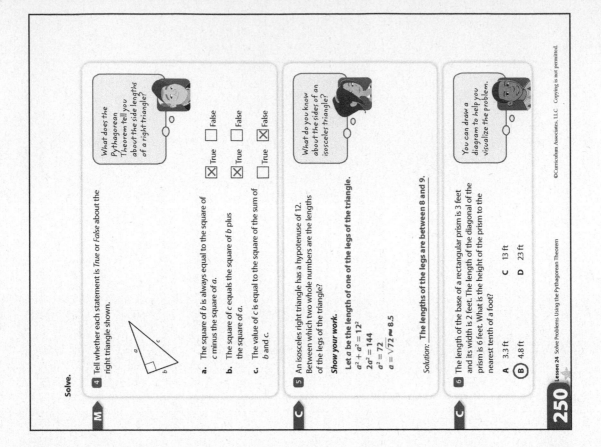

Lesson 25

Distance in the Coordinate Plane

Name: _____

Prerequisite: Solve Problems Using the Pythagorean Theorem

Study the example problem showing how to use the Pythagorean Theorem. Then solve problems 1–5.

Example

A wire stretches from the top of a 20-foot pole to the ground. The wire is secured to the ground 15 feet from the base of the pole. How long is the wire?

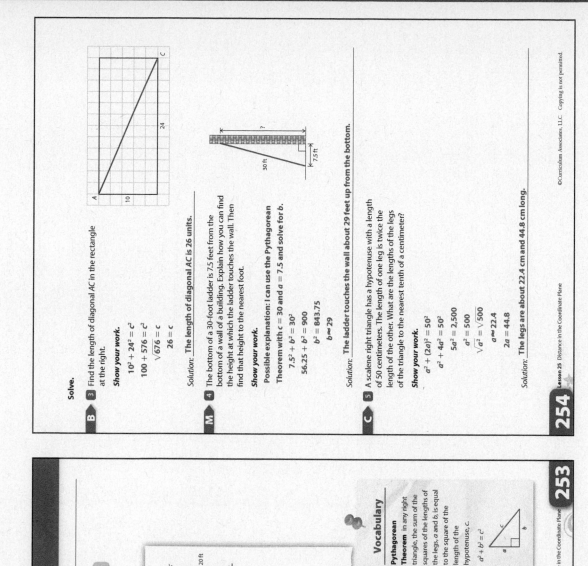

20 ft
15 ft

The pole, the ground, and the wire form a right triangle. Use the Pythagorean Theorem to find the length of the wire.

$a^2 + b^2 = c^2$
$20^2 + 15^2 = c^2$ Replace a with 20 and b with 15.
$400 + 225 = c^2$ Simplify.
$625 = c^2$ Add.
$\sqrt{625} = c$ Take the square root of each side.
$25 = c$ Simplify.

The wire is 25 feet long.

Vocabulary

Pythagorean Theorem in any right triangle, the sum of the squares of the lengths of the legs, a and b, is equal to the square of the length of the hypotenuse, c.
$a^2 + b^2 = c^2$

B 1 In the example, how do you know which sides are the legs and which side is the hypotenuse?
Possible answer: The pole and the ground are the legs that form the right angle. The wire is the hypotenuse, which is the side opposite the right angle.

B 2 Are the side lengths of the triangle in the example a Pythagorean triple? Explain.
Yes; Possible explanation: 15-20-25 is a multiple of the 3-4-5 triple.

Solve.

B 3 Find the length of diagonal AC in the rectangle at the right.
Show your work.
$10^2 + 24^2 = c^2$
$100 + 576 = c^2$
$\sqrt{676} = c$
$26 = c$
Solution: The length of diagonal AC is 26 units.

A, C, 10, 24

M 4 The bottom of a 30-foot ladder is 7.5 feet from the bottom of a wall of a building. Explain how you can find the height at which the ladder touches the wall. Then find that height to the nearest foot.
Show your work.
Possible explanation: I can use the Pythagorean Theorem with c = 30 and a = 7.5 and solve for b.
$7.5^2 + b^2 = 30^2$
$56.25 + b^2 = 900$
$b^2 = 843.75$
$b \approx 29$

30 ft   7.5 ft   ?

Solution: The ladder touches the wall about 29 feet up from the bottom.

C 5 A scalene right triangle has a hypotenuse with a length of 50 centimeters. The length of one leg is twice the length of the other. What are the lengths of the legs of the triangle to the nearest tenth of a centimeter?
Show your work.
$a^2 + (2a)^2 = 50^2$
$a^2 + 4a^2 = 50^2$
$5a^2 = 2,500$
$a^2 = 500$
$\sqrt{a^2} = \sqrt{500}$
$a \approx 22.4$
$2a = 44.8$
Solution: The legs are about 22.4 cm and 44.8 cm long.

Key

B Basic   **M** Medium   **C** Challenge

Lesson 25

Find the Distance Between Two Points

Study the example problem showing how to find the distance between two points. Then solve problems 1–6.

Example

What is the distance between points R and S?

Sketch right triangle RST by drawing a vertical line segment from R, a horizontal line segment from S, and a line segment connecting R and S.

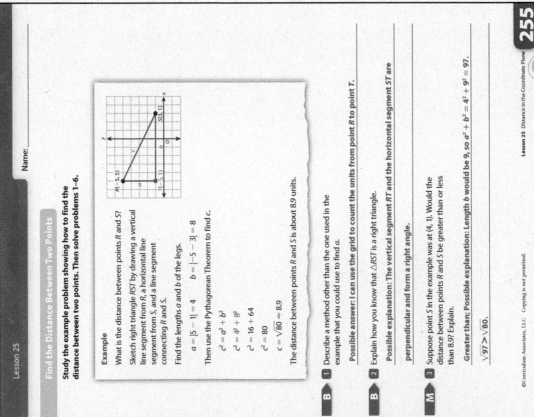

Find the lengths a and b of the legs.

$$a = |5 - 1| = 4 \qquad b = |-5 - 3| = 8$$

Then use the Pythagorean Theorem to find c.

$$c^2 = a^2 + b^2$$
$$c^2 = 4^2 + 8^2$$
$$c^2 = 16 + 64$$
$$c^2 = 80$$
$$c = \sqrt{80} \approx 8.9$$

The distance between points R and S is about 8.9 units.

B 1 Describe a method other than the one used in the example that you could use to find a.

Possible answer: I can use the grid to count the units from point R to point T.

B 2 Explain how you know that $\triangle RST$ is a right triangle.

Possible explanation: The vertical segment RT and the horizontal segment ST are perpendicular and form a right angle.

M 3 Suppose point S in the example was at $(4, 1)$. Would the distance between points R and S be greater than or less than 8.9? Explain.

Greater than; Possible explanation: Length b would be 9, so $a^2 + b^2 = 4^2 + 9^2 = 97$.
$\sqrt{97} > \sqrt{80}$.

255

Solve.

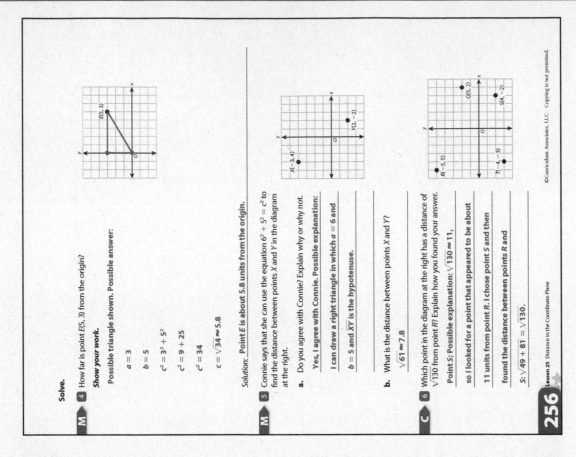

M 4 How far is point $E(5, 3)$ from the origin?

Show your work.

Possible triangle shown. Possible answer:

$$a = 3$$
$$b = 5$$
$$c^2 = 3^2 + 5^2$$
$$c^2 = 9 + 25$$
$$c^2 = 34$$
$$c = \sqrt{34} \approx 5.8$$

Solution: Point E is about 5.8 units from the origin.

M 5 Connie says that she can use the equation $6^2 + 5^2 = c^2$ to find the distance between points X and Y in the diagram at the right.

a. Do you agree with Connie? Explain why or why not.

Yes, I agree with Connie. Possible explanation:
I can draw a right triangle in which $a = 6$ and $b = 5$ and XY is the hypotenuse.

b. What is the distance between points X and Y?
$$\sqrt{61} \approx 7.8$$

C 6 Which point in the diagram at the right has a distance of $\sqrt{130}$ from point R? Explain how you found your answer.

Point S; Possible explanation: $\sqrt{130} \approx 11$, so I looked for a point that appeared to be about 11 units from point R. I chose point S and then found the distance between points R and
$$S: \sqrt{49 + 81} = \sqrt{130}.$$

256

Name: _____

Lesson 25

Distance in the Coordinate Plane

Solve the problems.

M

1 Find the distance between points L and M. Then find the distance between points L and N. Which distance is greater? How much greater?

Show your work.

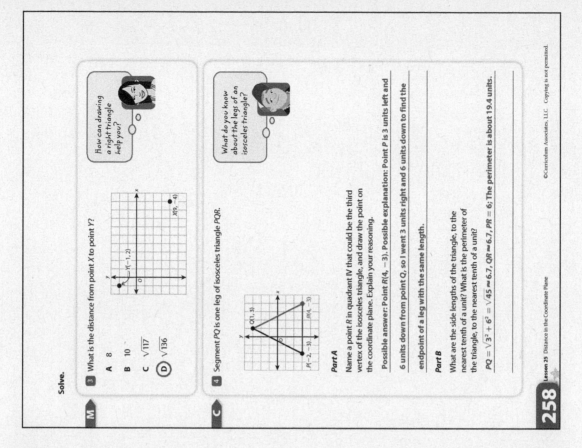

Distance between L and M:

$LM^2 = 4^2 + 3^2$

$LM^2 = 25$

$LM = \sqrt{25} = 5$

Distance between L and N:

$LN^2 = 1^2 + 6^2$

$LN^2 = 37$

$LN = \sqrt{37} \approx 6.1$

$6.1 - 5 = 1.1$

Solution: _The distance between L and N is about 1.1 units greater than the distance between L and M._

Use the Pythagorean Theorem to find both distances.

M

2 Which point has a distance of $\sqrt{5}$ units from the origin?

A Point A

B Point B

C Point C

D Point D

Ken chose A as the correct answer. How did he get that answer?

Possible answer: Ken chose the point that has a distance of 5 units from the origin.

The origin and which point form a hypotenuse that is $\sqrt{5}$ units long?

Solve.

M

3 What is the distance from point X to point Y?

A 8

B 10

C $\sqrt{117}$

D $\sqrt{136}$ ✓

How can drawing a right triangle help you?

C

4 Segment PQ is one leg of isosceles triangle PQR.

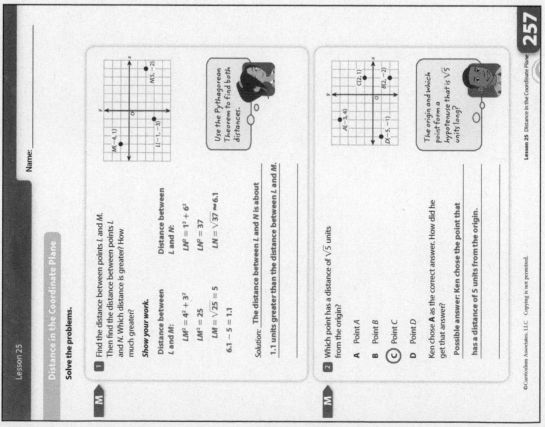

What do you know about the legs of an isosceles triangle?

Part A

Name a point R in quadrant IV that could be the third vertex of the isosceles triangle, and draw the point on the coordinate plane. Explain your reasoning.

Possible answer: Point $R(4, -3)$. Possible explanation: Point P is 3 units left and 6 units down from point Q, so I went 3 units right and 6 units down to find the endpoint of a leg with the same length.

Part B

What are the side lengths of the triangle, to the nearest tenth of a unit? What is the perimeter of the triangle, to the nearest tenth of a unit?

$PQ = \sqrt{3^2 + 6^2} = \sqrt{45} \approx 6.7$, $QR \approx 6.7$, $PR = 6$; The perimeter is about 19.4 units.

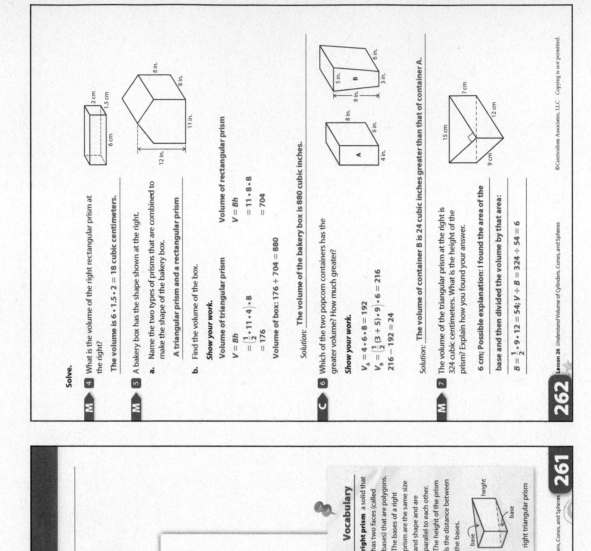

Lesson 26
Understand
Volume of Cylinders, Cones, and Spheres

Name: _____

Prerequisite: How can you find the volume of a right prism?

Study the example problem showing how to find the volume of a right prism. Then solve problems 1–7.

Example

A glass display case in the shape of a right triangular prism is shown at the right. What is the volume of the display case?

To find the volume of a right prism, you can use the formula $V = Bh$, where V is the volume, B is the area of the base, and h is the height of the prism.

First find B, the area of the base. The bases of a triangular prism are triangles, so use the formula for the area of a triangle.

$B = \frac{1}{2} \cdot 12 \cdot 8$
$B = 48$

Now find the volume of the prism, where $B = 48$ and $h = 15$.
$V = Bh$
$V = 48 \cdot 15$
$V = 720$

The volume of the display case is 720 cubic inches.

Vocabulary

right prism a solid that has two faces (called bases) that are polygons. The bases of a right prism are the same size and shape and are parallel to each other. The height of the prism is the distance between the bases.

right triangular prism

B 1 Why isn't the base of this prism the 12 in. by 15 in. rectangular face?

The bases of a right prism are the same size and shape and are parallel to each other.

B 2 If the bases of the case in the example were rectangles, what formula would you use to find B? $B = lw$

M 3 Suppose the area of the base of another triangular prism is 15 square inches and the height is 48 inches. What is the same about this prism and the prism in the example? What is different?

The volumes are the same. The shapes are different.

©Curriculum Associates, LLC Copying is not permitted.
Lesson 26 *Understand* Volume of Cylinders, Cones, and Spheres
261

Solve.

M 4 What is the volume of the right rectangular prism at the right?
The volume is $6 \cdot 1.5 \cdot 2 = 18$ cubic centimeters.

M 5 A bakery box has the shape shown at the right.

a. Name the two types of prisms that are combined to make the shape of the bakery box.
A triangular prism and a rectangular prism

b. Find the volume of the box.
Show your work.

Volume of triangular prism
$V = Bh$
$= \left(\frac{1}{2} \cdot 11 \cdot 4\right) \cdot 8$
$= 176$

Volume of rectangular prism
$V = Bh$
$= 11 \cdot 8 \cdot 8$
$= 704$

Volume of box: $176 + 704 = 880$

Solution: The volume of the bakery box is 880 cubic inches.

C 6 Which of the two popcorn containers has the greater volume? How much greater?
Show your work.
$V_A = 4 \cdot 6 \cdot 8 = 192$
$V_B = \left(\frac{1}{2}(3 + 5) \cdot 9\right) \cdot 6 = 216$
$216 - 192 = 24$

Solution: The volume of container B is 24 cubic inches greater than that of container A.

M 7 The volume of the triangular prism at the right is 324 cubic centimeters. What is the height of the prism? Explain how you found your answer.

6 cm; Possible explanation: I found the area of the base and then divided the volume by that area:
$B = \frac{1}{2} \cdot 9 \cdot 12 = 54; V \div B = 324 \div 54 = 6$

Lesson 26 *Understand* Volume of Cylinders, Cones, and Spheres
262

Key

B Basic   **M** Medium   **C** Challenge

Lesson 26

Name: _____

Use Volume Formulas

Study the example problem showing how to use formulas to find the volume of a cone and a cylinder. Then solve problems 1–7.

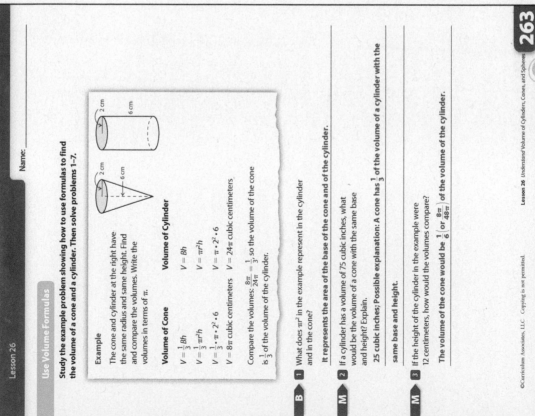

Example
The cone and cylinder at the right have the same radius and same height. Find and compare the volumes. Write the volumes in terms of π.

Volume of Cone	Volume of Cylinder
$V = \frac{1}{3}Bh$	$V = Bh$
$V = \frac{1}{3}\pi r^2 h$	$V = \pi r^2 h$
$V = \frac{1}{3} \cdot \pi \cdot 2^2 \cdot 6$	$V = \pi \cdot 2^2 \cdot 6$
$V = 8\pi$ cubic centimeters	$V = 24\pi$ cubic centimeters

Compare the volumes: $\frac{8\pi}{24\pi} = \frac{1}{3}$, so the volume of the cone is $\frac{1}{3}$ of the volume of the cylinder.

B 1 What does πr^2 in the example represent in the cylinder and in the cone?

It represents the area of the base of the cone and of the cylinder.

M 2 If a cylinder has a volume of 75 cubic inches, what would be the volume of a cone with the same base and height? Explain.

25 cubic inches; Possible explanation: A cone has $\frac{1}{3}$ of the volume of a cylinder with the same base and height.

M 3 If the height of the cylinder in the example were 12 centimeters, how would the volumes compare?

The volume of the cone would be $\frac{1}{6}$ (or $\frac{8\pi}{48\pi}$) of the volume of the cylinder.

Solve.

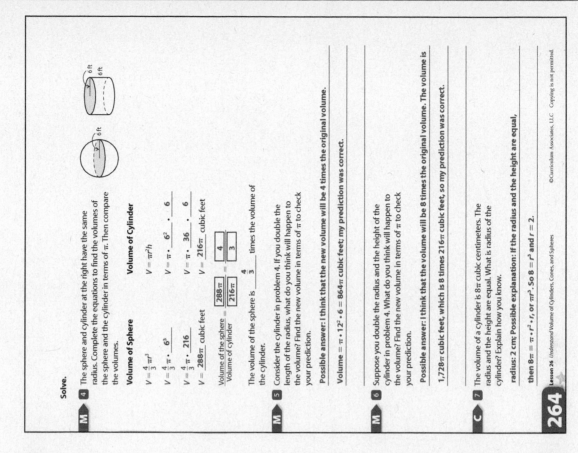

M 4 The sphere and cylinder at the right have the same radius. Complete the equations to find the volumes of the sphere and the cylinder in terms of π. Then compare the volumes.

Volume of Sphere	Volume of Cylinder
$V = \frac{4}{3}\pi r^3$	$V = \pi r^2 h$
$V = \frac{4}{3} \cdot 6^3$	$V = \pi \cdot 6^2 \cdot 6$
$V = \frac{4}{3} \cdot 216$	$V = \pi \cdot 36 \cdot 6$
$V = 288\pi$ cubic feet	$V = 216\pi$ cubic feet

$$\frac{\text{Volume of the sphere}}{\text{Volume of cylinder}} = \frac{288\pi}{216\pi} = \frac{4}{3}$$

The volume of the sphere is $\frac{4}{3}$ times the volume of the cylinder.

M 5 Consider the cylinder in problem 4. If you double the length of the radius, what do you think will happen to the volume? Find the new volume in terms of π to check your prediction.

Possible answer: I think that the new volume will be 4 times the original volume.

Volume $= \pi \cdot 12^2 \cdot 6 = 864\pi$ cubic feet; my prediction was correct.

M 6 Suppose you double the radius and the height of the cylinder in problem 4. What do you think will happen to the volume? Find the new volume in terms of π to check your prediction.

Possible answer: I think that the volume will be 8 times the original volume. The volume is 1,728π cubic feet, which is 8 times 216π cubic feet, so my prediction was correct.

C 7 The volume of a cylinder is 8π cubic centimeters. The radius and the height are equal. What is radius of the cylinder? Explain how you know.

radius: 2 cm; Possible explanation: If the radius and the height are equal,

then $8\pi = \pi \cdot r^2 \cdot r$, or πr^3. So $8 = r^3$ and $r = 2$.

Lesson 26

Reason and Write

Name: _____

Study the example. Underline two parts that you think make it a particularly good answer and a helpful example.

Example

Use the cone and cylinder shown below to complete the table. For both solid figures, compare the volume when the radius is halved to the original volume. Then compare the volume when the height is halved to the original volume. Describe the effects of halving the radius and halving the height.

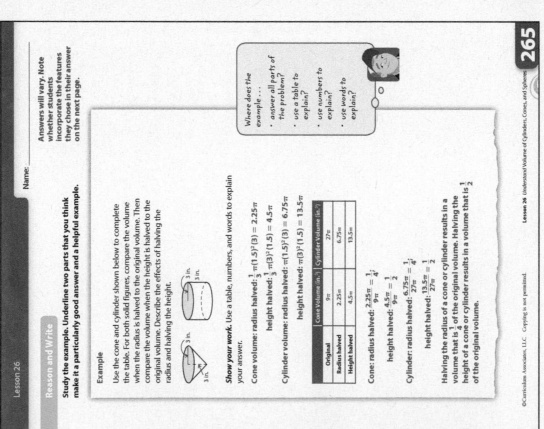

Show your work. Use a table, numbers, and words to explain your answer.

Cone volume: radius halved: $\frac{1}{3}\pi(1.5)^2(3) = 2.25\pi$

height halved: $\frac{1}{3}\pi(3)^2(1.5) = 4.5\pi$

Cylinder volume: radius halved: $\pi(1.5)^2(3) = 6.75\pi$

height halved: $\pi(3)^2(1.5) = 13.5\pi$

	Cone Volume (in.³)	Cylinder Volume (in.³)
Original	9π	27π
Radius halved	2.25π	6.75π
Height halved	4.5π	13.5π

Cone: radius halved: $\frac{2.25\pi}{9\pi} = \frac{1}{4}$;

height halved: $\frac{4.5\pi}{9\pi} = \frac{1}{2}$

Cylinder: radius halved: $\frac{6.75\pi}{27\pi} = \frac{1}{4}$;

height halved: $\frac{13.5\pi}{27\pi} = \frac{1}{2}$

Halving the radius of a cone or cylinder results in a volume that is $\frac{1}{4}$ of the original volume. Halving the height of a cone or cylinder results in a volume that is $\frac{1}{2}$ of the original volume.

Where does the example . . .
- *answer all parts of the problem?*
- *use a table to explain?*
- *use numbers to explain?*
- *use words to explain?*

Answers will vary. Note whether students incorporate the features they chose in their answer on the next page.

265

©Curriculum Associates, LLC   Copying is not permitted.   Lesson 26 *Understand* Volume of Cylinders, Cones, and Spheres

---

Solve the problem. Use what you learned from the model.

Use the cone and cylinder shown below to complete the table. For both solid figures, find the volume. Then compare the volume when the radius and height are both doubled to the original volume. Describe the effects of doubling both dimensions.

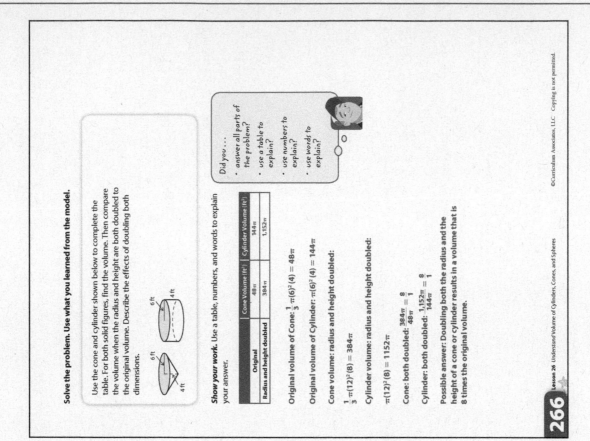

Show your work. Use a table, numbers, and words to explain your answer.

	Cone Volume (ft³)	Cylinder Volume (ft³)
Original	48π	144π
Radius and height doubled	384π	1,152π

Original volume of Cone: $\frac{1}{3}\pi(6)^2(4) = 48\pi$

Original volume of Cylinder: $\pi(6)^2(4) = 144\pi$

Cone volume: radius and height doubled:

$\frac{1}{3}\pi(12)^2(8) = 384\pi$

Cylinder volume: radius and height doubled:

$\pi(12)^2(8) = 1152\pi$

Cone: both doubled: $\frac{384\pi}{48\pi} = \frac{8}{1}$

Cylinder: both doubled: $\frac{1,152\pi}{144\pi} = \frac{8}{1}$

Possible answer: Doubling both the radius and the height of a cone or cylinder results in a volume that is 8 times the original volume.

Did you . . .
- *answer all parts of the problem?*
- *use a table to explain?*
- *use numbers to explain?*
- *use words to explain?*

266

Lesson 26 *Understand* Volume of Cylinders, Cones, and Spheres   ©Curriculum Associates, LLC   Copying is not permitted.

Lesson 27

Solve Problems with Cylinders, Cones, and Spheres

Name: _____

Prerequisite: Find the Volume of Cones and Cylinders

Study the example problem showing how to find the volume of a cylinder and a cone. Then solve problems 1–7.

Example

Find the volumes of the cone and the cylinder. Write the volumes in terms of π.

Volume of Cone	Volume of Cylinder
$V = \frac{1}{3} Bh$	$V = Bh$
$= \frac{1}{3} \pi r^2 h$	$= \pi r^2 h$
$= \frac{1}{3} \cdot 6^2 \cdot 5$	$= \pi \cdot 6^2 \cdot 5$
$= 60\pi$	$= 180\pi$

The volume of the cone is 60π cubic centimeters, and the volume of the cylinder is 180π cubic centimeters.

Vocabulary

cylinder a solid figure with two congruent and parallel circular bases.

cone a solid figure with one vertex and one circular base.

B 1 In the example, what measurements are the same in the cone and the cylinder?

They both have a radius of 6 cm and a height of 5 cm.

B 2 How does the volume of the cone in the example compare to the volume of the cylinder?

The volume of the cone is $\frac{1}{3}$ of the volume of the cylinder.

M 3 Suppose the height of the cone in the example was tripled. How would the volume of the cone compare to the volume of the cylinder? Explain how you know.

The volumes would be equal. Possible explanation: The volume of the cone is $\frac{1}{3}$ of the volume of the cylinder. If the height of the cone were tripled, the volume would be tripled, and $3 \cdot 60\pi = 180\pi$.

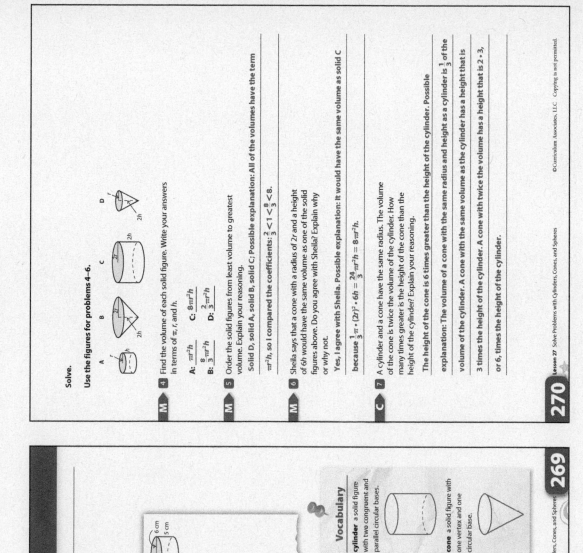

Solve.

Use the figures for problems 4–6.

A B C D

M 4 Find the volume of each solid figure. Write your answers in terms of π, r, and h.

A: $\pi r^2 h$ C: $8\pi r^2 h$

B: $\frac{8}{3} \pi r^2 h$ D: $\frac{2}{3} \pi r^2 h$

M 5 Order the solid figures from least volume to greatest volume. Explain your reasoning.

Solid D, solid B, solid C; Possible explanation: All of the volumes have the term $\pi r^2 h$, so I compared the coefficients: $\frac{2}{3} < 1 < \frac{8}{3} < 8$.

M 6 Sheila says that a cone with a radius of $2r$ and a height of $6h$ would have the same volume as one of the solid figures above. Do you agree with Sheila? Explain why or why not.

Yes, I agree with Sheila. Possible explanation: It would have the same volume as solid C

because $\frac{1}{3} \pi \cdot (2r)^2 \cdot 6h = \frac{24}{3} \pi r^2 h = 8\pi r^2 h$.

C 7 A cylinder and a cone have the same radius. The volume of the cone is twice the volume of the cylinder. How many times greater is the height of the cone than the height of the cylinder? Explain your reasoning.

The height of the cone is 6 times greater than the height of the cylinder. Possible explanation: The volume of a cone with the same radius and height as a cylinder is $\frac{1}{3}$ of the volume of the cylinder. A cone with the same volume as the cylinder has a height that is 3 times the height of the cylinder. A cone with twice the volume has a height that is $2 \cdot 3$, or 6, times the height of the cylinder.

Key

B Basic   **M** Medium   **C** Challenge

Name: _____

Lesson 27

Solve Volume Problems

Study the example problem showing how to solve a volume problem. Then solve problems 1–8.

Example

Two solid glass paperweights are shown at the right. What is the volume of glass used to make each paperweight? Write the volumes in terms of π.

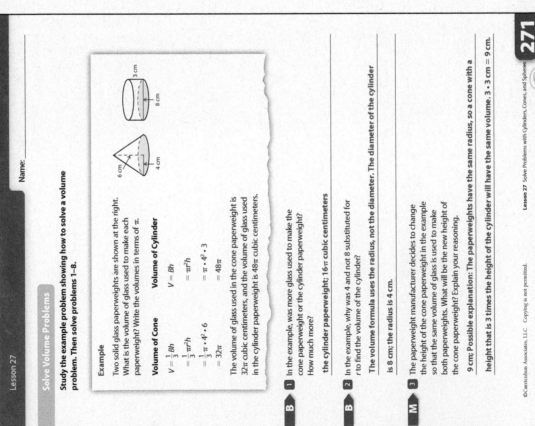

Volume of Cone	Volume of Cylinder
$V = \frac{1}{3} Bh$	$V = Bh$
$= \frac{1}{3} \pi r^2 h$	$= \pi r^2 h$
$= \frac{1}{3} \pi \cdot 4^2 \cdot 6$	$= \pi \cdot 4^2 \cdot 3$
$= 32\pi$	$= 48\pi$

The volume of glass used in the cone paperweight is 32π cubic centimeters, and the volume of glass used in the cylinder paperweight is 48π cubic centimeters.

B 1 In the example, was more glass used to make the cone paperweight or the cylinder paperweight? How much more?

the cylinder paperweight; 16π cubic centimeters

B 2 In the example, why was 4 and not 8 substituted for r to find the volume of the cylinder?

The volume formula uses the radius, not the diameter. The diameter of the cylinder is 8 cm; the radius is 4 cm.

M 3 The paperweight manufacturer decides to change the height of the cone paperweight in the example so that the same volume of glass is used to make both paperweights. What will be the new height of the cone paperweight? Explain your reasoning.

9 cm; Possible explanation: The paperweights have the same radius, so a cone with a height that is 3 times the height of the cylinder will have the same volume. 3 • 3 cm = 9 cm.

Solve.

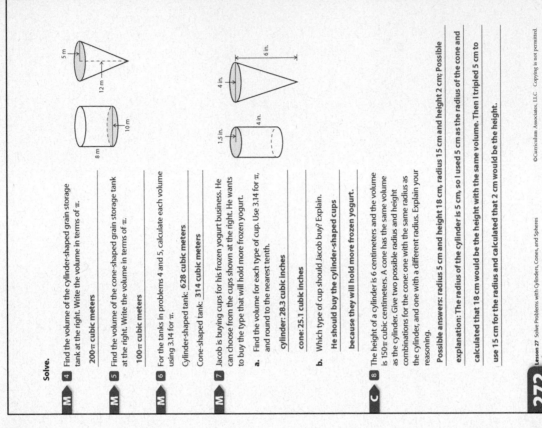

M 4 Find the volume of the cylinder-shaped grain storage tank at the right. Write the volume in terms of π.

200π cubic meters

M 5 Find the volume of the cone-shaped grain storage tank at the right. Write the volume in terms of π.

100π cubic meters

M 6 For the tanks in problems 4 and 5, calculate each volume using 3.14 for π.

Cylinder-shaped tank: 628 cubic meters

Cone-shaped tank: 314 cubic meters

M 7 Jacob is buying cups for his frozen yogurt business. He can choose from the cups shown at the right. He wants to buy the type that will hold more frozen yogurt.

a. Find the volume for each type of cup. Use 3.14 for π, and round to the nearest tenth.

cylinder: 28.3 cubic inches

cone: 25.1 cubic inches

b. Which type of cup should Jacob buy? Explain.

He should buy the cylinder-shaped cups

because they will hold more frozen yogurt.

C 8 The height of a cylinder is 6 centimeters and the volume is 150π cubic centimeters. A cone has the same volume as the cylinder. Give two possible radius and height combinations for the cone: one with the same radius as the cylinder, and one with a different radius. Explain your reasoning.

Possible answers: radius 5 cm and height 18 cm, radius 15 cm and height 2 cm; Possible explanation: The radius of the cylinder is 5 cm, so I used 5 cm as the radius of the cone and calculated that 18 cm would be the height with the same volume. Then I tripled 5 cm to use 15 cm for the radius and calculated that 2 cm would be the height.

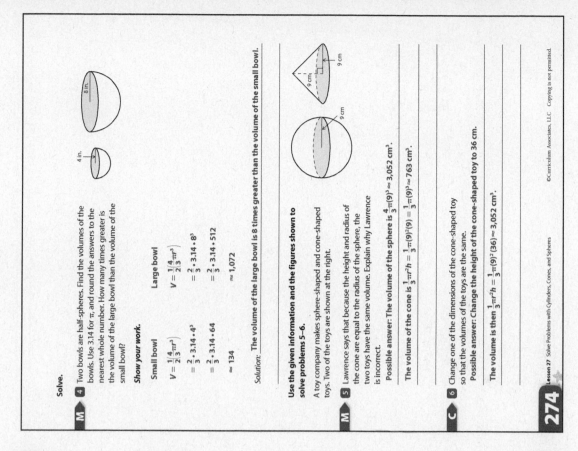

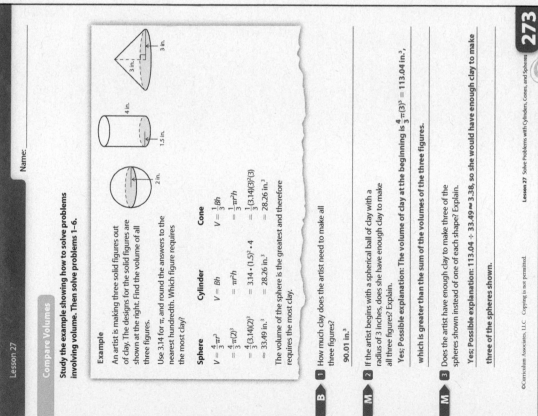

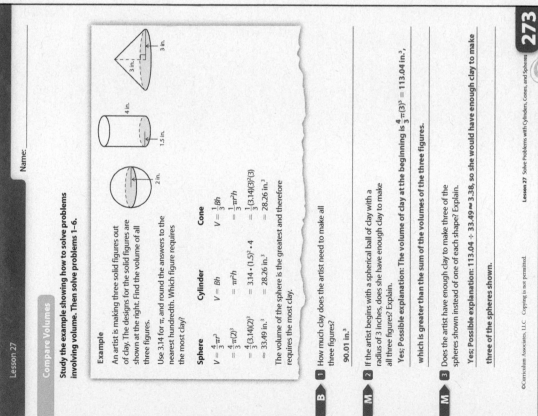

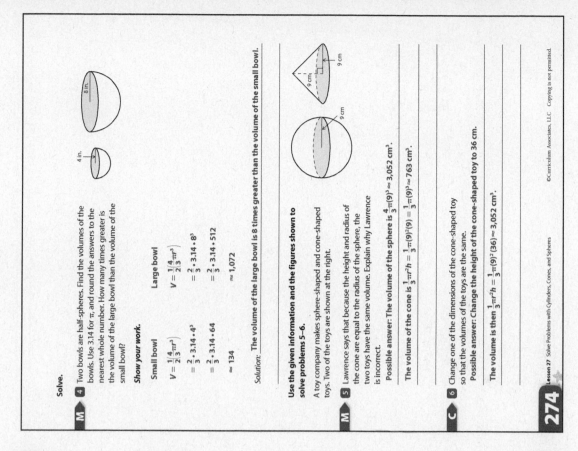

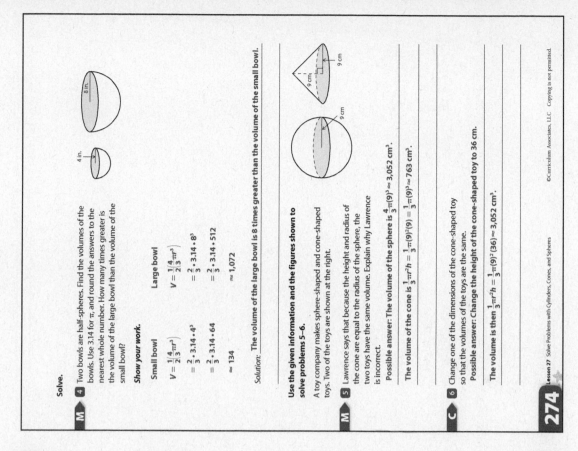

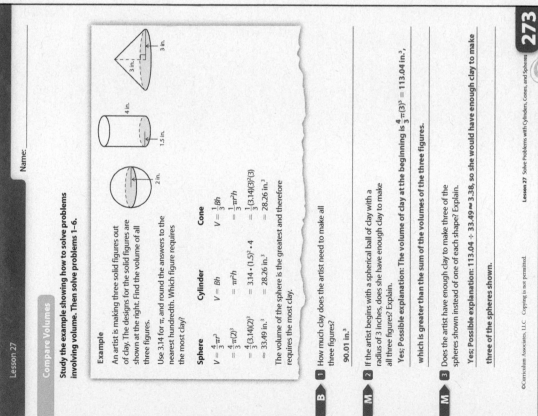

Practice Lesson 27 Solve Problems with Cylinders, Cones, and Spheres

Unit 4

Lesson 27

Compare Volumes

Study the example showing how to solve problems involving volume. Then solve problems 1–6.

Example

An artist is making three solid figures out of clay. The designs for the solid figures are shown at the right. Find the volume of all three figures.

Use 3.14 for π, and round the answers to the nearest hundredth. Which figure requires the most clay?

Sphere	Cylinder	Cone
$V = \frac{4}{3}\pi r^3$	$V = Bh$	$V = \frac{1}{3}Bh$
$= \frac{4}{3}\pi(2)^3$	$= \pi r^2 h$	$= \frac{1}{3}\pi r^2 h$
$= \frac{4}{3}(3.14)(2)^3$	$= 3.14 \cdot (1.5)^2 \cdot 4$	$= \frac{1}{3}(3.14)(3)^2(3)$
≈ 33.49 in.^{3}	$= 28.26$ in.^{3}	$= 28.26$ in.^{3}

The volume of the sphere is the greatest and therefore requires the most clay.

B 1 How much clay does the artist need to make all three figures?

90.01 in.^{3}

M 2 If the artist begins with a spherical ball of clay with a radius of 3 inches, does she have enough clay to make all three figures? Explain.

Yes; Possible explanation: The volume of clay at the beginning is $\frac{4}{3}\pi(3)^3 = 113.04$ in.^{3},

which is greater than the sum of the volumes of the three figures.

M 3 Does the artist have enough clay to make three of the spheres shown instead of one of each shape? Explain.

Yes; Possible explanation: 113.04 ÷ 33.49 ≈ 3.38, so she would have enough clay to make

three of the spheres shown.

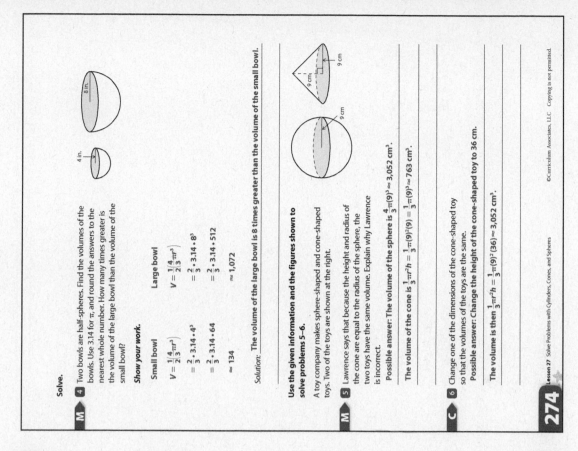

Solve.

M 4 Two bowls are half-spheres. Find the volumes of the bowls. Use 3.14 for π, and round the answers to the nearest whole number. How many times greater is the volume of the large bowl than the volume of the small bowl?

Show your work.

Small bowl

$V = \frac{1}{2}\left(\frac{4}{3}\pi r^3\right)$

$= \frac{2}{3} \cdot 3.14 \cdot 4^3$

$= \frac{2}{3} \cdot 3.14 \cdot 64$

≈ 134

Large bowl

$V = \frac{1}{2}\left(\frac{4}{3}\pi r^3\right)$

$= \frac{2}{3} \cdot 3.14 \cdot 8^3$

$= \frac{2}{3} \cdot 3.14 \cdot 512$

$\approx 1,072$

Solution: ____The volume of the large bowl is 8 times greater than the volume of the small bowl.____

Use the given information and the figures shown to solve problems 5–6.

A toy company makes sphere-shaped and cone-shaped toys. Two of the toys are shown at the right.

M 5 Lawrence says that because the height and radius of the cone are equal to the radius of the sphere, the two toys have the same volume. Explain why Lawrence is incorrect.

Possible answer: The volume of the sphere is $\frac{4}{3}\pi(9)^3 \approx 3,052$ cm^3.

The volume of the cone is $\frac{1}{3}\pi r^2 h = \frac{1}{3}\pi(9)^2(9) = \frac{1}{3}\pi(9)^3 \approx 763$ cm^3.

C 6 Change one of the dimensions of the cone-shaped toy so that the volumes of the toys are the same.

Possible answer: Change the height of the cone-shaped toy to 36 cm.

The volume is then $\frac{1}{3}\pi r^2 h = \frac{1}{3}\pi(9)^2(36) \approx 3,052$ cm^3.

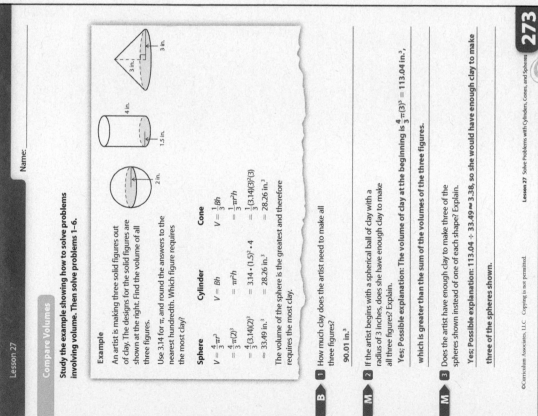

273

Lesson 27 Solve Problems with Cylinders, Cones, and Spheres

©Curriculum Associates, LLC   Copying is not permitted.

274

Lesson 27 Solve Problems with Cylinders, Cones, and Spheres

©Curriculum Associates, LLC   Copying is not permitted.

Name: _____

Lesson 27

Solve Problems with Cylinders, Cones, and Spheres

Solve the problems.

1 The propane storage tank shown is a cylinder with a half-sphere on each end.

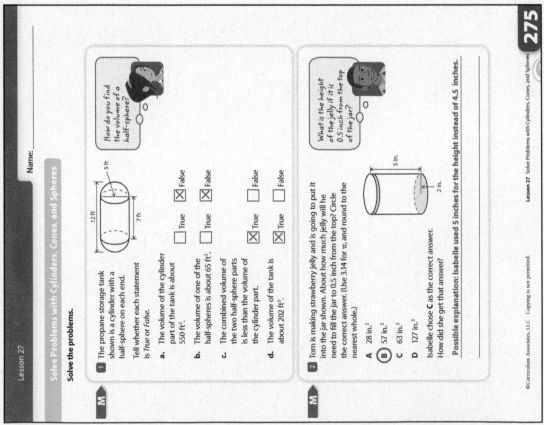

Tell whether each statement is *True* or *False*.

a. The volume of the cylinder part of the tank is about 550 ft³. ☐ True ☒ False

b. The volume of one of the half-spheres is about 65 ft³. ☐ True ☒ False

c. The combined volume of the two half-sphere parts is less than the volume of the cylinder part. ☒ True ☐ False

d. The volume of the tank is about 202 ft³. ☒ True ☐ False

How do you find the volume of a half-sphere?

2 Tom is making strawberry jelly and is going to put it into the jar shown. About how much jelly will he need to fill the jar to 0.5 inch from the top? Circle the correct answer. (Use 3.14 for π, and round to the nearest whole.)

A 28 in.³

B 57 in.³

C 63 in.³

D 127 in.³

Isabelle chose **C** as the correct answer. How did she get that answer?

Possible explanation: Isabelle used 5 inches for the height instead of 4.5 inches.

What is the height of the jelly if it is 0.5 inch from the top of the jar?

Solve.

3 Juan cut a section shaped like a cone out of the center of a piece of wood that is shaped like a cylinder, as shown below. What is the volume of the piece of wood left after Juan cut out the cone-shaped section? Use 3.14 for π, and round to the nearest whole cubic centimeter.

What is the radius of the cone that Juan cut out of the cylinder?

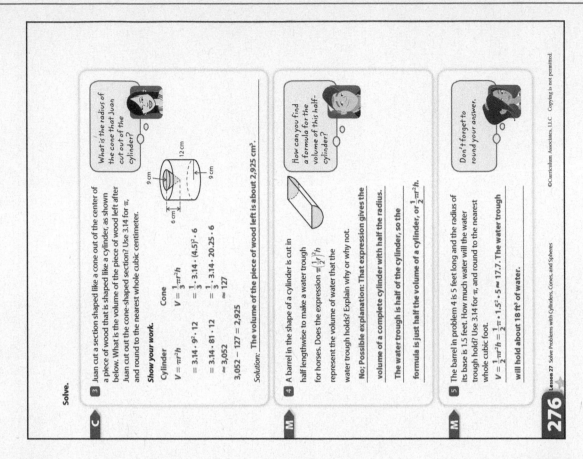

Show your work.

Cylinder	Cone
$V = \pi r^2 h$	$V = \frac{1}{3}\pi r^2 h$
$= 3.14 \cdot 9^2 \cdot 12$	$= \frac{1}{3} \cdot 3.14 \cdot (4.5)^2 \cdot 6$
$= 3.14 \cdot 81 \cdot 12$	$= \frac{1}{3} \cdot 3.14 \cdot 20.25 \cdot 6$
$\approx 3{,}052$	≈ 127

$3{,}052 - 127 = 2{,}925$

Solution: The volume of the piece of wood left is about 2,925 cm³.

4 A barrel in the shape of a cylinder is cut in half lengthwise to make a water trough for horses. Does the expression $\pi\left(\frac{1}{2}\right)^2 h$ represent the volume of water that the water trough holds? Explain why or why not.

How can you find a formula for the volume of this half-cylinder?

No; Possible explanation: That expression gives the volume of a complete cylinder with half the radius.

The water trough is half of the cylinder, so the formula is just half the volume of a cylinder, or $\frac{1}{2}\pi r^2 h$.

5 The barrel in problem 4 is 5 feet long and the radius of its base is 1.5 feet. How much water will the water trough hold? Use 3.14 for π, and round to the nearest whole cubic foot.

Don't forget to round your answer.

$V = \frac{1}{2}\pi r^2 h = \frac{1}{2} \cdot \pi \cdot 1.5^2 \cdot 5 \approx 17.7$. The water trough will hold about 18 ft³ of water.

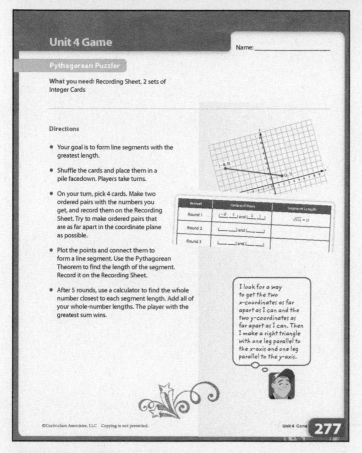

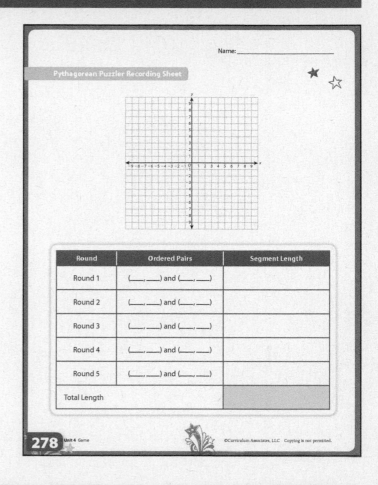

STEP BY STEP

CCSS Focus - 8.G.B.8 *Embedded SMPs* - 1, 2, 4, 5, 6, 7	**Materials** For each pair: Recording Sheets (1 for each player) (TR 7), 2 sets of Integer Cards (TR 3)
Objective • Use the Pythagorean Theorem to find the distance between two points in the coordinate plane.	

• Your goal is to form line segments with the greatest length.

• Shuffle the cards and place them in a pile facedown. Players take turns.

• On your turn, pick 4 cards. Make two ordered pairs with the numbers you get, and record them on the Recording Sheet. Try to make ordered pairs that are as far apart in the coordinate plane as possible.

• Plot the points and connect them to form a line segment. Use the Pythagorean Theorem to find the length of the segment. Record it on the Recording Sheet.

• After 5 rounds, use a calculator to find the whole number closest to each segment length. Add all of your whole-number lengths. The player with the greatest sum wins.

• Model one round for students before they play. Discuss strategies for creating ordered pairs that will give the greatest lengths.

Vary the Game Twice during the game a player may choose to return one card to the bottom of the pile and draw a new one.

Challenge After 5 rounds, do not add the segment lengths. Instead, players pick 3 of the points on their grid to make a triangle. They find the perimeter of their triangles. The player with the longest perimeter wins.

Unit 4 Practice

Name: _____

Geometry

In this unit you learned to:

	Lesson
demonstrate the properties of translations, rotations, and reflections.	18
give the new coordinates of a figure in the coordinate plane after a translation, rotation, or reflection.	19, 20
identify pairs of congruent angles when a transversal intersects parallel lines.	21
identify similar triangles based on angle measurements.	22
demonstrate why the sum of the angle measures in any triangle is 180°.	22
explain a proof of the Pythagorean Theorem.	23
apply the Pythagorean Theorem to solve problems.	24
find distance in the coordinate plane.	25
compare the volumes of cones, cylinders, and spheres.	26
apply volume formulas of cones, cylinders, and spheres to solve problems.	27

Use these skills to solve problems 1–6.

B **1** What is the image of the point $(4, -1)$ after a reflection over the x-axis and a translation 6 units left and 2 units up?

A $(-10, 1)$ C $(6, -5)$
(B) $(-2, 3)$ D $(10, 3)$

M **3** In the drawing below, the two horizontal lines are parallel.

What are the values of x, y, and z?

$x = 144$, $y = 36$, $z = 54$

M **2** A rectangle has a length that is 7 inches longer than its width. The length of a diagonal is 13 inches. What is the perimeter of the rectangle?

A 5 inches   (C) 34 inches
B 12 inches   D 40 inches

283

Solve.

M **4** A flagpole is 48 feet tall. A 50-foot-long support wire connects the top of the flagpole to a stake in the ground. How far from the base of the flagpole is the stake?

[diagram: 50 ft, 48 ft]

Show your work.

$n^2 + 48^2 = 50^2$
$n^2 + 2,304 = 2,500$
$n^2 = 196$
$n = 14$

Solution: __The stake is 14 feet from the base of the flagpole.__

M **5** An ice cream cone is 8 cm tall and the radius of the opening is 3 cm. A scoop of ice cream is a sphere with a radius of 3 cm. If the entire scoop of ice cream melts into the cone, how much of the ice cream will spill over the cone? Use 3.14 for π.

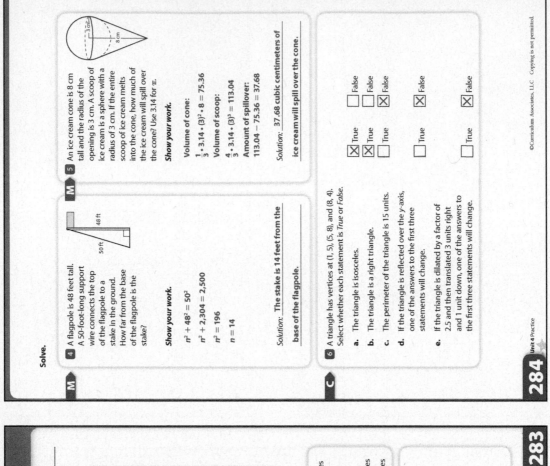

Show your work.

Volume of cone:
$\frac{1}{3} \cdot 3.14 \cdot (3)^2 \cdot 8 = 75.36$

Volume of scoop:
$\frac{4}{3} \cdot 3.14 \cdot (3)^3 = 113.04$

Amount of spillover:
$113.04 - 75.36 = 37.68$

Solution: __37.68 cubic centimeters of ice cream will spill over the cone.__

C **6** A triangle has vertices at $(1, 5)$, $(5, 8)$, and $(8, 4)$. Select whether each statement is *True* or *False*.

a. The triangle is isosceles. [X] True [ ] False
b. The triangle is a right triangle. [X] True [ ] False
c. The perimeter of the triangle is 15 units. [ ] True [X] False
d. If the triangle is reflected over the y-axis, one of the answers to the first three statements will change. [ ] True [X] False
e. If the triangle is dilated by a factor of 2.5 and then translated 3 units right and 1 unit down, one of the answers to the first three statements will change. [ ] True [X] False

284

Key

B Basic   **M** Medium   **C** Challenge

TEACHER NOTES

Common Core Standards: 8.G.B.7, 8.NS.A.2
Standards for Mathematical Practice: 1, 2, 3, 4, 5, 6, 7
DOK: 3
Materials: None

About the Task

To complete this task, students solve a multi-step problem that involves finding the hypotenuse lengths of right triangles and determining the triangles' areas. The task requires that students specify lengths of the triangles' legs, find their areas, calculate the length of each hypotenuse, and explain how the triangles meet the criteria given.

Getting Started

Read the problem out loud with students and go over the checklist. Have them identify the goal. Have students suggest strategies for designing triangles whose legs and areas will meet the criteria. You might suggest using parts of the sides of the rectangle as the legs of the triangles as one possible approach. **(SMP 1)**

Completing the Task

Students may choose to begin by drawing a diagram or by specifying lengths of each triangle's legs. Knowing the lengths of the legs will enable them to find the area. They must use the Pythagorean Theorem to find the length of the hypotenuse of each triangle. **(SMP 1, 5)**

The diagram is an integral requirement of this task. Encourage students to use the diagram to help them work out the details of the task, including the dimensions and placement of the triangles. **(SMP 4)**

As you circulate, help students stay connected to the problem context by asking them to explain what the numbers, formulas, and diagram mean. **(SMP 2, 3)**

When students are finished, post their diagrams and have a "poster session" in which students explain their work to small groups of classmates. Students should explain how they approached their work, the decisions they made, and how they organized their calculations to ensure that they met the requirements of the task. **(SMP 3, 5, 7)**

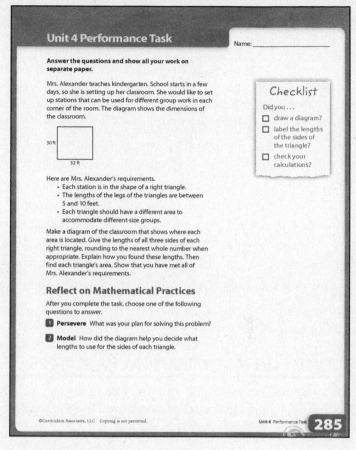

Extension

If students have more time to spend on this problem, you can have them solve this extension:

One of the stations is too large. Mrs. Alexander wants a triangular area that is similar to the largest one that you drew but with sides that are $\frac{3}{4}$ as long. How long is each side of the new triangle and what is its area?

SAMPLE RESPONSE AND RUBRIC

4-Point Solution

I can use the Pythagorean Theorem, $a^2 + b^2 = c^2$, to find the length of the hypotenuse c in each triangle. The area of a triangle is $\frac{1}{2}bh$, or $bh \div 2$, where b is the length of the base and h is the height. In a right triangle, the legs are the base and height. I located the legs on the sides of the rectangle and chose dimensions that would allow for plenty of space in the middle of the room.

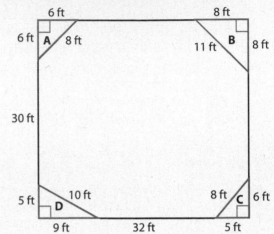

Triangle A: Area = (6)(6) ÷ 2 = 36 ÷ 2, or 18 square feet.
$6^2 + 6^2 = c^2$, so $36 + 36 = c^2$ and $c = \sqrt{72}$, or about 8 feet.

Triangle B: Area = (8)(8) ÷ 2 = 64 ÷ 2, or 32 square feet.
$8^2 + 8^2 = c^2$, so $64 + 64 = c^2$ and $c = \sqrt{128}$, or about 11 feet.

Triangle C: Area = (5)(6) ÷ 2 = 30 ÷ 2, or 15 square feet.
$5^2 + 6^2 = c^2$, so $25 + 36 = c^2$ and $c = \sqrt{61}$, or about 8 feet.

Triangle D: Area = (5)(9) ÷ 2 = 45 ÷ 2, or 22.5 square feet.
$5^2 + 9^2 = c^2$, so $25 + 81 = c^2$ and $c = \sqrt{106}$, or about 10 feet.

The legs of the triangles are all between 5 and 10 feet long and the areas are all different.

REFLECT ON MATHEMATICAL PRACTICES

1. Students should be able to articulate how their plan used the formula for the area of a triangle along with the Pythagorean Theorem and accounted for the requirements of the problem. *(SMP 1)*

2. Look for evidence of visual thinking, such as drawing the triangles to look different or trying to create some kind of scale for the dimensions. *(SMP 4)*

SCORING RUBRIC

4 points   All parts of the problem are complete and correct. Triangles are correctly placed and their legs are between 5 and 10 feet long. Area and hypotenuse calculations and rounding are correct and reflect the diagram. The diagram is properly labeled. Explanations are complete and correct.

3 points   The student has completed all parts of the problem, with one or two errors. Possible errors might include triangle legs outside the specified range, calculation or rounding errors, incomplete explanations, or an incomplete or improperly labeled diagram.

2 points   The student has attempted all parts of the problem, with a number of errors. Triangles may not meet specifications. The diagram contains errors. There are errors in area and/or hypotenuse calculations. Explanations may be incomplete or missing.

1 point   Much of the problem is incomplete, with several errors. Calculations and explanations are incomplete, incorrect, or missing. The diagram and triangle dimensions contain errors and do not reflect the requirements.

SOLUTION TO THE EXTENSION

Possible Solution

The largest triangle has legs that are both 8 feet long, and $\frac{3}{4}$ of 8 feet is 6 feet.

Area = (6)(6) ÷ 2 = 36 ÷ 2, or 18 square feet.

$6^2 + 6^2 = c^2$, so $36 + 36 = c^2$ and $c = \sqrt{72}$, or about 8 feet.

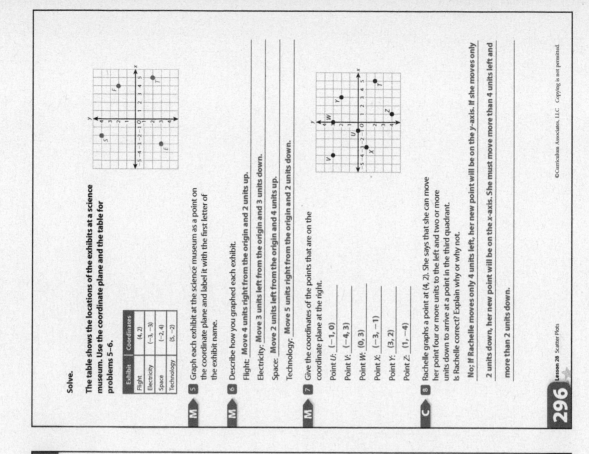

Lesson 28

Scatter Plots

Prerequisite: Graph Points on the Coordinate Plane

Study the example showing how to graph points on the coordinate plane. Then solve problems 1–8.

Example

Graph and label each of the points on the coordinate plane.

$A(5, 3)$ $B(-4, -2)$ $C(-1, 3)$ $D(0, -1)$ $E(4, -4)$

Start from the origin for each point.
For point A: Move 5 units right and 3 units up.
For point B: Move 4 units left and 2 units down.
For point C: Move 1 unit left and 3 units up.
For point D: Move 1 unit down.
For point E: Move 4 units right and 4 units down.

B   **1**   Point B in the example is in which quadrant?
quadrant III

B   **2**   Suppose both coordinates of a point are positive. In which quadrant is the point located?   quadrant I

B   **3**   Without graphing, in which quadrant is $F(-2, 4)$ located? Explain.
quadrant II; The x-coordinate is negative and the y-coordinate is positive.

B   **4**   When a point is on the y-axis, like point D in the example, what do you know about the x-coordinate? What is the y-coordinate when a point is on the x-axis?
The x-coordinate of a point on the y-axis is 0. The y-coordinate of a point on the x-axis is 0.

Vocabulary

origin the point on the coordinate plane where the x-axis and y-axis intersect.

quadrants the four regions of the coordinate plane that are created by the x-axis and the y-axis.

Lesson 28 Scatter Plots **295**

©Curriculum Associates, LLC Copying is not permitted.

Solve.

The table shows the locations of the exhibits at a science museum. Use the coordinate plane and the table for problems 5–6.

Exhibit	Coordinates
Flight	(4, 2)
Electricity	(−3, −3)
Space	(−2, 4)
Technology	(5, −2)

M   **5**   Graph each exhibit at the science museum as a point on the coordinate plane and label it with the first letter of the exhibit name.

M   **6**   Describe how you graphed each exhibit.
Flight: Move 4 units right from the origin and 2 units up.
Electricity: Move 3 units left from the origin and 3 units down.
Space: Move 2 units left from the origin and 4 units up.
Technology: Move 5 units right from the origin and 2 units down.

M   **7**   Give the coordinates of the points that are on the coordinate plane at the right.
Point U: (−1, 0)
Point V: (−4, 3)
Point W: (0, 3)
Point X: (−3, −1)
Point Y: (3, 2)
Point Z: (1, −4)

C   **8**   Rachelle graphs a point at (4, 2). She says that she can move her point four or more units to the left and two or more units down to arrive at a point in the third quadrant. Is Rachelle correct? Explain why or why not.
No; If Rachelle moves only 4 units left, her new point will be on the y-axis. If she moves only 2 units down, her new point will be on the x-axis. She must move more than 4 units left and more than 2 units down.

296   Lesson 28 Scatter Plots

©Curriculum Associates, LLC Copying is not permitted.

Key

B Basic   **M** Medium   **C** Challenge

Page 297

Name: _____

Lesson 28

Identify Positive and Negative Associations

Study the example showing how to analyze a scatter plot. Then solve problems 1–7.

Example

The scatter plot represents data comparing the incomes of a company's employees and the number of years of experience they have. What trends do you notice?

There appears to be a positive association between income and years of experience because there is an upward trend in the data. The income increases as the number of years of experience increases.

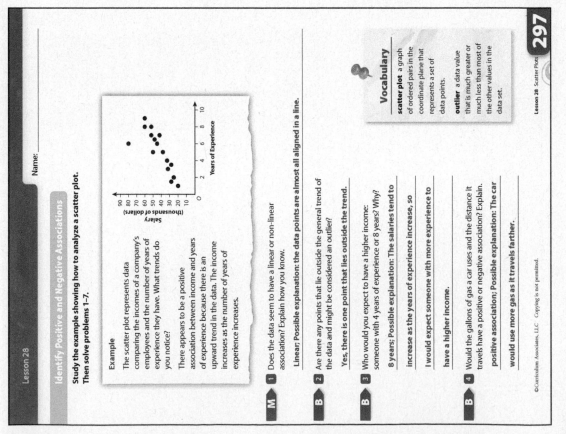

M **1** Does the data seem to have a linear or non-linear association? Explain how you know.

Linear; Possible explanation: the data points are almost all aligned in a line.

B **2** Are there any points that lie outside the general trend of the data and might be considered an outlier?

Yes, there is one point that lies outside the trend.

B **3** Who would you expect to have a higher income: someone with 4 years of experience or 8 years? Why?

8 years; Possible explanation: The salaries tend to increase as the years of experience increase, so I would expect someone with more experience to have a higher income.

B **4** Would the gallons of gas a car uses and the distance it travels have a positive or negative association? Explain.

positive association; Possible explanation: The car would use more gas as it travels farther.

Vocabulary

scatter plot a graph of ordered pairs in the coordinate plane that represents a set of data points.

outlier a data value that is much greater or much less than most of the other values in the data set.

©Curriculum Associates, LLC   Copying is not permitted.

Lesson 28 Scatter Plots **297**

Page 298

Solve.

The scatter plot compares the ages of cars to their values. Use the scatter plot for problems 5–6.

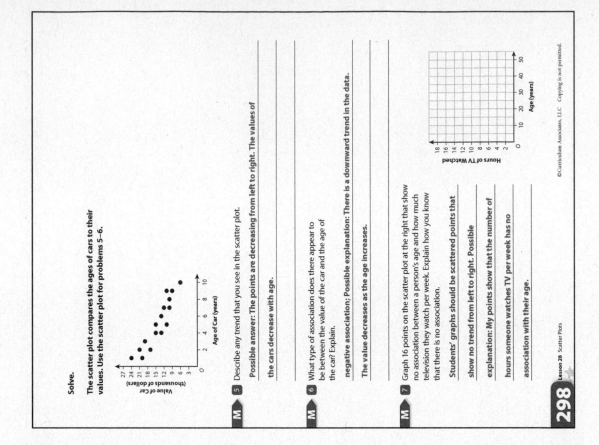

M **5** Describe any trend that you see in the scatter plot.

Possible answer: The points are decreasing from left to right. The values of

the cars decrease with age.

M **6** What type of association does there appear to be between the value of the car and the age of the car? Explain.

negative association; Possible explanation: There is a downward trend in the data.

The value decreases as the age increases.

M **7** Graph 16 points on the scatter plot at the right that show no association between a person's age and how much television they watch per week. Explain how you know that there is no association.

Students' graphs should be scattered points that

show no trend from left to right. Possible

explanation: My points show that the number of

hours someone watches TV per week has no

association with their age.

298 Lesson 28 Scatter Plots

©Curriculum Associates, LLC   Copying is not permitted.

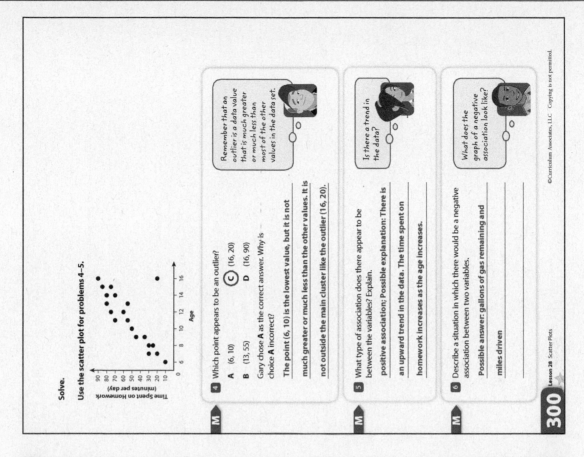

Lesson 28

Scatter Plots

Name: _____

1 What type of association does the scatter plot show?

Is there a trend in the shoe size as the math quiz score increases?

Scatter plot — Shoe Size (vertical axis 1–9) vs. Math Quiz Score (horizontal axis 50–90)

A positive   C none

B negative   D non-linear

2 Use the scatter plot in problem 1 to decide whether each statement is *True* or *False*.

What does each point in the scatter plot represent?

a. There are no outliers. [X] True [ ] False

b. There are 10 data points. [ ] True [X] False

c. The person with the highest score has a size 7 shoe. [X] True [ ] False

d. The scatter plot shows that people with higher test scores have smaller feet. [ ] True [X] False

3 Describe a situation in which there would be a positive association between two variables.

What does the graph of a positive association look like?

Possible answer: distance traveled and time

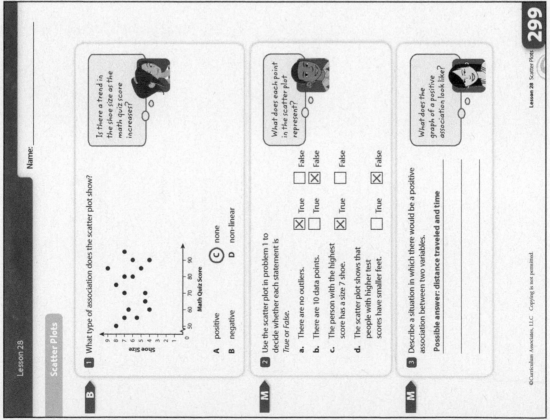

Solve.

Use the scatter plot for problems 4–5.

Scatter plot — Time Spent on Homework (minutes per day) (vertical axis 10–90) vs. Age (horizontal axis 6–16)

4 Which point appears to be an outlier?

Remember that an outlier is a data value that is much greater or much less than most of the other values in the data set.

A (6, 10)   (C) (16, 20)

B (13, 55)   D (16, 90)

Gary chose **A** as the correct answer. Why is choice **A** incorrect?

The point (6, 10) is the lowest value, but it is not much greater or much less than the other values. It is not outside the main cluster like the outlier (16, 20).

5 What type of association does there appear to be between the variables? Explain.

Is there a trend in the data?

positive association; Possible explanation: There is an upward trend in the data. The time spent on homework increases as the age increases.

6 Describe a situation in which there would be a negative association between two variables.

What does the graph of a negative association look like?

Possible answer: gallons of gas remaining and miles driven

Lesson 29

Scatter Plots and Linear Models

Name: _____

Prerequisite: Analyze a Bivariate Data Set

Study the example showing how to analyze a bivariate data set in a scatter plot. Then solve problems 1–6.

Example

The scatter plot represents data comparing the number of Calories burned and the number of minutes of exercise for a group of fitness club members.

There appears to be a positive association between Calories burned and minutes of exercise because there is an upward trend in the data. The number of Calories burned increases as the number of minutes of exercise increases.

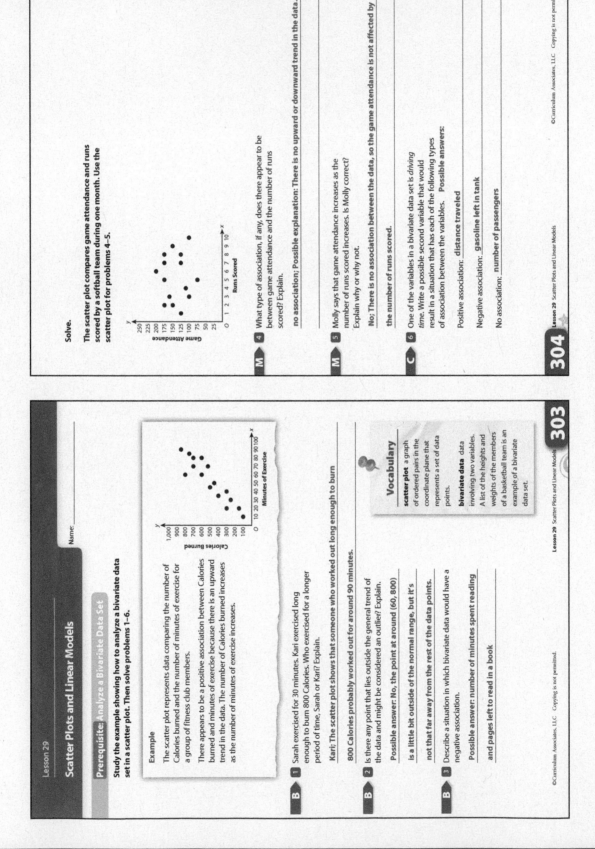

1 Sarah exercised for 30 minutes. Kari exercised long enough to burn 800 Calories. Who exercised for a longer period of time, Sarah or Kari? Explain.

Kari; The scatter plot shows that someone who worked out long enough to burn

800 Calories probably worked out for around 90 minutes.

2 Is there any point that lies outside the general trend of the data and might be considered an outlier? Explain.

Possible answer: No, the point at around (60, 800)

is a little bit outside of the normal range, but it's

not that far away from the rest of the data points.

3 Describe a situation in which bivariate data would have a negative association.

Possible answer: number of minutes spent reading

and pages left to read in a book

Vocabulary

scatter plot a graph of ordered pairs in the coordinate plane that represents a set of data points.

bivariate data data involving two variables. A list of the heights and weights of the members of a basketball team is an example of a bivariate data set.

©Curriculum Associates, LLC   Copying is not permitted.   Lesson 29 Scatter Plots and Linear Models **303**

Solve.

The scatter plot compares game attendance and runs scored by a softball team during one month. Use the scatter plot for problems 4–5.

M 4 What type of association, if any, does there appear to be between game attendance and the number of runs scored? Explain.

no association; Possible explanation: There is no upward or downward trend in the data.

_____

M 5 Molly says that game attendance increases as the number of runs scored increases. Is Molly correct? Explain why or why not.

No; There is no association between the data, so the game attendance is not affected by

the number of runs scored.

C 6 One of the variables in a bivariate data set is *driving time*. Write a possible second variable that would result in a situation that has each of the following types of association between the variables.   Possible answers:

Positive association: **distance traveled**

Negative association: **gasoline left in tank**

No association: **number of passengers**

304 Lesson 29 Scatter Plots and Linear Models   ©Curriculum Associates, LLC   Copying is not permitted.

Key

B Basic   **M** Medium   **C** Challenge

Lesson 29

Evaluate Trend Lines

Study the example problem showing how to evaluate a trend line. Then solve problems 1–5.

Example

The trend lines that Carlota and Julie drew for a data set are shown. Whose line seems to be a better fit for the data?

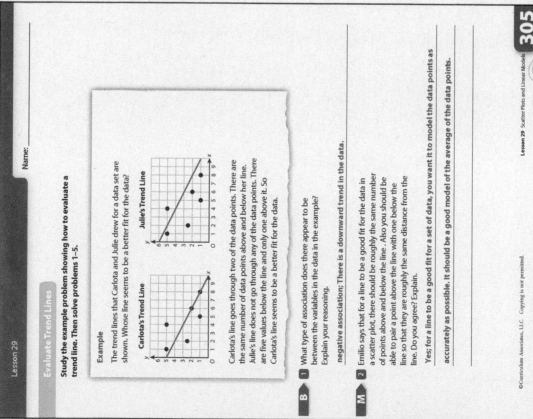

Carlota's line goes through two of the data points. There are the same number of data points above and below her line. Julie's line does not go through any of the data points. There are five values below the line and only one above it. So Carlota's line seems to be a better fit for the data.

B 1 What type of association does there appear to be between the variables in the data in the example? Explain your reasoning.

negative association; There is a downward trend in the data.

M 2 Emilio says that for a line to be a good fit for the data in a scatter plot, there should be roughly the same number of points above and below the line . Also you should be able to pair a point above the line with one below the line so that they are roughly the same distance from the line. Do you agree? Explain.

Yes; for a line to be a good fit for a set of data, you want it to model the data points as accurately as possible. It should be a good model of the average of the data points.

©Curriculum Associates, LLC   Copying is not permitted.

Lesson 29 Scatter Plots and Linear Models **305**

Solve.

M 3 Which line is a better fit for the data in the scatter plot? Explain your choice.

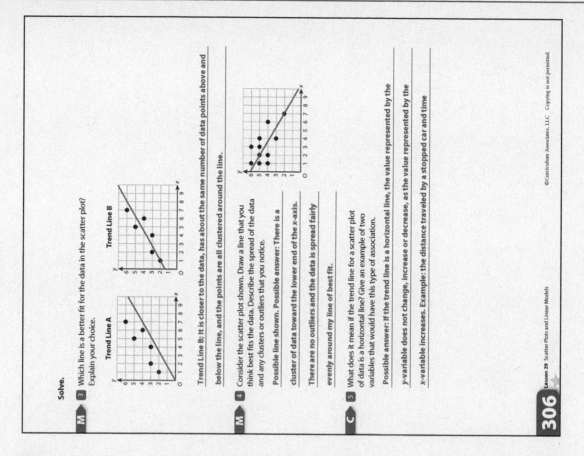

Trend Line B; It is closer to the data, has about the same number of data points above and below the line, and the points are all clustered around the line.

M 4 Consider the scatter plot shown. Draw a line that you think best fits the data. Describe the spread of the data and any clusters or outliers that you notice.

Possible line shown. Possible answer: There is a cluster of data toward the lower end of the x-axis. There are no outliers and the data is spread fairly evenly around my line of best fit.

C 5 What does it mean if the trend line for a scatter plot of data is a horizontal line? Give an example of two variables that would have this type of association.

Possible answer: If the trend line is a horizontal line, the value represented by the y-variable does not change, increase or decrease, as the value represented by the x-variable increases. Example: the distance traveled by a stopped car and time

306 **Lesson 29** Scatter Plots and Linear Models

©Curriculum Associates, LLC   Copying is not permitted.

Practice Lesson 29 Scatter Plots and Linear Models

Lesson 29

Scatter Plots and Linear Models

Solve the problems.

1 Which line is the best fit for the data?

How do you draw a trend line?

A   B   C   D

(B circled)

2 Tell whether each statement is *True* or *False*.

Remember that trend lines show the average values of all of the data.

a. Data points that lie above the trend line should be about the same distance as data points below the line. [X] True [ ] False

b. A line of best fit must go through at least one data point. [ ] True [X] False

c. A trend line is a good fit for the data if all of the data points are fairly close to it. [X] True [ ] False

d. A trend line must go through the origin. [ ] True [X] False

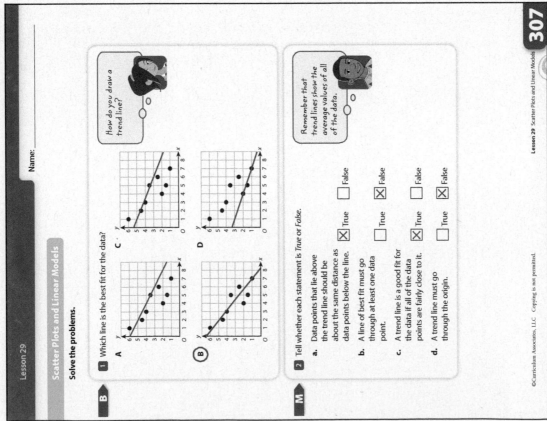

Lesson 29 Scatter Plots and Linear Models **307**

Solve.

3 The scatter plot compares ten daily high temperatures and the number of snow cones sold. Jon drew the following trend line to represent the data.

When drawing a trend line, be careful not to let an outlier pull the trend line in its direction.

Jon's Trend Line

Mary thinks there is a better trend line. What might she be thinking?

Possible answer: Jon included the outlier which does not follow the general upward data trend. A better trend line would ignore the point (91, 10).

4 Draw a trend line for each of the following scatterplots. If the data has no association, write *no association*.

Look for a trend in each of the scatter plots.

Possible trend lines shown.

Scatter Plot E   Scatter Plot F   Scatter Plot G

no association

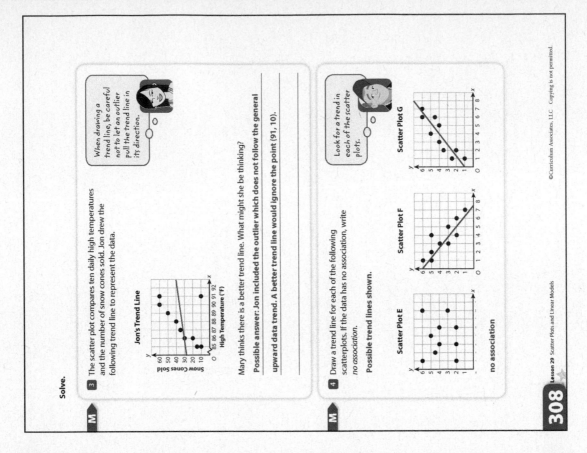

308 Lesson 29 Scatter Plots and Linear Models

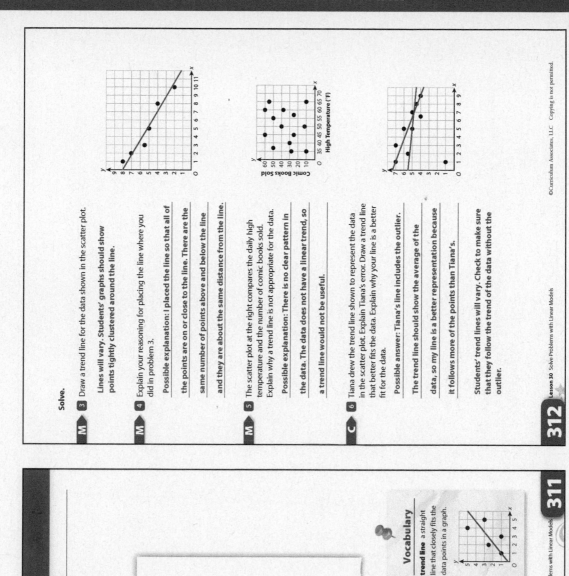

Lesson 30

Solve Problems with Linear Models

Name: _____

Prerequisite: Use Trend Lines to Analyze Scatter Plots

Study the example problem showing how to fit a trend line to data in a scatter plot. Then solve problems 1–6.

Example

The trend lines that Robert and Michael drew for the set of data are shown. Whose line seems to be a better fit for the data?

Robert's Trend Line   Michael's Trend Line

Robert's line goes through one of the data points, and all of the other data points lie above his line. Michael's line goes through two of the data points. There are the same number of data points above and below his line and they appear to be about the same distance away from his line. So Michael's line seems to be a better fit for the data.

B 1 In the example, is there an association between the variables in the data? If so, what type of association?

Yes, there is a positive linear association.

B 2 Sheldon draws a trend line for the data in the example that goes through the points (1, 2) and (8, 6). Is his trend line a better fit for the data than Michael's? Explain.

No, Sheldon's trend line is a fairly good trend line, but Michael's is better because it goes through the center of the data more than Sheldon's line does.

Vocabulary

trend line a straight line that closely fits the data points in a graph.

311

©Curriculum Associates, LLC   Copying is not permitted.

Solve.

M 3 Draw a trend line for the data shown in the scatter plot.

Lines will vary. Students' graphs should show points tightly clustered around the line.

M 4 Explain your reasoning for placing the line where you did in problem 3.

Possible explanation: I placed the line so that all of the points are on or close to the line. There are the same number of points above and below the line and they are about the same distance from the line.

M 5 The scatter plot at the right compares the daily high temperature and the number of comic books sold. Explain why a trend line is not appropriate for the data.

Possible explanation: There is no clear pattern in the data. The data does not have a linear trend, so a trend line would not be useful.

C 6 Tiana drew the trend line shown to represent the data in the scatter plot. Explain Tiana's error. Draw a trend line that better fits the data. Explain why your line is a better fit for the data.

Possible answer: Tiana's line includes the outlier. The trend line should show the average of the data, so my line is a better representation because it follows more of the points than Tiana's.

Students' trend lines will vary. Check to make sure that they follow the trend of the data without the outlier.

312

©Curriculum Associates, LLC   Copying is not permitted.

Key

B Basic   **M** Medium   **C** Challenge

Lesson 30

Use an Equation for the Line of Best Fit

Study the example showing how to write an equation for the line of best fit to analyze data. Then solve problems 1–6.

Example

Devon is practicing for a spelling competition. The scatter plot at the right compares his study time and the number of words he spelled correctly. He drew a line to fit the data. Write an equation for the line.

You can write an equation of the form $y = mx + b$. The points (2, 15) and (3, 21) are on the line. Use the points to find the slope m: $m = \frac{21 - 15}{3 - 2} = \frac{6}{1} = 6$.

Substitute the slope into the equation to get $y = 6x + b$. Use this equation and either one of the points, say (2, 15), to find the y-intercept.

$15 = 6(2) + b$
$3 = b$

The equation of the line is $y = 6x + 3$.

Spelling Competition

B 1 What do the slope and y-intercept mean as they relate to the study time and the number of words spelled correctly?

The slope is 6. It means that as Devon's study time increases by 1 hour, the number of words he spells correctly increases by 6. The y-intercept is 3. It means that if Devon does not study he will spell 3 words correctly.

B 2 Use the graph in the example to estimate how many words Devon will spell correctly if he studies for 4.5 hours. Then use the equation to estimate how many words he will spell correctly if he studies for 4.5 hours. How do the estimates compare?

graph: about 30 words; equation: $y = 6(4.5) + 3 = 30$; Possible answer: The estimates are the same.

Solve.

Use the scatter plot and the information below for problems 3–6.

The scatter plot shows the results of a survey of students about how long it took them to write their most recent research report.

Research Reports

M 3 Write an equation for the line of best fit.

Show your work.

Possible answer: Looking at the graph, the y-intercept appears to be 2. Two points on the line are (0, 2) and (5, 8).

$m = \frac{8 - 2}{5 - 0} = \frac{6}{5} = 1.2$

So the equation is $y = 1.2x + 2$.

Solution: $y = 1.2x + 2$

B 4 What does the slope tell you about how the time to write a research report changes as the number of pages increases?

The slope tells me that each time the number of pages increases by 1, the amount of time to write the report increases by about 1.2 hours.

M 5 Micah's next research report needs to be 9 pages long. Use your equation to find out how long it will take Micah to write the report.

$y = 1.2(9) + 2$; $y = 12.8$; It will take Micah about 12.8 hours to write the report.

C 6 Rita spent 10 hours writing a research report. Use two different methods to estimate the number of pages in her report. Explain your methods.

Possible explanation: Method 1: There are two data points on the graph that have a y-value of 10: (6, 10) and (7, 10). I estimate that Rita's paper was about 6.5 pages long.

Method 2: I substituted 10 for y in my equation and solved for x: $10 = 1.2x + 2$; $x ≈ 6.7$. I estimate her paper was about 6.7 pages long.

Name: _____

Lesson 30

Solve Problems with Linear Models

Solve the problems.

M **1** The table and scatter plot show the total weight for quart containers of strawberries at Marty's Market.

Number of Containers	Weight (lb)
1	1.5
2	3.7
2	4.8
5	5.5
5	7.25
6	8.75
6	9.5
8	13
9	13.5
10	14.25

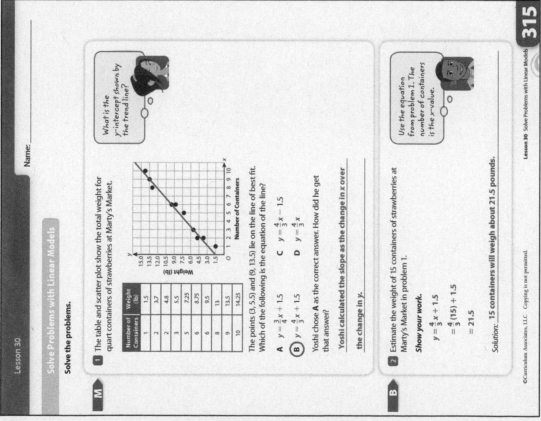

What is the y-intercept shown by the trend line?

The points (3, 5.5) and (9, 13.5) lie on the line of best fit. Which of the following is the equation of the line?

A $y = \frac{3}{4}x + 1.5$

B $y = \frac{4}{3}x + 1.5$ (circled)

C $y = \frac{4}{3}x - 1.5$

D $y = \frac{4}{3}x$

Yoshi chose **A** as the correct answer. How did he get that answer?

Yoshi calculated the slope as the change in x over the change in y.

_____

B **2** Estimate the weight of 15 containers of strawberries at Marty's Market in problem 1.

Use the equation from problem 1. The number of containers is the x-value.

Show your work.

$$y = \frac{4}{3}x + 1.5$$
$$= \frac{4}{3}(15) + 1.5$$
$$= 21.5$$

Solution: 15 containers will weigh about 21.5 pounds.

Solve.

M **3** The scatter plot compares the number of mistakes Koby makes playing a song on his trumpet and the number of hours he practices the song. A line of best fit is shown.

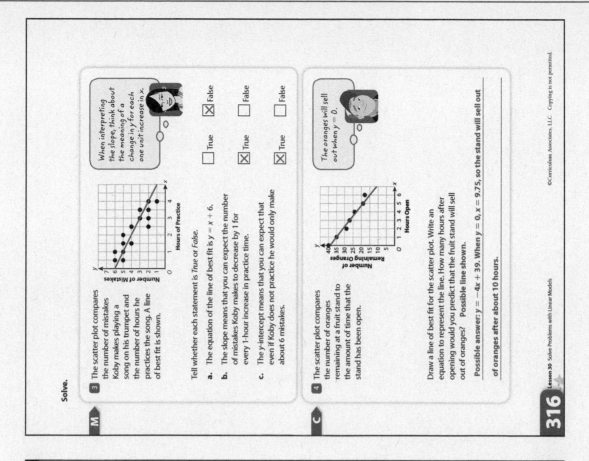

When interpreting the slope, think about the meaning of a change in y for each one unit increase in x.

Tell whether each statement is *True* or *False*.

a. The equation of the line of best fit is $y = x + 6$.   ☐ True   ☒ False

b. The slope means that you can expect the number of mistakes Koby makes to decrease by 1 for every 1-hour increase in practice time.   ☒ True   ☐ False

c. The y-intercept means that you can expect that even if Koby does not practice he would only make about 6 mistakes.   ☒ True   ☐ False

C **4** The scatter plot compares the number of oranges remaining at a fruit stand to the amount of time that the stand has been open.

The oranges will sell out when y = 0.

Draw a line of best fit for the scatter plot. Write an equation to represent the line. How many hours after opening would you predict that the fruit stand will sell out of oranges?   Possible line shown.

Possible answer: $y = -4x + 39$. When $y = 0$, $x = 9.75$, so the stand will sell out of oranges after about 10 hours.

Lesson 31

Categorical Data in Frequency Tables

Name: _____

Prerequisite: Express a Ratio as a Percent

Study the example showing how to express a ratio as a percent. Then solve problems 1–6.

Example

Team A won 18 out of the 25 games they played. Team B won 15 out of the 20 games they played. Which team won a greater percent of the games they played?

You can write ratios that compare the number of games won to the total number of games played by each team:

Team A: $\frac{18}{25}$ Team B: $\frac{15}{20}$

Next, make a table of equivalent ratios.

Team A

Wins	18	36	54	72
Total Games	25	50	75	100

Team B

Wins	15	30	45	60	75
Total Games	20	40	60	80	100

Last, you can use the table to write each ratio as a percent.

Team A: $\frac{18}{25} = \frac{72}{100} = 72\%$ Team B: $\frac{15}{20} = \frac{75}{100} = 75\%$

Compare the percents: 75% > 72%. So Team B won a greater percent of the games they played.

B 1 Explain why the example showed how to find ratios of the number of wins out of 100 games played.

Possible explanation: The problem is about comparing percents, and a percent is a rate "per 100."

M 2 Suppose Team C won 32 out of 50 games. What percent of the games they played did they win? How does this compare to the percents for Teams A and B?

64%; It is less than the percents for Team A and Team B.

Solve.

B 3 Complete the tables and equations to write each ratio as a percent.

a.

8	16	32
25	50	100

$\frac{8}{25} = \frac{\boxed{32}}{100} = \boxed{32}\%$

b.

23	46
50	100

$\frac{23}{50} = \frac{\boxed{46}}{100} = \boxed{46}\%$

M 4 In Walter's class, 14 of the 25 students ride the bus. In Sasha's class, 11 of the 20 students ride the bus. Which class has a greater percent of students who ride the bus? Explain.

Walter's class; Possible explanation:

$\frac{14}{25} = \frac{56}{100} = 56\%$; $\frac{11}{20} = \frac{55}{100} = 55\%$; 56% > 55%.

M 5 At Anthony's school, the ratio of girls to total students is $\frac{260}{500}$. At Theresa's school, the ratio of girls to total students is $\frac{360}{600}$. Explain how you can find percents for each of the ratios. Then tell whose school has a greater percent of girls.

Possible explanation: For $\frac{260}{500}$, I divide both numbers by 5 to get the percent: $\frac{260 \div 5}{500 \div 5} = $. For $\frac{360}{600}$, I divide both numbers by 6 to get the percent: $\frac{360 \div 6}{600 \div 6} = \frac{60}{100} = 60\%$.

$\frac{52}{100} = 52\%$. So Theresa's school has a greater percent of girls.

60% > 52%, so Theresa's school has a greater percent of girls.

C 6 Emma's two methods for writing the ratio $\frac{9}{40}$ as a percent are shown at the right. Use one of Emma's methods to write the ratio $\frac{3}{8}$ as a percent. Compare your percent to 22.5%.

Possible answer: $\frac{3}{8} \times \frac{12.5}{12.5} = \frac{37.5}{100} = 37.5\%$;

37.5% > 22.5%.

Method 1
$\frac{9}{40} = \frac{9}{40} \times \frac{2.5}{2.5} = \frac{22.5}{100} = 22.5\%$

Method 2
$\frac{9}{40} = 9 \div 40 = 0.225 = 22.5\%$

Key

B Basic   **M** Medium   **C** Challenge

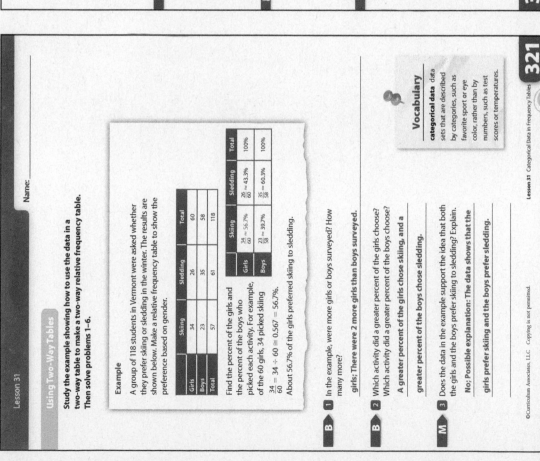

Lesson 31

Name: _____

Using Two-Way Tables

Study the example showing how to use the data in a two-way table to make a two-way relative frequency table. Then solve problems 1–6.

Example

A group of 118 students in Vermont were asked whether they prefer skiing or sledding in the winter. The results are shown below. Make a relative frequency table to show the preference based on gender.

	Skiing	Sledding	Total
Girls	34	26	60
Boys	23	35	58
Total	57	61	118

Find the percent of the girls and the percent of the boys who picked each activity. For example, of the 60 girls, 34 picked skiing.

$\frac{34}{60} = 34 \div 60 \approx 0.567 \approx 56.7\%$

About 56.7% of the girls preferred skiing to sledding.

	Skiing	Sledding	Total
Girls	$\frac{34}{60} \approx 56.7\%$	$\frac{26}{60} \approx 43.3\%$	100%
Boys	$\frac{23}{58} \approx 39.7\%$	$\frac{35}{58} \approx 60.3\%$	100%

Vocabulary

categorical data data sets that are described by categories, such as favorite sport or eye color, rather than by numbers, such as test scores or temperatures.

B **1** In the example, were more girls or boys surveyed? How many more?

girls; There were 2 more girls than boys surveyed.

B **2** Which activity did a greater percent of the girls choose? Which activity did a greater percent of the boys choose?

A greater percent of the girls chose skiing, and a greater percent of the boys chose sledding.

M **3** Does the data in the example support the idea that both the girls and the boys prefer skiing to sledding? Explain.

No; Possible explanation: The data shows that the girls prefer skiing and the boys prefer sledding.

Solve.

Use the information and the table below for problems 4–6.

The two-way table shows the results of a survey that asked students whether they watch animated movies.

	Age (years)				
	11–12	13–14	15–16	17–18	Total
Watch Animated Movies	44	32	39	15	130
Do Not Watch Animated Movies	16	20	36	45	117
Total	60	52	75	60	247

B **4** Complete the relative frequency table to show the percent, to the nearest tenth, of each age group that do and do not watch animated movies.

	Age (years)			
	11–12	13–14	15–16	17–18
Watch Animated Movies	$\frac{44}{60} \approx 73.3\%$	61.5%	52%	25%
Do Not Watch Animated Movies	$\frac{16}{60} \approx 26.7\%$	38.5%	48%	75%
Total	100%	100%	100%	100%

M **5** Use the relative frequency table in problem 4 to determine if there is an association between age and watching animated movies. Explain.

Yes; Possible explanation: A greater percent of the younger students watch animated movies. As students get older, the percent of students who do not watch animated movies increases. It appears there is an association.

C **6** Instead of finding the relative frequencies based on age group, Ahanti found the relative frequencies based on whether they watch animated movies or not. Complete Ahanti's table. Can you draw the same conclusions using Ahanti's table that you drew in problem 5? Explain.

	Age (years)				
	11–12	13–14	15–16	17–18	Total
Watch Animated Movies	$\frac{44}{130} \approx 33.8\%$	24.6%	30%	11.5%	≈ 100%
Do Not Watch Animated Movies	13.7%	17.1%	30.8%	38.5%	≈ 100%

Yes; Possible explanation: Out of the total number of people who watched animated movies, the majority were younger. Out of the total number of people who did not watch animated movies, the majority were older.

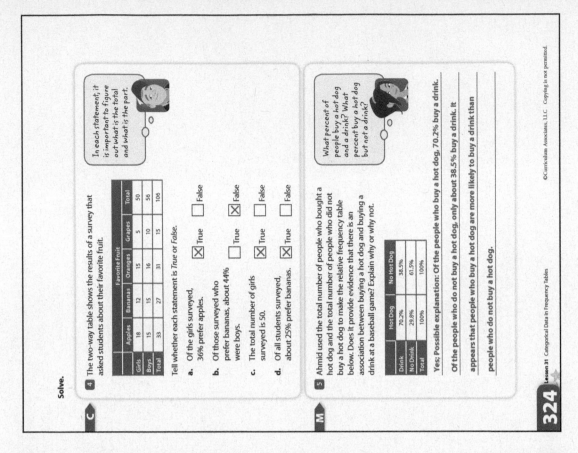

Name: _____

Lesson 31

Categorical Data in Frequency Tables

Solve the problems.

Use the information below and the table for problems 1–3.

The two-way table shows the results of a survey that asked students whether or not they were going to the school play.

	Sixth Graders	Seventh Graders	Eighth Graders	Total
Yes	82	70	64	216
No	76	85	96	257
Total	158	155	160	473

1 How many students said they were planning to go to the play? Circle the letter of the correct answer.

A 158 students   C 257 students

B 216 students   D 473 students

Robin chose **C** as the correct answer. How did she get that answer?

Possible answer: Robin found the sum of the data in the No row instead of the Yes row.

> What is the sum of the data in the Yes row?

2 Complete the relative frequency table to show the percent of *Yes* and *No* responses for each grade level.

	Sixth Graders	Seventh Graders	Eighth Graders
Yes	51.9%	45.2%	40%
No	48.1%	54.8%	60%
Total	100%	100%	100%

> Should you compute the percents for each column or for each row?

3 Do you think that there is an association between grade level and going to the play? Explain.

Yes; Possible explanation: A greater percent of the younger students are going to the play, and a smaller percent of the older students are going to the play. So the lower the grade level, the more likely a student is to go to the play.

> What are the differences in the percent for each grade level?

©Curriculum Associates, LLC   Copying is not permitted.   Lesson 31 Categorical Data in Frequency Tables **323**

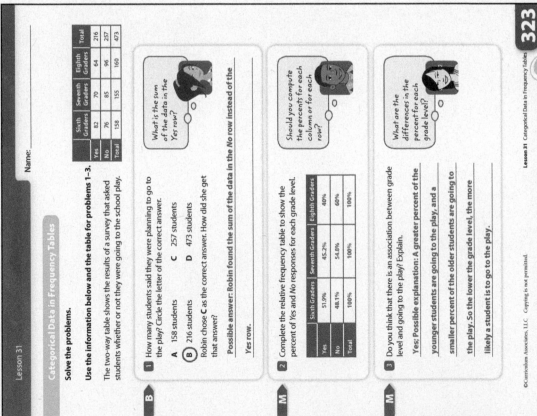

Solve.

> In each statement, it is important to figure out what is the total and what is the part.

4 The two-way table shows the results of a survey that asked students about their favorite fruit.

	Favorite Fruit				
	Apples	Bananas	Oranges	Grapes	Total
Girls	18	12	15	5	50
Boys	15	15	16	10	56
Total	33	27	31	15	106

Tell whether each statement is *True* or *False*.

a. Of the girls surveyed, 36% prefer apples. [X] True [ ] False

b. Of those surveyed who prefer bananas, about 44% were boys. [ ] True [X] False

c. The total number of girls surveyed is 50. [X] True [ ] False

d. Of all students surveyed, about 25% prefer bananas. [X] True [ ] False

5 Ahmid used the total number of people who bought a hot dog and the total number of people who did not buy a hot dog to make the relative frequency table below. Does it provide evidence that there is an association between buying a hot dog and buying a drink at a baseball game? Explain why or why not.

> What percent of people buy a hot dog and a drink? What percent buy a hot dog but not a drink?

	Hot Dog	No Hot Dog
Drink	70.2%	38.5%
No Drink	29.8%	61.5%
Total	100%	100%

Yes; Possible explanation: Of the people who buy a hot dog, 70.2% buy a drink. Of the people who do not buy a hot dog, only about 38.5% buy a drink. It appears that people who buy a hot dog are more likely to buy a drink than people who do not buy a hot dog.

©Curriculum Associates, LLC   Copying is not permitted.   **324** Lesson 31 Categorical Data in Frequency Tables

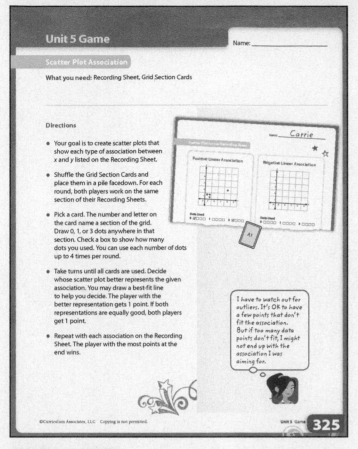

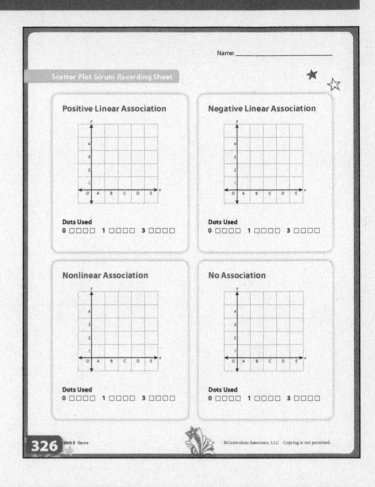

STEP BY STEP

CCSS Focus - 8.SP.A.1, 8.SP.A.2 *Embedded SMPs* - 1, 2, 3, 4, 5, 6, 7 **Objectives** • Construct a scatter plot that models a linear or nonlinear association. • Use best-fit lines to describe scatter plots.	**Materials** For each pair: Recording Sheets (1 for each player) (TR 8), Grid Section Cards (TR 9)

- Your goal is to create scatter plots that show each type of association between *x* and *y* listed on the Recording Sheet.

- Shuffle the Game Cards and place them in a pile facedown. For each round, both players work on the same section of their Recording Sheets.

- Pick a card. The number and letter on the card name a section of the grid. Draw 0, 1, or 3 dots anywhere in that section. Check a box to show how many dots you used. You can use each number of dots up to 4 times per round.

- Take turns until all cards are used. Decide whose scatter plot better represents the given association. You may draw a best-fit line to help you decide.

- The player with the better representation gets 1 point. If both representations are equally good, both players get 1 point.

- Repeat with each association on the Recording Sheet. The player with the most points at the end wins.

- Model one round for students before they play. Have students discuss ways to place dots to create desired associations.

Vary the Game Play the same game, but put no limit on the number of times you can draw 0, 1, or 3 dots.

Extra Support Draw only 1 dot or 0 dots in each square, with no limit on how many times you may use 1 or 0.

Unit 5 Practice

Statistics and Probability

Name: _____

In this unit you learned to:

	Lesson
construct a scatter plot of bivariate data.	28
fit a trend line to a scatter plot.	29
interpret the slope and y-intercept of trend lines in scatter plots to solve problems.	30
display data in a two-way frequency table.	31
interpret a two-way frequency table to identify possible associations between two categorical variables.	31

Use these skills to solve problems 1–4.

B

1 The scatter plot shows the relationship between two variables. Which line appears to be the line of best fit?

A Line a   C Line c

B Line b   D The relationship is not linear.

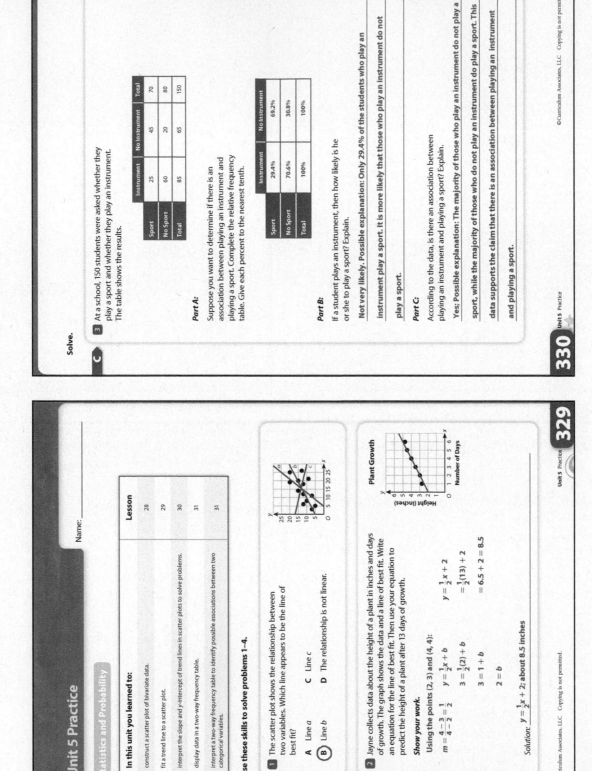

M

2 Jayne collects data about the height of a plant in inches and days of growth. The graph shows the data and a line of best fit. Write an equation for the line of best fit. Then use your equation to predict the height of a plant after 13 days of growth.

Show your work.

Using the points (2, 3) and (4, 4):

$m = \dfrac{4-3}{4-2} = \dfrac{1}{2}$

$y = \dfrac{1}{2}x + b$

$3 = \dfrac{1}{2}(2) + b$

$3 = 1 + b$

$2 = b$

$y = \dfrac{1}{2}x + 2$

$= \dfrac{1}{2}(13) + 2$

$= 6.5 + 2 = 8.5$

Plant Growth

Solution: $y = \dfrac{1}{2}x + 2$; **about 8.5 inches**

Solve.

C

3 At a school, 150 students were asked whether they play a sport and whether they play an instrument. The table shows the results.

	Instrument	No Instrument	Total
Sport	25	45	70
No Sport	60	20	80
Total	85	65	150

Part A:

Suppose you want to determine if there is an association between playing an instrument and playing a sport. Complete the relative frequency table. Give each percent to the nearest tenth.

	Instrument	No Instrument
Sport	29.4%	69.2%
No Sport	70.6%	30.8%
Total	100%	100%

Part B:

If a student plays an instrument, then how likely is he or she to play a sport? Explain.

Not very likely. Possible explanation: Only 29.4% of the students who play an instrument play a sport. It is more likely that those who play an instrument do not play a sport.

Part C:

According to the data, is there an association between playing an instrument and playing a sport? Explain.

Yes; Possible explanation: The majority of those who play an instrument do not play a sport, while the majority of those who do not play an instrument do play a sport. This data supports the claim that there is an association between playing an instrument and playing a sport.

Key

B Basic   **M** Medium   **C** Challenge

TEACHER NOTES

Common Core Standards: 8.SP.A.1, 8.SP.A.2, 8.SP.A.3
Standards for Mathematical Practice: 1, 2, 3, 4, 5, 6, 7
DOK: 3
Materials: None

About the Task

To complete this task, students solve a multi-step problem that involves creating a scatter plot and best-fit line. The task requires them to write an equation for the line and write a report summarizing the relationship of sales and advertising expenditures suggested by the scatter plot.

Getting Started

Read the problem out loud with students and go over the checklist. Have them identify the goal. Discuss the data, and have students note any general patterns they see. (*SMP 1, 7*)

Completing the Task

Students must interpret the table and plot the data. They must use the sales and advertising expense figures for each month as pairs for the data points. The scatter plot will show how these two variables are related. (*SMP 2, 4*)

Next, students will begin analyzing the scatter plot to determine the best-fit line. They need to observe the patterns in the data, consider any outliers and clusters, and describe the association. It will be helpful to try several different lines before deciding which one fits best. (*SMP 3, 5, 7*)

Once the line is drawn, students need to figure out the equation that represents the line. If they extend the line to the y-axis, they can determine the y-intercept. To find the slope, they need to find two points that are easy to read and write a ratio that compares the increase in y-values to the increase in x-values. (*SMP 4, 6, 7*)

The report uses the information that students have gathered from the scatter plot and the best-fit line. They must address the relationship between advertising and sales as shown by the best-fit line. (*SMP 2, 3, 4*)

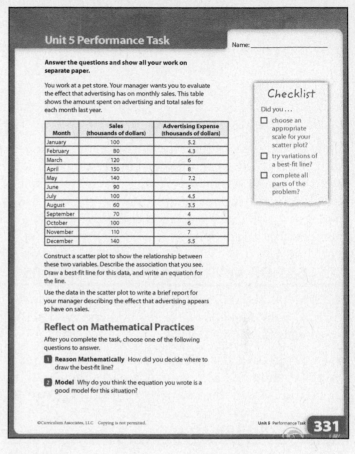

Unit 5 Performance Task

Name: _____

Answer the questions and show all your work on separate paper.

You work at a pet store. Your manager wants you to evaluate the effect that advertising has on monthly sales. This table shows the amount spent on advertising and total sales for each month last year.

Month	Sales (thousands of dollars)	Advertising Expense (thousands of dollars)
January	100	5.2
February	80	4.3
March	120	6
April	150	8
May	140	7.2
June	90	5
July	100	4.5
August	60	3.5
September	70	4
October	100	6
November	110	7
December	140	5.5

Construct a scatter plot to show the relationship between these two variables. Describe the association that you see. Draw a best-fit line for this data, and write an equation for the line.

Use the data in the scatter plot to write a brief report for your manager describing the effect that advertising appears to have on sales.

Reflect on Mathematical Practices

After you complete the task, choose one of the following questions to answer.

1 **Reason Mathematically** How did you decide where to draw the best-fit line?

2 **Model** Why do you think the equation you wrote is a good model for this situation?

Checklist

Did you . . .
- ☐ choose an appropriate scale for your scatter plot?
- ☐ try variations of a best-fit line?
- ☐ complete all parts of the problem?

©Curriculum Associates, LLC   Copying is not permitted.   Unit 5 Performance Task **331**

Extension

If students have more time to spend on this problem, you can have them solve this extension:

The manager is considering increasing the advertising budget. She wants you to find the average monthly advertising expense and then double it to calculate the advertising expense for the upcoming month. Based on this amount and your equation, predict next month's sales. Explain and show all of your work.

SAMPLE RESPONSE AND RUBRIC

4-Point Solution

The graph shows a linear trend. The best-fit line goes through some points and is close to all but one of other points. Using points (5, 90) and (4, 70), the slope is 20. Then $70 = 20(4) + b$, so $b = -10$. The equation of the line is $y = 20x - 10$. As the advertising expense rises, the sales also rise. Here is my report:

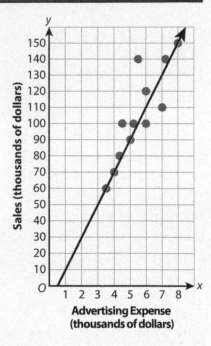

The data shows a positive relationship between money spent on advertising and sales. It looks like when we spend more money on advertising, our sales increase. When we spend less on advertising, we earn less money from sales. I can't say for sure that increasing our advertising will cause us to sell more and make more money. But I do think we should consider increasing our budget for advertising based on this information.

REFLECT ON MATHEMATICAL PRACTICES

1. Students should explain how the data supports their placement of the best-fit line. They should address any outliers and describe how well the best-fit line models the data. (*SMP 2*)

2. This question also addresses the question of fit, but from the perspective of the equation. Students should address how well the slope fits the data and the relationship of the data points to the line. (*SMP 4*)

SCORING RUBRIC

4 points   All parts of the problem are complete and correct. The scatter plot accurately represents the data. The equation represents the line. The best-fit line is a good model of the data. The report is clear and it correctly describes the relationship between the two variables.

3 points   The student has completed all parts of the problem, with one or two errors. Possible errors might include omitting or incorrectly plotting a data point, an error in the slope or y-intercept of the equation, or missing information in the report.

2 points   The student has attempted all parts of the problem, with a number of errors. Points may be missing or are plotted incorrectly. The best-fit line may not fit very well. The equation may not accurately represent the line. The report makes incorrect statements or neglects some important information.

1 point   Much of the problem is incomplete, with several errors. A number of data points are missing or are plotted incorrectly. The best-fit line is missing or does not reflect the data. The equation is incorrect or missing. The report is inaccurate, incomplete, and does not reflect the data.

SOLUTION TO THE EXTENSION

Possible Solution

To find the average monthly advertising expense, add the amounts for each month and divide by 12.

$5.2 + 4.3 + 6 + 8 + 7.2 + 5 + 4.5 + 3.5 + 4 + 6 + 7 + 5.5 = 66.2$ and $66.2 \div 12 \approx 5.5$. Double 5.5 and use an advertising expense of 11 (thousand). Substitute 11 for x in the equation $y = 20x - 10$; $y = 20(11) - 10$, so $y = 210$. If the advertising expense is $11,000, I would predict sales to be $210,000.

Rational and Irrational Numbers— Skills Practice

Name: _____

Form A

Evaluate square roots and cube roots. Simplify each expression.

1 $\sqrt{16} =$ _4_

2 $\sqrt[3]{0} =$ _0_

3 $\sqrt{1} =$ _1_

4 $\sqrt{64} =$ _8_

5 $\sqrt{144} =$ _12_

6 $\sqrt{169} =$ _13_

7 $\sqrt[3]{8} =$ _2_

8 $\sqrt{100} =$ _10_

9 $\sqrt{49} =$ _7_

10 $\sqrt[3]{27} =$ _3_

11 $\sqrt[3]{125} =$ _5_

12 $\sqrt{2,500} =$ _50_

13 $\sqrt[3]{64} =$ _4_

14 $\sqrt{900} =$ _30_

15 $\sqrt{36} =$ _6_

16 $\sqrt{441} =$ _21_

17 $\sqrt[3]{1,000} =$ _10_

18 $\sqrt{25} =$ _5_

Rational and Irrational Numbers— Skills Practice

Name: _____

Form B

Evaluate square roots and cube roots. Simplify each expression.

1 $\sqrt{9} =$ _3_

2 $\sqrt[3]{1} =$ _1_

3 $\sqrt{0} =$ _0_

4 $\sqrt{81} =$ _9_

5 $\sqrt{121} =$ _11_

6 $\sqrt[3]{1,000} =$ _10_

7 $\sqrt[3]{27} =$ _3_

8 $\sqrt{25} =$ _5_

9 $\sqrt{4} =$ _2_

10 $\sqrt{225} =$ _15_

11 $\sqrt{400} =$ _20_

12 $\sqrt[3]{216} =$ _6_

13 $\sqrt{64} =$ _8_

14 $\sqrt{1,600} =$ _40_

15 $\sqrt{625} =$ _25_

16 $\sqrt[3]{8} =$ _2_

17 $\sqrt[3]{512} =$ _8_

18 $\sqrt{961} =$ _31_

Rational and Irrational Numbers— Skills Practice

Name: _____

Form A

Solve equations of the form $x^2 = p$ and $x^3 = p$.

1. $x^2 = 1$; $x =$ ___1, −1___

2. $x^2 = 49$; $x =$ ___7, −7___

3. $x^3 = 8$; $x =$ ___2___

4. $x^2 = 100$; $x =$ ___10, −10___

5. $x^2 = \frac{4}{9}$; $x =$ ___$\frac{2}{3}, -\frac{2}{3}$___

6. $x^2 = 144$; $x =$ ___12, −12___

7. $x^3 = \frac{1}{8}$; $x =$ ___$\frac{1}{2}$___

8. $x^2 = \frac{81}{100}$; $x =$ ___$\frac{9}{10}, -\frac{9}{10}$___

9. $x^2 = 16$; $x =$ ___4, −4___

10. $x^3 = 64$; $x =$ ___4___

11. $x^2 = 900$; $x =$ ___30, −30___

12. $x^2 = \frac{1}{49}$; $x =$ ___$\frac{1}{7}, -\frac{1}{7}$___

13. $x^3 = 125$; $x =$ ___5___

14. $x^2 = \frac{36}{49}$; $x =$ ___$\frac{6}{7}, -\frac{6}{7}$___

15. $x^2 = \frac{9}{25}$; $x =$ ___$\frac{3}{5}, -\frac{3}{5}$___

16. $x^2 = 2{,}500$; $x =$ ___50, −50___

17. $x^3 = \frac{1}{27}$; $x =$ ___$\frac{1}{3}$___

18. $x^2 = 36$; $x =$ ___6, −6___

Rational and Irrational Numbers— Skills Practice

Name: _____

Form B

Solve equations of the form $x^2 = p$ and $x^3 = p$.

1. $x^2 = 121$; $x =$ ___11, −11___

2. $x^3 = 1{,}000$; $x =$ ___10___

3. $x^2 = \frac{25}{49}$; $x =$ ___$\frac{5}{7}, -\frac{5}{7}$___

4. $x^2 = 25$; $x =$ ___5, −5___

5. $x^2 = \frac{9}{64}$; $x =$ ___$\frac{3}{8}, -\frac{3}{8}$___

6. $x^3 = 1$; $x =$ ___1___

7. $x^2 = 9$; $x =$ ___3, −3___

8. $x^2 = \frac{27}{64}$; $x =$ ___$\frac{3}{4}$___

9. $x^2 = 0$; $x =$ ___0___

10. $x^2 = \frac{121}{144}$; $x =$ ___$\frac{11}{12}, -\frac{11}{12}$___

11. $x^2 = 1{,}600$; $x =$ ___40, −40___

12. $x^3 = \frac{64}{125}$; $x =$ ___$\frac{4}{5}$___

13. $x^2 = 441$; $x =$ ___21, −21___

14. $x^2 = \frac{49}{81}$; $x =$ ___$\frac{7}{9}, -\frac{7}{9}$___

15. $x^2 = 225$; $x =$ ___15, −15___

16. $x^3 = 216$; $x =$ ___6___

17. $x^2 = 625$; $x =$ ___25, −25___

18. $x^2 = \frac{1}{9}$; $x =$ ___$\frac{1}{3}, -\frac{1}{3}$___

Rational and Irrational Numbers— Skills Practice

Name: _____

Form A

Approximate irrational numbers.

Write the two consecutive whole numbers that the given number is between.

1. $\sqrt{5}$ ___ 2 and 3
2. $\sqrt{10}$ ___ 3 and 4
3. $\sqrt{8}$ ___ 2 and 3
4. $\sqrt{28}$ ___ 5 and 6
5. $\sqrt{23}$ ___ 4 and 5
6. $\sqrt{84}$ ___ 9 and 10
7. $\sqrt{45}$ ___ 6 and 7
8. $\sqrt{29}$ ___ 5 and 6
9. $\sqrt{70}$ ___ 8 and 9

Approximate to the nearest whole number.

10. $\sqrt{5} \approx$ 2
11. $\sqrt{10} \approx$ 3
12. $\sqrt{8} \approx$ 3
13. $\sqrt{28} \approx$ 5
14. $\sqrt{23} \approx$ 5
15. $\sqrt{84} \approx$ 9
16. $\sqrt{45} \approx$ 7
17. $\sqrt{29} \approx$ 5
18. $\sqrt{70} \approx$ 8

Approximate to the nearest tenth.

19. $\sqrt{5} \approx$ 2.2
20. $\sqrt{10} \approx$ 3.2
21. $\sqrt{8} \approx$ 2.8
22. $\sqrt{28} \approx$ 5.3
23. $\sqrt{23} \approx$ 4.8
24. $\sqrt{84} \approx$ 9.2

Approximate to the nearest hundredth.

25. $\sqrt{5} \approx$ 2.24
26. $\sqrt{10} \approx$ 3.16
27. $\sqrt{8} \approx$ 2.83

Rational and Irrational Numbers— Skills Practice

Name: _____

Form B

Approximate irrational numbers.

Write the two consecutive whole numbers that the given number is between.

1. $\sqrt{2}$ ___ 1 and 2
2. $\sqrt{3}$ ___ 1 and 2
3. $\sqrt{7}$ ___ 2 and 3
4. $\sqrt{14}$ ___ 3 and 4
5. $\sqrt{55}$ ___ 7 and 8
6. $\sqrt{39}$ ___ 6 and 7
7. $\sqrt{99}$ ___ 9 and 10
8. $\sqrt{39}$ ___ 6 and 7
9. $\sqrt{24}$ ___ 4 and 5

Approximate to the nearest whole number.

10. $\sqrt{2} \approx$ 1
11. $\sqrt{3} \approx$ 2
12. $\sqrt{7} \approx$ 3
13. $\sqrt{14} \approx$ 4
14. $\sqrt{55} \approx$ 7
15. $\sqrt{39} \approx$ 6
16. $\sqrt{99} \approx$ 10
17. $\sqrt{39} \approx$ 6
18. $\sqrt{24} \approx$ 5

Approximate to the nearest tenth.

19. $\sqrt{2} \approx$ 1.4
20. $\sqrt{3} \approx$ 1.7
21. $\sqrt{7} \approx$ 2.6
22. $\sqrt{14} \approx$ 3.7
23. $\sqrt{55} \approx$ 7.4
24. $\sqrt{39} \approx$ 6.2

Approximate to the nearest hundredth.

25. $\sqrt{2} \approx$ 1.41
26. $\sqrt{3} \approx$ 1.73
27. $\sqrt{7} \approx$ 2.65

Rational and Irrational Numbers— Skills Practice

Name: _____   Form A

Approximate expressions with irrational numbers.

Give the two consecutive whole numbers that the given expression is between.

1. $2\sqrt{3}$ ___ 3 and 4
2. 2π ___ 6 and 7
3. $\sqrt{35} + 2$ ___ 7 and 8
4. $\frac{4}{3}\pi$ ___ 4 and 5
5. $4\sqrt{5}$ ___ 8 and 9
6. $\sqrt{48} - 2$ ___ 4 and 5

Approximate the value of the expression to the nearest whole number.

7. $\sqrt{5} + \sqrt{2} \approx$ ___ 4
8. $\pi^2 \approx$ ___ 10
9. $\frac{\sqrt{82}}{4} \approx$ ___ 2
10. $3\pi \approx$ ___ 9
11. $(\sqrt{2})^3 \approx$ ___ 3
12. $3\sqrt{24} \approx$ ___ 15

Approximate the value of the expression to the nearest tenth.

13. $\sqrt{3} - \sqrt{2} \approx$ ___ 0.3
14. $\frac{\sqrt{2}}{2} \approx$ ___ 0.7
15. $\frac{1}{\sqrt{3}} \approx$ ___ 0.6
16. $\frac{\pi}{2} \approx$ ___ 1.6
17. $\frac{2}{\sqrt{2}} \approx$ ___ 1.4
18. $5 - \pi \approx$ ___ 1.9

Rational and Irrational Numbers— Skills Practice

Name: _____   Form B

Approximate expressions with irrational numbers.

Give the two consecutive whole numbers that the given expression is between.

1. $2\sqrt{2}$ ___ 2 and 3
2. 4π ___ 12 and 13
3. $\sqrt{35} - 2$ ___ 3 and 4
4. $\frac{2}{3}\pi$ ___ 2 and 3
5. $4\sqrt{8}$ ___ 11 and 12
6. $\sqrt{48} + 2$ ___ 8 and 9

Approximate the value of the expression to the nearest whole number.

7. $\sqrt{3} + \sqrt{2} \approx$ ___ 3
8. $\pi^3 \approx$ ___ 31
9. $\frac{\sqrt{65}}{3} \approx$ ___ 3
10. $\frac{\pi}{3} \approx$ ___ 1
11. $(\sqrt{3})^3 \approx$ ___ 5
12. $4\sqrt{26} \approx$ ___ 20

Approximate the value of the expression to the nearest tenth.

13. $\sqrt{5} - \sqrt{3} \approx$ ___ 0.5
14. $\frac{\sqrt{3}}{2} \approx$ ___ 0.9
15. $\frac{1}{\sqrt{2}} \approx$ ___ 0.7
16. $5\pi \approx$ ___ 15.7
17. $\frac{2}{\sqrt{3}} \approx$ ___ 1.2
18. $6 - \pi \approx$ ___ 2.9

Rational and Irrational Numbers— Skills Practice

Form A

Name: _____

Rewrite a repeating decimal as a fraction.

1. $0.\overline{6} = $ ____ $\frac{2}{3}$ or $\frac{6}{9}$

2. $0.\overline{63} = $ ____ $\frac{7}{11}$ or $\frac{63}{99}$

3. $0.\overline{4} = $ ____ $\frac{4}{9}$

4. $0.\overline{83} = $ ____ $\frac{5}{6}$ or $\frac{75}{90}$

5. $0.1\overline{3} = $ ____ $\frac{2}{15}$ or $\frac{12}{90}$

6. $0.2\overline{7} = $ ____ $\frac{5}{18}$ or $\frac{25}{90}$

7. $0.6\overline{1} = $ ____ $\frac{11}{18}$ or $\frac{55}{90}$

8. $0.0\overline{6} = $ ____ $\frac{1}{15}$ or $\frac{6}{90}$

9. $0.9\overline{4} = $ ____ $\frac{17}{18}$ or $\frac{85}{90}$

10. $0.\overline{36} = $ ____ $\frac{4}{11}$ or $\frac{36}{99}$

11. $0.\overline{7} = $ ____ $\frac{7}{9}$

12. $0.\overline{54} = $ ____ $\frac{6}{11}$ or $\frac{54}{99}$

13. $0.41\overline{6} = $ ____ $\frac{5}{12}$ or $\frac{375}{900}$

14. $0.8\overline{6} = $ ____ $\frac{13}{15}$ or $\frac{78}{90}$

15. $0.08\overline{3} = $ ____ $\frac{1}{12}$ or $\frac{75}{900}$

16. $0.\overline{27} = $ ____ $\frac{3}{11}$ or $\frac{27}{99}$

17. $0.\overline{1} = $ ____ $\frac{1}{9}$

18. $0.\overline{90} = $ ____ $\frac{10}{11}$ or $\frac{90}{99}$

Rational and Irrational Numbers— Skills Practice

Form B

Name: _____

Rewrite a repeating decimal as a fraction.

1. $0.\overline{3} = $ ____ $\frac{1}{3}$ or $\frac{3}{9}$

2. $0.\overline{81} = $ ____ $\frac{9}{11}$ or $\frac{81}{99}$

3. $0.\overline{5} = $ ____ $\frac{5}{9}$

4. $0.1\overline{6} = $ ____ $\frac{1}{6}$ or $\frac{15}{90}$

5. $0.7\overline{3} = $ ____ $\frac{11}{15}$ or $\frac{66}{90}$

6. $0.3\overline{8} = $ ____ $\frac{7}{18}$ or $\frac{35}{90}$

7. $0.7\overline{2} = $ ____ $\frac{13}{18}$ or $\frac{65}{90}$

8. $0.2\overline{6} = $ ____ $\frac{4}{15}$ or $\frac{24}{90}$

9. $0.5\overline{3} = $ ____ $\frac{8}{15}$ or $\frac{48}{90}$

10. $0.\overline{18} = $ ____ $\frac{2}{11}$ or $\frac{18}{99}$

11. $0.\overline{2} = $ ____ $\frac{2}{9}$

12. $0.\overline{45} = $ ____ $\frac{5}{11}$ or $\frac{45}{99}$

13. $0.58\overline{3} = $ ____ $\frac{7}{12}$ or $\frac{525}{900}$

14. $0.0\overline{5} = $ ____ $\frac{1}{18}$ or $\frac{5}{90}$

15. $0.91\overline{6} = $ ____ $\frac{11}{12}$ or $\frac{825}{900}$

16. $0.\overline{09} = $ ____ $\frac{1}{11}$ or $\frac{9}{99}$

17. $0.\overline{8} = $ ____ $\frac{8}{9}$

18. $0.\overline{72} = $ ____ $\frac{8}{11}$ or $\frac{72}{99}$

Integer Exponents—Skills Practice

Name: _____ Form A

Simplify expressions with exponents.

Rewrite each expression using a single nonnegative exponent.

1 $y^5 \cdot y^7 =$ ___ y^{12}

2 $(m^3)^4 =$ ___ m^{12}

3 $n^6 \cdot n^5 =$ ___ n^{11}

4 $\dfrac{m^3}{m^9} =$ ___ $\dfrac{1}{m^6}$

5 $(n^9)^3 =$ ___ n^{27}

6 $\dfrac{w^8}{w^4} =$ ___ w^4

Evaluate each expression.

7 $4^2 \cdot 4^1 =$ ___ 64

8 $2^3 \cdot 5^3 =$ ___ 1,000

9 $(2^3)^4 =$ ___ 4,096

10 $(5^2)^3 =$ ___ 15,625

11 $6^2 \cdot 7^2 =$ ___ 1,764

12 $\dfrac{3^3}{3^5} =$ ___ $\dfrac{1}{9}$

13 $3^3 \cdot 3^3 =$ ___ 243

14 $\dfrac{8^3}{2^3} =$ ___ 64

15 $\dfrac{2^6}{2^3} =$ ___ 8

16 $2^4 \cdot 3^4 =$ ___ 1,296

17 $\dfrac{4^2}{2^2} =$ ___ 4

18 $\dfrac{5^3}{5^2} =$ ___ 5

Rational and Irrational Numbers—Repeated Reasoning

Name: _____

Find patterns in repeating decimals. Rewrite each decimal as a fraction.

Set A

1 $0.\overline{3} =$ ___ $\dfrac{3}{9}$ or $\dfrac{1}{3}$

2 $0.0\overline{3} =$ ___ $\dfrac{3}{90}$ or $\dfrac{1}{30}$

3 $0.00\overline{3} =$ ___ $\dfrac{3}{900}$ or $\dfrac{1}{300}$

4 $0.\overline{4} =$ ___ $\dfrac{4}{9}$

5 $0.0\overline{4} =$ ___ $\dfrac{4}{90}$ or $\dfrac{2}{45}$

6 $0.00\overline{4} =$ ___ $\dfrac{4}{900}$ or $\dfrac{1}{225}$

7 $0.\overline{5} =$ ___ $\dfrac{5}{9}$

8 $0.0\overline{5} =$ ___ $\dfrac{5}{90}$ or $\dfrac{1}{18}$

9 $0.00\overline{5} =$ ___ $\dfrac{5}{900}$ or $\dfrac{1}{180}$

Set B

1 $0.\overline{3} =$ ___ $\dfrac{3}{9}$ or $\dfrac{1}{3}$

2 $0.\overline{03} =$ ___ $\dfrac{3}{99}$ or $\dfrac{1}{33}$

3 $0.\overline{003} =$ ___ $\dfrac{3}{999}$ or $\dfrac{1}{333}$

4 $0.\overline{4} =$ ___ $\dfrac{4}{9}$

5 $0.\overline{04} =$ ___ $\dfrac{4}{99}$

6 $0.\overline{004} =$ ___ $\dfrac{4}{999}$

7 $0.\overline{5} =$ ___ $\dfrac{5}{9}$

8 $0.\overline{05} =$ ___ $\dfrac{5}{99}$

9 $0.\overline{005} =$ ___ $\dfrac{5}{999}$

Describe a pattern you see in one of the sets of problems above.

Answers will vary. Sample answer: In Set A, as the digit that repeats moves one decimal place to the right, the fraction is $\dfrac{1}{10}$ of the fraction in the previous problem.

_____

_____

Integer Exponents—Skills Practice

Name: _____

Form A

Simplify more expressions with exponents.

Rewrite each expression using a single exponent.

1. $y^{-3} \cdot y^{-7} = \underline{\hspace{1.5cm}}\quad y^{-10} \text{ or } \dfrac{1}{y^{10}}$

2. $(m^{-2})^3 = \underline{\hspace{1.5cm}}\quad m^{-6} \text{ or } \dfrac{1}{m^6}$

3. $n^{-2} \cdot n^8 = \underline{\hspace{1.5cm}}\quad n^6$

4. $\dfrac{m^{-10}}{m^{-5}} = \underline{\hspace{1.5cm}}\quad m^{-5} \text{ or } \dfrac{1}{m^5}$

5. $(n^{-4})^{-4} = \underline{\hspace{1.5cm}}\quad n^{16}$

6. $\dfrac{w^6}{w^{-5}} = \underline{\hspace{1.5cm}}\quad w^{11}$

Evaluate each expression.

7. $2^{-4} \cdot 2^{-2} = \underline{\hspace{1.5cm}}\quad \dfrac{1}{64}$

8. $0^4 \cdot 2^7 = \underline{\hspace{1.5cm}}\quad 0$

9. $(2^{-3})^{-3} = \underline{\hspace{1.5cm}}\quad 512$

10. $(3^{-4})^0 = \underline{\hspace{1.5cm}}\quad 1$

11. $(-2)^{-2} \cdot (-2)^{-2} = \underline{\hspace{1.5cm}}\quad \dfrac{1}{16}$

12. $\dfrac{(-6)^3}{(-6)^2} = \underline{\hspace{1.5cm}}\quad -6$

13. $3^0 \cdot 3^{-4} = \underline{\hspace{1.5cm}}\quad \dfrac{1}{81}$

14. $\dfrac{7^{-2}}{3^{-2}} = \underline{\hspace{1.5cm}}\quad \dfrac{9}{49}$

15. $\dfrac{4^{-2}}{4^{-5}} = \underline{\hspace{1.5cm}}\quad 64$

16. $(-5)^4 \cdot (-5)^{-3} = \underline{\hspace{1.5cm}}\quad -5$

17. $\dfrac{(-8)^{10}}{(-7)^0} = \underline{\hspace{1.5cm}}\quad 1$

18. $\dfrac{(-4)^3}{(-6)^3} = \underline{\hspace{1.5cm}}\quad \dfrac{8}{27}$

Fluency Practice **349**

Integer Exponents—Skills Practice

Name: _____

Form B

Simplify expressions with exponents.

Rewrite each expression using a single nonnegative exponent.

1. $y^4 \cdot y^{11} = \underline{\hspace{1.5cm}}\quad y^{15}$

2. $(m^2)^7 = \underline{\hspace{1.5cm}}\quad m^{14}$

3. $n^8 \cdot n^5 = \underline{\hspace{1.5cm}}\quad n^{13}$

4. $\dfrac{m^2}{m^6} = \underline{\hspace{1.5cm}}\quad \dfrac{1}{m^4}$

5. $(n^8)^7 = \underline{\hspace{1.5cm}}\quad n^{56}$

6. $\dfrac{w^{10}}{w^5} = \underline{\hspace{1.5cm}}\quad w^5$

Evaluate each expression.

7. $5^2 \cdot 5^4 = \underline{\hspace{1.5cm}}\quad 15,625$

8. $2^1 \cdot 6^1 = \underline{\hspace{1.5cm}}\quad 12$

9. $(2^2)^5 = \underline{\hspace{1.5cm}}\quad 1,024$

10. $(3^2)^2 = \underline{\hspace{1.5cm}}\quad 81$

11. $4^2 \cdot 2^2 = \underline{\hspace{1.5cm}}\quad 64$

12. $\dfrac{3^6}{3^6} = \underline{\hspace{1.5cm}}\quad 1$

13. $2^3 \cdot 2^3 = \underline{\hspace{1.5cm}}\quad 64$

14. $\dfrac{10^3}{2^3} = \underline{\hspace{1.5cm}}\quad 125$

15. $\dfrac{2^5}{2^3} = \underline{\hspace{1.5cm}}\quad 4$

16. $4^3 \cdot 2^3 = \underline{\hspace{1.5cm}}\quad 512$

17. $\dfrac{4^2}{8^2} = \underline{\hspace{1.5cm}}\quad \dfrac{1}{4}$

18. $\dfrac{4^3}{4^2} = \underline{\hspace{1.5cm}}\quad 4$

348 Fluency Practice

Integer Exponents—Skills Practice

Name: _____ Form B

Simplify more expressions with exponents.

Rewrite each expression using a single exponent.

1. $y^{-4} \cdot y^{-5} =$ _____ y^{-9} or $\frac{1}{y^9}$

2. $(m^{-3})^5 =$ _____ m^{-15} or $\frac{1}{m^{15}}$

3. $n^{-3} \cdot n^6 =$ _____ n^3

4. $\frac{m^{-12}}{m^{-6}} =$ _____ m^{-6} or $\frac{1}{m^6}$

5. $(n^{-2})^{-2} =$ _____ n^4

6. $\frac{w^6}{w^{-7}} =$ _____ w^{12}

Evaluate each expression.

7. $2^{-3} \cdot 2^{-2} =$ _____ $\frac{1}{32}$

8. $(-6)^4 \cdot (-6)^{-3} =$ _____ -6

9. $(4 \cdot 6)^0 =$ _____ 1

10. $(3^{-2})^{-2} =$ _____ 81

11. $(-3)^{-2} \cdot (-4)^{-2} =$ _____ $\frac{1}{144}$

12. $\frac{(-5)^4}{(-5)^3} =$ _____ -5

13. $4^0 \cdot 4^{-3} =$ _____ $\frac{1}{64}$

14. $\frac{8^{-2}}{3^{-2}} =$ _____ $\frac{9}{64}$

15. $\frac{3^{-2}}{3^{-5}} =$ _____ 27

16. $0^6 \cdot 2^6 =$ _____ 0

17. $\frac{(-6)^3}{(3)^3} =$ _____ -8

18. $\frac{(-6)^0}{(-5)^0} =$ _____ 1

Integer Exponents—Repeated Reasoning

Name: _____

Find patterns in products of powers with the same base.

Expand each factor. Write the product in expanded form. Then write the product using an exponent. The first one is done for you.

1. $2^3 \times 2^2 = (2 \times 2 \times 2) \times (2 \times 2) = 2 \times 2 \times 2 \times 2 \times 2 = 2^5$

2. $3^3 \times 3^2 = (3 \times 3 \times 3) \times (3 \times 3) = 3 \times 3 \times 3 \times 3 \times 3 = 3^5$

3. $4^3 \times 4^2 = (4 \times 4 \times 4) \times (4 \times 4) = 4 \times 4 \times 4 \times 4 \times 4 = 4^5$

4. $5^3 \times 5^2 = (5 \times 5 \times 5) \times (5 \times 5) = 5 \times 5 \times 5 \times 5 \times 5 = 5^5$

5. $6^3 \times 6^2 = (6 \times 6 \times 6) \times (6 \times 6) = 6 \times 6 \times 6 \times 6 \times 6 = 6^5$

6. $7^3 \times 7^2 = (7 \times 7 \times 7) \times (7 \times 7) = 7 \times 7 \times 7 \times 7 \times 7 = 7^5$

7. $8^3 \times 8^2 = (8 \times 8 \times 8) \times (8 \times 8) = 8 \times 8 \times 8 \times 8 \times 8 = 8^5$

8. $9^3 \times 9^2 = (9 \times 9 \times 9) \times (9 \times 9) = 9 \times 9 \times 9 \times 9 \times 9 = 9^5$

9. $n^3 \times n^2 = (n \times n \times n) \times (n \times n) = n \times n \times n \times n \times n = n^5$

10. $4.2^3 \times 4.2^2 = (4.2 \times 4.2 \times 4.2) \times (4.2 \times 4.2) = 4.2 \times 4.2 \times 4.2 \times 4.2 \times 4.2 = 4.2^5$

Describe a pattern or relationship you see between the problems and the answers. Explain what the pattern means or why it happens.

Answers will vary. Sample answer: When the factors have the same base, the exponent of the product is equal to the sum of the exponents of the factors. Three factors of n multiplied by two factors of n is a total of five factors of n.

Integer Exponents—Repeated Reasoning   Name: _____

Find more patterns in products of powers with the same base. Write each expression as a power of a single number.

Set A

1. $3^2 \times 3^1 =$ _____ 3^3
2. $3^{-2} \times 3^{-1} =$ _____ 3^{-3}
3. $3^2 \times 3^2 =$ _____ 3^4
4. $3^{-2} \times 3^{-2} =$ _____ 3^{-4}
5. $3^2 \times 3^3 =$ _____ 3^5
6. $3^{-2} \times 3^{-3} =$ _____ 3^{-5}
7. $3^2 \times 3^4 =$ _____ 3^6
8. $3^{-2} \times 3^{-4} =$ _____ 3^{-6}
9. $3^2 \times 3^5 =$ _____ 3^7
10. $3^{-2} \times 3^{-5} =$ _____ 3^{-7}
11. $3^2 \times 3^6 =$ _____ 3^8
12. $3^{-2} \times 3^{-6} =$ _____ 3^{-8}

Set B

1. $3^{-2} \times 3^1 =$ _____ 3^{-1}
2. $3^{-2} \times 3^2 =$ _____ 3^0
3. $3^{-2} \times 3^3 =$ _____ 3^1
4. $3^2 \times 3^{-1} =$ _____ 3^1
5. $3^2 \times 3^{-2} =$ _____ 3^0
6. $3^2 \times 3^{-3} =$ _____ 3^{-1}

Describe a pattern you see in one of the sets of problems above.

Answers will vary. Students may notice in Set A that as the exponent of one factor increases by 1 the exponent of the answer increases by 1.

Integer Exponents—Repeated Reasoning   Name: _____

Find patterns in quotients of powers with the same base.

Expand each term in the quotient of powers. Write the quotient in expanded form. Then write the quotient using an exponent. The first one has been done for you.

1. $2^5 \div 2^3 = (2 \cdot 2 \cdot 2 \cdot 2 \cdot 2) \div (2 \cdot 2 \cdot 2) = 2 \cdot 2 = 2^2$
2. $3^5 \div 3^3 = (3 \cdot 3 \cdot 3 \cdot 3 \cdot 3) \div (3 \cdot 3 \cdot 3) = 3 \cdot 3 = 3^2$
3. $4^5 \div 4^3 = (4 \cdot 4 \cdot 4 \cdot 4 \cdot 4) \div (4 \cdot 4 \cdot 4) = 4 \cdot 4 = 4^2$
4. $5^5 \div 5^3 = (5 \cdot 5 \cdot 5 \cdot 5 \cdot 5) \div (5 \cdot 5 \cdot 5) = 5 \cdot 5 = 5^2$
5. $6^5 \div 6^3 = (6 \cdot 6 \cdot 6 \cdot 6 \cdot 6) \div (6 \cdot 6 \cdot 6) = 6 \cdot 6 = 6^2$
6. $7^5 \div 7^3 = (7 \cdot 7 \cdot 7 \cdot 7 \cdot 7) \div (7 \cdot 7 \cdot 7) = 7 \cdot 7 = 7^2$
7. $8^5 \div 8^3 = (8 \cdot 8 \cdot 8 \cdot 8 \cdot 8) \div (8 \cdot 8 \cdot 8) = 8 \cdot 8 = 8^2$
8. $9^5 \div 9^3 = (9 \cdot 9 \cdot 9 \cdot 9 \cdot 9) \div (9 \cdot 9 \cdot 9) = 9 \cdot 9 = 9^2$
9. $n^5 \div n^3 = (n \cdot n \cdot n \cdot n \cdot n) \div (n \cdot n \cdot n) = n \cdot n = n^2$
10. $6.3^5 \div 6.3^3 = (6.3 \cdot 6.3 \cdot 6.3 \cdot 6.3 \cdot 6.3) \div (6.3 \cdot 6.3 \cdot 6.3) = 6.3 \cdot 6.3 = 6.3^2$

Describe a pattern or relationship you see between the problems and the answers. Explain what the pattern means or why it happens.

Answers will vary. Sample answer: Students may see that when the dividend and divisor have the same base, the exponent of the quotient is equal to the difference of the exponents of the dividend and divisor. Five factors of n divided by three factors of n is a total of two factors of n.

Integer Exponents—Repeated Reasoning

Name: _____

Find patterns in products of powers with different bases.

Expand each factor. Rewrite the expanded form as a power of a product. Then simplify. The first one has been done for you.

Set A

1. $2^2 \times 4^2 = 2 \times 2 \times 4 \times 4 = (2 \times 4)^2 = 8^2$

2. $2^3 \times 4^3 = 2 \times 2 \times 2 \times 4 \times 4 \times 4 = (2 \times 4)^3 = 8^3$

3. $2^4 \times 4^4 = 2 \times 2 \times 2 \times 2 \times 4 \times 4 \times 4 \times 4 = (2 \times 4)^4 = 8^4$

4. $3^2 \times 5^2 = 3 \times 3 \times 5 \times 5 = (3 \times 5)^2 = 15^2$

5. $3^3 \times 5^3 = 3 \times 3 \times 3 \times 5 \times 5 \times 5 = (3 \times 5)^3 = 15^3$

6. $n^5 \times m^5 = n \times n \times n \times n \times n \times m \times m \times m \times m \times m = (n \times m)^5 = (nm)^5$

Write the base as a product of two factors. Use the exponent to expand the product. Then write it as a product of two exponential expressions. The first one has been done for you.

Set B

1. $10^2 = (2 \times 5)^2 = 2 \times 5 \times 2 \times 5 = 2^2 \times 5^2$

2. $10^3 = (2 \times 5)^3 = 2 \times 5 \times 2 \times 5 \times 2 \times 5 = 2^3 \times 5^3$

3. $10^4 = (2 \times 5)^4 = 2 \times 5 \times 2 \times 5 \times 2 \times 5 \times 2 \times 5 = 2^4 \times 5^4$

4. $6^2 = (2 \times 3)^2 = 2 \times 3 \times 2 \times 3 = 2^2 \times 3^2$

5. $6^3 = (2 \times 3)^3 = 2 \times 3 \times 2 \times 3 \times 2 \times 3 = 2^3 \times 3^3$

6. $(mn)^5 = (m \times n)^5 = m \times n \times m \times n \times m \times n \times m \times n \times m \times n = m^5 \times n^5$

Describe a pattern you see in one of the sets of problems above.

Answers will vary. Sample answer: Students may see in Set B that when there is more than one factor inside the parentheses, each factor is raised to the power.

Integer Exponents—Repeated Reasoning

Name: _____

Find more patterns in quotients of powers with the same base.

Expand each term in the quotient of powers. Write the quotient in expanded form. Then write the quotient using an exponent. The first one has been done for you.

1. $2^4 \div 2^1 = (2 \times 2 \times 2 \times 2) \div (2) = 2 \times 2 \times 2 = 2^3$

2. $2^4 \div 2^2 = (2 \times 2 \times 2 \times 2) \div (2 \times 2) = 2 \times 2 = 2^2$

3. $2^4 \div 2^3 = (2 \times 2 \times 2 \times 2) \div (2 \times 2 \times 2) = 2 = 2^1$

4. $2^4 \div 2^4 = (2 \times 2 \times 2 \times 2) \div (2 \times 2 \times 2 \times 2) = 1 = 2^0$

5. $2^4 \div 2^5 = (2 \times 2 \times 2 \times 2) \div (2 \times 2 \times 2 \times 2 \times 2) = 1 \div 2 = 2^{-1}$

6. $2^4 \div 2^6 = (2 \times 2 \times 2 \times 2) \div (2 \times 2 \times 2 \times 2 \times 2 \times 2) = 1 \div (2 \times 2) = 2^{-2}$

7. $2^4 \div 2^7 = (2 \times 2 \times 2 \times 2) \div (2 \times 2 \times 2 \times 2 \times 2 \times 2 \times 2) = 1 \div (2 \times 2 \times 2) = 2^{-3}$

8. $4.3^5 \div 4.3^2 = (4.3 \times 4.3 \times 4.3 \times 4.3 \times 4.3) \div (4.3 \times 4.3) = 4.3 \times 4.3 \times 4.3 = 4.3^3$

Describe a pattern or relationship you see between the problems and the answers. Explain what the pattern means or why it happens.

Answers will vary. Students may notice that if the exponent in the divisor increases by 1, the exponent in the quotient decreases by 1. That happens because you are dividing by one more factor, so the result has one fewer factor.

Form A

Name: _____

Scientific Notation—Skills Practice

Write the numbers in scientific notation.

1 4,500 = _____ 4.5×10^3

2 0.0578 = _____ 5.78×10^{-2}

3 57 = _____ 5.7×10^1

4 0.006256 = _____ 6.256×10^{-3}

5 730 = _____ 7.3×10^2

6 0.000042 = _____ 4.2×10^{-5}

7 0.007 = _____ 7.0×10^{-3}

8 25.63 = _____ 2.563×10^1

9 300.25 = _____ 3.0025×10^2

10 0.1456 = _____ 1.456×10^{-1}

11 56,325.2 = _____ 5.63252×10^4

12 9,214.3 = _____ 9.2143×10^3

Write the numbers in standard form.

13 7.65×10^3 = _____ 7,650

14 5.21×10^{-1} = _____ 0.521

15 7.528×10^2 = _____ 752.8

16 2.169×10^{-4} = _____ 0.0002169

17 2.7345×10^1 = _____ 27.345

18 4.6×10^{-5} = _____ 0.000046

19 8.752×10^5 = _____ 875,200

20 5.0×10^{-3} = _____ 0.005

21 8.0×10^7 = _____ 80,000,000

22 5.639×10^{-2} = _____ 0.05639

23 5.3725×10^4 = _____ 53,725

24 1.3×10^{-6} = _____ 0.0000013

Form B

Name: _____

Scientific Notation—Skills Practice

Write the numbers in scientific notation.

1 6,500 = _____ 6.5×10^3

2 0.0354 = _____ 3.54×10^{-2}

3 69 = _____ 6.9×10^1

4 0.007257 = _____ 7.257×10^{-3}

5 820 = _____ 8.2×10^2

6 0.000053 = _____ 5.3×10^{-5}

7 0.002 = _____ 2.0×10^{-3}

8 37.85 = _____ 3.785×10^1

9 400.75 = _____ 4.0075×10^2

10 0.2531 = _____ 2.531×10^{-1}

11 76,213.8 = _____ 7.62138×10^4

12 1,876.4 = _____ 1.8764×10^3

Write the numbers in standard form.

13 8.72×10^3 = _____ 8,720

14 3.79×10^{-1} = _____ 0.379

15 3.628×10^2 = _____ 362.8

16 9.786×10^{-4} = _____ 0.0009786

17 1.4278×10^1 = _____ 14.278

18 3.4×10^{-5} = _____ 0.000034

19 6.251×10^5 = _____ 625,100

20 4.0×10^{-3} = _____ 0.004

21 9.0×10^7 = _____ 90,000,000

22 6.213×10^{-2} = _____ 0.06213

23 4.1723×10^4 = _____ 41,723

24 4.6×10^{-6} = _____ 0.0000046

Scientific Notation—Skills Practice

Name: _____

Form A

Perform operations with numbers written in scientific notation. Write your answers in standard form.

1. $(4.2 \times 10^4) \times (2 \times 10^3) =$ __84,000,000__

2. $(2.8 \times 10^5) \div (7 \times 10^{-2}) =$ __4,000,000__

3. $(3.9 \times 10^6) + (4.1 \times 10^7) =$ __44,900,000__

4. $(5.05 \times 10^{-3}) \div (5.05 \times 10^{-2}) =$ __0.1__

5. $(3.21 \times 10^{-3}) \times (4.6 \times 10^3) =$ __14.766__

6. $(4.5 \times 10^4) + (1.1 \times 10^3) =$ __45,011__

7. $(2.65 \times 10^3) - (1.21 \times 10^3) =$ __1,440__

8. $(7.5 \times 10^{-2}) + (8.6 \times 10^2) =$ __860.075__

9. $(6.21 \times 10^{-2}) - (4.32 \times 10^{-4}) =$ __0.061668__

10. $(8.6 \times 10^2) + (9.4 \times 10^2) =$ __1,800__

11. $(2.6 \times 10^2) \cdot (3.8 \times 10^0) =$ __988__

12. $(1.7 \times 10^{-1}) + (2.59 \times 10^{-2}) =$ __0.1959__

13. $\dfrac{4.62 \times 10^6}{2.2 \times 10^3} =$ __2,100__

14. $(4.25 \times 10^3) \cdot (3.5 \times 10^{-6}) =$ __14.875__

Scientific Notation—Skills Practice

Name: _____

Form B

Perform operations with numbers written in scientific notation. Write your answers in standard form.

1. $(3.1 \times 10^4) \times (3 \times 10^3) =$ __93,000,000__

2. $(3.6 \times 10^5) \div (4 \times 10^{-2}) =$ __9,000,000__

3. $(2.7 \times 10^6) + (5.1 \times 10^7) =$ __53,700,000__

4. $(6.39 \times 10^{-3}) \div (3 \times 10^{-3}) =$ __21.3__

5. $(4.78 \times 10^{-3}) \times (2.1 \times 10^3) =$ __10.038__

6. $(5.84 \times 10^4) + (6.2 \times 10^1) =$ __58,462__

7. $(3.85 \times 10^3) - (1.41 \times 10^3) =$ __2,440__

8. $(3.5 \times 10^{-2}) + (7.9 \times 10^2) =$ __790.035__

9. $(5.31 \times 10^{-2}) - (2.34 \times 10^{-4}) =$ __0.052866__

10. $(7.2 \times 10^2) + (8.7 \times 10^2) =$ __1,590__

11. $(4.6 \times 10^2) \times (2.8 \times 10^0) =$ __1,288__

12. $(1.9 \times 10^{-1}) + (3.69 \times 10^{-2}) =$ __0.2269__

13. $\dfrac{1{,}725 \times 10^6}{7.5 \times 10^3} =$ __230__

14. $(4.87 \times 10^6) \times (4.3 \times 10^{-5}) =$ __209.41__

Solutions to Linear Equations— Skills Practice

Form A

Name: _____

Solve and tell whether the equation has 1 solution, no solution, or infinitely many solutions.

1 $-3x + 8 - 5x = 21 - 8x$
no solution

2 $-2y - 7 + 5y = 13 - 2y$
1 solution: $y = 4$

3 $12 - 8z = -20 - 4z$
1 solution: $z = 8$

4 $7 + 2f = 9 + 4f$
1 solution: $f = -1$

5 $6 + 3m - 4 = -5 + 3m + 7$
infinitely many solutions

6 $d + 6 + 2d = 4d + 9$
1 solution: $d = -3$

7 $4p - 4 = 3p - 3$
1 solution: $x = 1$

8 $4c + 12 = c - 3$
1 solution: $c = -5$

9 $7d - 8 = 3d - 8$
1 solution: $d = 0$

10 $-9n - 8 = -10n - 7$
1 solution: $n = 1$

11 $6 + 8b = -6 + 2b$
1 solution: $b = -2$

12 $7g + 5 - 2g = 5 + 5g$
infinitely many solutions

Solutions to Linear Equations— Skills Practice

Form B

Name: _____

Solve and tell whether the equation has 1 solution, no solution, or infinitely many solutions.

1 $-3x - 8 + 5x = 17 - 3x$
1 solution: $x = 5$

2 $-4a + 6 - 2a = 12 - 6a$
no solution

3 $14 - 7z = -22 - 3z$
1 solution: $z = 9$

4 $9 + 4g - 6 = -3 + 4g + 6$
infinitely many solutions

5 $8 + 3d = 10 + 5d$
1 solution: $d = -1$

6 $5w - 5 = 4w - 4$
1 solution: $w = 1$

7 $c + 7 + 3c = 5c + 11$
1 solution: $c = -4$

8 $9 + 6p = -9 - 3p$
1 solution: $p = -2$

9 $5f + 14 = f - 6$
1 solution: $f = -5$

10 $9h - 7 = 4h - 7$
1 solution: $h = 0$

11 $6z + 3 - 3z = 3 + 3z$
infinitely many solutions

12 $-9b - 10 = -10b - 9$
1 solution: $b = 1$

Solutions to Linear Equations—Skills Practice

Name: _____ Form A

Use the distributive property as needed to solve and tell whether the equation has 1 solution, no solution, or infinitely many solutions.

1 $6x - 12 = 6(x - 2)$
infinitely many solutions

2 $\frac{4}{5} - \frac{3}{10}m = \frac{1}{10}m - \frac{4}{5}$
1 solution: $m = 4$

3 $-15x - 4 + 6x = -4 - 9x$
infinitely many solutions

4 $7(y - 6) = 7y + 42$
no solution

5 $4(p + 5) = 6p + 20$
1 solution: $p = 0$

6 $3m + 11 = \frac{1}{3}(9m + 33)$
infinitely many solutions

7 $15y - 4 = 12y - 28$
1 solution: $y = -8$

8 $-8 + 2n + 14 = 4n - 16$
1 solution: $n = 11$

9 $-\frac{1}{2}(4a + 8) = -2a + 4$
no solution

10 $3(m - 4) = 6m - 15$
1 solution: $m = 1$

11 $8(2y + 5) = 9y + 12$
1 solution: $y = -4$

12 $2n + 14 = 3n + 5$
1 solution: $n = 9$

Solutions to Linear Equations—Skills Practice

Name: _____ Form B

Use the distributive property as needed to solve and tell whether the equation has 1 solution, no solution, or infinitely many solutions.

1 $\frac{2}{3} - \frac{1}{6}m = \frac{1}{6}m - \frac{2}{3}$
1 solution: $m = 4$

2 $7x - 14 = 7(x - 2)$
infinitely many solutions

3 $7(p + 4) = 9p + 28$
1 solution: $p = 0$

4 $-16x - 8 + 9x = -8 - 7x$
infinitely many solutions

5 $4m + 11 = \frac{1}{8}(32m + 88)$
infinitely many solutions

6 $8(y - 7) = 8y + 56$
no solution

7 $-9 + 4n + 18 = 7n - 24$
1 solution: $n = 11$

8 $14y - 6 = 11y - 27$
1 solution: $y = -7$

9 $5(m - 3) = 7m - 17$
1 solution: $m = 1$

10 $-\frac{1}{4}(8a + 20) = -2a + 5$
no solution

11 $7(4y + 5) = 19y + 8$
1 solution: $y = -3$

12 $-9n - 8 - 3n = 6n - 8$
1 solution: $n = 0$

Systems of Equations—Skills Practice

Form B

Name: _____

Solve systems of equations using substitution.

1 $x = 7y$
$3x + 2y = 23$
$x = 7, y = 1$

2 $x = 4y$
$0.5y + 2x = 85$
$x = 40, y = 10$

3 $x - 6 = 5y$
$5y + x = -24$
$x = -9, y = -3$

4 $x = 9y$
$5x + 3y = -48$
$x = -9, y = -1$

5 $y = \frac{1}{5}x$
$-7x + 5y = 60$
$x = -10, y = -2$

6 $x - 8 = \frac{1}{6}y$
$\frac{1}{6}y + x = 10$
$x = 9, y = 6$

7 $y = 3x$
$-2x + y = 5$
$x = 5, y = 15$

8 $x + 7 = -3y$
$-3y + x = 41$
$x = 17, y = -8$

9 $y = 1.5x$
$10y - 3x = 96$
$x = 8, y = 12$

10 $x + 7 = 8y$
$8y + x = 9$
$x = 1, y = 1$

©Curriculum Associates, LLC   Copying is permitted for classroom use.

Systems of Equations—Skills Practice

Form A

Name: _____

Solve systems of equations using substitution.

1 $y = 4x$
$2y + 2.5x = 105$
$x = 10, y = 40$

2 $x + 10 = -8y$
$-8y + x = 6$
$x = -2, y = -1$

3 $x = -6y$
$3x + 6y = -24$
$x = -12, y = 2$

4 $x - 9 = 7y$
$7y + x = -19$
$x = -5, y = -2$

5 $y = 7x$
$-2x + y = 15$
$x = 3, y = 21$

6 $x + 5 = -4y$
$-4y + x = 43$
$x = 19, y = -6$

7 $x - 1 = \frac{1}{2}y$
$\frac{1}{2}y + x = 11$
$x = 6, y = 10$

8 $y = \frac{1}{3}x$
$-6x + 3y = 30$
$x = -6, y = -2$

9 $x = 1.5y$
$-8x - 2y = -84$
$x = 9, y = 6$

10 $y = 0.5x$
$8y - 6x = -20$
$x = 10, y = 5$

©Curriculum Associates, LLC   Copying is permitted for classroom use.

Systems of Equations—Skills Practice

Name: _____

Form A

Solve systems of equations using any method.

1 $3x - 4y = 7$
$3x - 4y = 9$
no solution

2 $10x - 15y = 30$
$2x - 4y = 4$
$x = 6, y = 2$

3 $y = 2x$
$4y + 3x = 55$
$x = 5, y = 10$

4 $6x + 2y = 20$
$3x + 2y = 8$
$x = 4, y = -2$

5 $14y - 7x = 21$
$x - 2y = -3$
infinitely many solutions

6 $9x - 6y = 3$
$-9x + 4y = 7$
$x = -3, y = -5$

7 $7y + 8x = 15$
$3y + 8x = 11$
$x = 1, y = 1$

8 $7x - 6y = 4$
$-6y + 7x = 5$
no solution

9 $5x - 4y = 9$
$3x + 8y = -5$
$x = 1, y = -1$

10 $x + 4 = 6y$
$6y + x = 8$
$x = 2, y = 1$

Systems of Equations—Skills Practice

Name: _____

Form B

Solve systems of equations using any method.

1 $20x - 10y = 50$
$10x - 15y = -5$
$x = 4, y = 3$

2 $2x - 6y = 8$
$2x - 6y = 3$
no solution

3 $y = 3x$
$5y + 5x = 40$
$x = 2, y = 6$

4 $7x + 4y = 30$
$3x + 4y = 6$
$x = 6, y = -3$

5 $8x - 4y = 4$
$-8x + 2y = 6$
$x = -2, y = -5$

6 $15y - 5x = 20$
$x - 3y = -4$
infinitely many solutions

7 $8x - 4y = 3$
$-4y + 8x = 9$
no solution

8 $9y + 6x = 15$
$2y + 6x = 8$
$x = 1, y = 1$

9 $10x + 4y = 8$
$5x + 8y = 16$
$x = 0, y = 2$

10 $x = -2y$
$3y + 5x = -21$
$x = -6, y = 3$

Systems of Equations—Skills Practice

Name: _____ **Form A**

Solve systems of equations involving fractions and decimals.

1 $x = 0.5y$
$6x + 2y = 20$
$x = 2, y = 4$

2 $2x + 3y = 5$
$0.25x + 0.25y = 0.5$
$x = 1, y = 1$

3 $\frac{3}{2}x + \frac{7}{10}y = 20$
$2x - 7y = -120$
$x = 10, y = 20$

4 $x = \frac{1}{4}y$
$12x - 4y = 8$
$x = -2, y = -8$

5 $4x + 5y = 42$
$\frac{2}{3}x - \frac{1}{6}y = 1$
$x = 3, y = 6$

6 $-8x - 7y = 3$
$\frac{4}{5}x + \frac{7}{10}y = \frac{3}{10}$
no solution

7 $\frac{1}{8}x + \frac{1}{4}y = 2$
$x + 2y = 16$
infinitely many solutions

8 $x = \frac{1}{6}y$
$36x - 2y = 24$
$x = 1, y = 6$

9 $6x - 5y = 36$
$0.5x + 2.5y = 3$
$x = 6, y = 0$

10 $2.5x + 5y = 50$
$1.25x + 1.5y = 21$
$x = 12, y = 4$

Systems of Equations—Skills Practice

Name: _____ **Form B**

Solve systems of equations involving fractions and decimals.

1 $x = -0.5y$
$8x + 6y = 12$
$x = -3, y = 6$

2 $-6x + 12y = 14$
$1.5x - 3y = -3.5$
infinitely many solutions

3 $4x - 7y = 32$
$0.5x + 3.5y = 4$
$x = 8, y = 0$

4 $2x + 6y = 8$
$0.25x + 0.25y = 0.5$
$x = 1, y = 1$

5 $\frac{4}{5}x + \frac{3}{10}y = 13$
$2x - 3y = -80$
$x = 5, y = 30$

6 $y = \frac{1}{5}x$
$3x - 25y = 20$
$x = -10, y = -2$

7 $\frac{1}{5}x + \frac{1}{10}y = 3$
$2x + y = 30$
infinitely many solutions

8 $4x + y = 12$
$\frac{1}{3}x - \frac{1}{6}y = -2$
$x = 0, y = 12$

9 $-6x - 3y = 5$
$\frac{3}{4}x + \frac{3}{8}y = \frac{5}{8}$
no solution

10 $2x + 5y = 24$
$\frac{1}{2}x - \frac{3}{4}y = -2$
$x = 2, y = 4$

Linear Functions—Skills Practice

Name: _____ Form A

Find the slope of the line through two given points.

1. $(7, 7)$ and $(9, 9)$
slope = ___ 1

2. $(8, 11)$ and $(5, 5)$
slope = ___ 2

3. $(2, 5)$ and $(5, 8)$
slope = ___ 1

4. $(-2, -3)$ and $(-1, -6)$
slope = ___ -3

5. $(-1, -4)$ and $(3, 12)$
slope = ___ 4

6. $(0, 0)$ and $(6, 5)$
slope = ___ $\frac{5}{6}$

7. $(5, 6)$ and $(9, 8)$
slope = ___ $\frac{1}{2}$

8. $(-2, -13)$ and $(-4, -3)$
slope = ___ -5

9. $(5, 9)$ and $(3, 11)$
slope = ___ -1

10. $(-8, 17)$ and $(-5, 19)$
slope = ___ $\frac{2}{3}$

11. $\left(\frac{1}{4}, 4\right)$ and $\left(\frac{3}{4}, 5\right)$
slope = ___ 2

12. $(6, 3)$ and $(-6, 6)$
slope = ___ $-\frac{1}{4}$

13. $(8, 5)$ and $(4, -7)$
slope = ___ 3

14. $\left(\frac{1}{8}, -2\right)$ and $\left(\frac{5}{8}, -4\right)$
slope = ___ -4

15. $(0, 4)$ and $(-10, 0)$
slope = ___ $\frac{2}{5}$

16. $(3, 8)$ and $(4, 6)$
slope = ___ -2

17. $(4, 9)$ and $(7, 9)$
slope = ___ 0

18. $(-3, 0)$ and $(0, 9)$
slope = ___ 3

19. $(-2, 3)$ and $(4, -2)$
slope = ___ $-\frac{5}{6}$

20. $(1, 1)$ and $(-3, 9)$
slope = ___ -2

21. $\left(-\frac{1}{4}, \frac{1}{4}\right)$ and $(-2, 2)$
slope = ___ -1

©Curriculum Associates, LLC   Copying is permitted for classroom use.

Linear Functions—Skills Practice

Name: _____ Form B

Find the slope of the line through two given points.

1. $(7, 10)$ and $(4, 4)$
slope = ___ 2

2. $(6, 6)$ and $(14, 14)$
slope = ___ 1

3. $(-3, -4)$ and $(-2, -7)$
slope = ___ -3

4. $(0, 0)$ and $(9, 4)$
slope = ___ $\frac{4}{9}$

5. $(-1, -10)$ and $(4, 15)$
slope = ___ 5

6. $(2, 4)$ and $(4, 6)$
slope = ___ 1

7. $\left(\frac{1}{4}, -3\right)$ and $\left(\frac{3}{4}, -5\right)$
slope = ___ -4

8. $\left(-\frac{1}{5}, \frac{1}{5}\right)$ and $(-2, 2)$
slope = ___ -1

9. $(2, 7)$ and $(6, 9)$
slope = ___ $\frac{1}{2}$

10. $(-2, -5)$ and $(-4, -11)$
slope = ___ 3

11. $(-7, 16)$ and $(-4, 18)$
slope = ___ $\frac{2}{3}$

12. $(9, 6)$ and $(-9, 9)$
slope = ___ $-\frac{1}{6}$

13. $\left(\frac{1}{8}, 6\right)$ and $\left(\frac{5}{8}, 7\right)$
slope = ___ 2

14. $(1, 1)$ and $(-2, 7)$
slope = ___ -2

15. $(-2, 0)$ and $(0, -10)$
slope = ___ -5

16. $(0, -6)$ and $(-8, 0)$
slope = ___ $-\frac{3}{4}$

17. $(4, 12)$ and $(5, 10)$
slope = ___ -2

18. $(6, 7)$ and $(1, 12)$
slope = ___ -1

19. $(9, 6)$ and $(4, -9)$
slope = ___ 3

20. $(2, -1)$ and $(7, 2)$
slope = ___ $\frac{3}{5}$

21. $(6, 8)$ and $(9, 8)$
slope = ___ 0

©Curriculum Associates, LLC   Copying is permitted for classroom use.

Form A

Linear Functions—Skills Practice

Name: _____

Determine the rate of change and the initial value of the line through two given points.

1 (5, 14) and (3, 10)
Rate of change = 2
Initial value = 4

2 (9, 32) and (4, 17)
Rate of change = 3
Initial value = 5

3 (8, 5) and (4, 7)
Rate of change = $-\dfrac{1}{2}$
Initial value = 9

4 (4, 8) and (12, 10)
Rate of change = $\dfrac{1}{4}$
Initial value = 7

5 (3, 13) and (6, 14)
Rate of change = $\dfrac{1}{3}$
Initial value = 12

6 (0, 4) and (7, 4)
Rate of change = 0
Initial value = 4

7 (1, 6) and (6, 1)
Rate of change = -1
Initial value = 7

8 (3, 8) and (12, 2)
Rate of change = $-\dfrac{2}{3}$
Initial value = 10

9 (4, 1) and (8, 2)
Rate of change = $\dfrac{1}{4}$
Initial value = 0

10 (1, 3) and (3, 9)
Rate of change = 3
Initial value = 0

11 (2, 8) and (4, 8)
Rate of change = 0
Initial value = 8

12 (5, 12) and (2, 6)
Rate of change = 2
Initial value = 2

Give the rate of change and the initial value from each description.

13 Yamini starts a savings account with $12. She will put in an equal amount each week. After 6 weeks, she will have $54.
Rate of change per week = $7
Initial value = $12

14 Jordan has some music books. He will buy 9 new music books each year. He will have 52 music books in 5 years.
Rate of change per year = 9
Initial value = 7

Form B

Linear Functions—Skills Practice

Name: _____

Determine the rate of change and the initial value of the line through two given points.

1 (1, 4) and (3, 12)
Rate of change = 4
Initial value = 0

2 (5, 18) and (2, 9)
Rate of change = 3
Initial value = 3

3 (5, 1) and (10, 2)
Rate of change = $\dfrac{1}{5}$
Initial value = 0

4 (0, 5) and (8, 5)
Rate of change = 0
Initial value = 5

5 (1, 6) and (6, 16)
Rate of change = 2
Initial value = 4

6 (8, 30) and (5, 21)
Rate of change = 3
Initial value = 6

7 (1, 3) and (3, 1)
Rate of change = -1
Initial value = 4

8 (4, 7) and (12, 9)
Rate of change = $\dfrac{1}{4}$
Initial value = 6

9 (3, 11) and (5, 11)
Rate of change = 0
Initial value = 11

10 (8, 4) and (4, 6)
Rate of change = $-\dfrac{1}{2}$
Initial value = 8

11 (6, 16) and (9, 17)
Rate of change = $\dfrac{1}{3}$
Initial value = 14

12 (6, 8) and (15, 2)
Rate of change = $-\dfrac{2}{3}$
Initial value = 12

Give the rate of change and the initial value from each description.

13 Kahn starts a savings account with $14. He will put in an equal amount each week. After 7 weeks, he will have $56.
Rate of change per week = $6
Initial value = $14

14 Addison has some puzzle books. She will buy 7 new puzzle books each year. She will have 43 puzzle books in 5 years.
Rate of change per year = 7
Initial value = 8

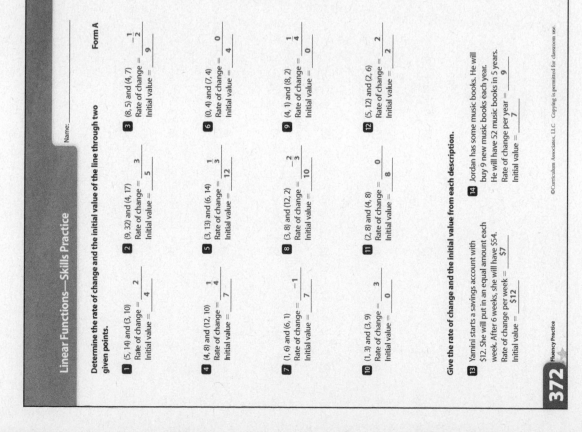

Linear Functions—Skills Practice

Name: _____

Form A

Identify another point on the line given one point and the slope. One possible answer is given.

1 (−4, 0) and slope = −2
(−3, −2)

2 (−5, 2) and slope = −1
(−4, 1)

3 (4, 5) and slope = 0
(5, 5)

4 (−3, −2) and slope = 5
(−2, 3)

5 (5, 6) and slope = 1
(6, 7)

6 (0, 0) and slope = 3
(1, 3)

7 (−1, −1) and slope = $-\frac{1}{2}$
(1, −2)

8 (1, 1) and slope = −4
(2, −3)

9 (−2, −2) and slope = $\frac{1}{4}$
(2, −1)

10 (0, −2) and slope = −5
(1, −7)

11 (1, 2) and slope = $-\frac{1}{3}$
(4, 1)

12 (3, −6) and slope = 4
(4, −2)

13 (2, −3) and slope = 0
(3, −3)

14 (4, 4) and slope = −3
(5, 1)

15 (3, 5) and slope = $-\frac{3}{5}$
(8, 2)

16 (2, 7) and slope = 1
(3, 8)

17 (3, −3) and slope = −6
(4, −9)

18 (2, 2) and slope = 2
(3, 4)

19 (−2, 1) and slope = $\frac{1}{6}$
(4, 2)

20 (4, 2) and slope = −2
(5, 0)

21 (0, 0) and slope = $\frac{2}{3}$
(3, 2)

22 (2, 4) and slope = −1
(3, 3)

23 (1, −1) and slope = 3
(2, 2)

24 (−1, 1) and slope = 8
(0, 9)

Linear Functions—Skills Practice

Name: _____

Form B

Identify another point on the line given one point and the slope. One possible answer is given.

1 (6, 7) and slope = 0
(7, 7)

2 (−4, −5) and slope = 5
(−3, 0)

3 (−4, 3) and slope = −1
(−3, 2)

4 (−6, 0) and slope = −2
(−5, −2)

5 (3, 11) and slope = 1
(4, 12)

6 (0, 0) and slope = $\frac{1}{4}$
(4, 1)

7 (−1, −1) and slope = $-\frac{3}{5}$
(4, −4)

8 (1, 2) and slope = $-\frac{1}{2}$
(3, 1)

9 (0, −3) and slope = −5
(1, −8)

10 (4, −8) and slope = 3
(5, −5)

11 (4, −9) and slope = 0
(5, −9)

12 (−3, 3) and slope = $-\frac{1}{3}$
(0, 2)

13 (5, 5) and slope = −2
(6, 3)

14 (5, −5) and slope = −6
(6, −11)

15 (8, 9) and slope = 1
(9, 10)

16 (−2, 3) and slope = $\frac{2}{3}$
(1, 5)

17 (3, 4) and slope = −4
(4, 0)

18 (−3, 1) and slope = $\frac{1}{6}$
(3, 2)

19 (1, 1) and slope = −3
(2, −2)

20 (0, 0) and slope = 4
(1, 4)

21 (−1, 1) and slope = 2
(0, 3)

22 (8, 8) and slope = 8
(9, 16)

23 (1, −1) and slope = −1
(2, −2)

24 (6, 2) and slope = 3
(7, 5)

Unit Game Teacher Resource
Table of Contents

TR 1

Triple-E: Equivalent Exponential Expressions Recording Sheet

Round	Exponential Expression	Equivalent Form
1		
2		
3		
4		
5		
6		
7		
8		
9		
10		

Name: _____

Triple-E: Equivalent Exponential Expressions Game Board

−9	−8	−7	−6	−5
−4	−3	−2	−1	0
1	2	3	4	5
6	7	8	9	10

0	1	−1	2	−2
3	−3	4	−4	5
−5	6	−6	7	−7
8	−8	9	−9	10

TR 4

Slippery Slopes Recording Sheet

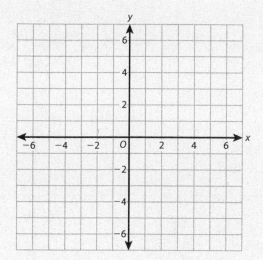

Slope = _____ **Points** _____

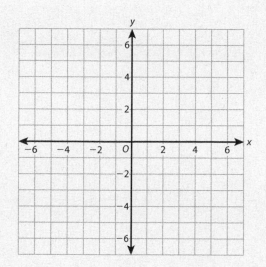

Slope = _____ **Points** _____

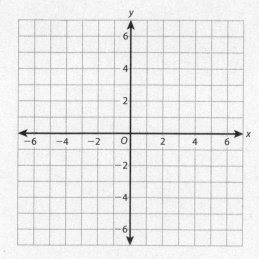

Slope = _____ **Points** _____

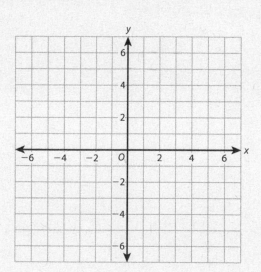

Slope = _____ **Points** _____

Name: _____

TR 5

It's Systematic Recording Sheet

Round	Roll 1	Equation 1	Roll 2	Equation 2	Solution	Points
1						
2						
3						
4						
5						

TR 6

Equation Cards

✂

$y = \underline{\quad}x$	$y = \underline{\quad}x + \underline{\quad}$	$y = \underline{\quad}x - \underline{\quad}$
$y = \underline{\quad}x$	$y = \underline{\quad}x + \underline{\quad}$	$y = \underline{\quad}x - \underline{\quad}$
$y = \underline{\quad}x$	$y = \underline{\quad}x + \underline{\quad}$	$y = \underline{\quad}x - \underline{\quad}$
$y = \underline{\quad}x$	$y = \underline{\quad}x + \underline{\quad}$	$y = \underline{\quad}x - \underline{\quad}$

TR 7

Pythagorean Puzzler Recording Sheet

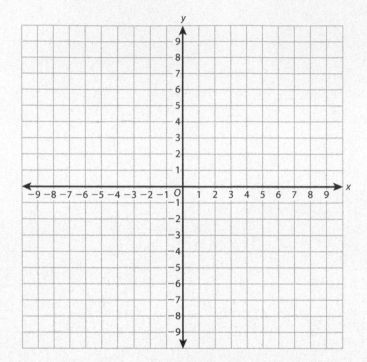

Round	Ordered Pairs	Segment Length
Round 1	(___, ___) and (___, ___)	
Round 2	(___, ___) and (___, ___)	
Round 3	(___, ___) and (___, ___)	
Round 4	(___, ___) and (___, ___)	
Round 5	(___, ___) and (___, ___)	
Total Length		

TR 8

Scatter Plot Association Recording Sheet

Positive Linear Association

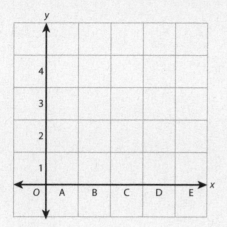

Dots Used

0 ☐☐☐☐   1 ☐☐☐☐   3 ☐☐☐☐

Negative Linear Association

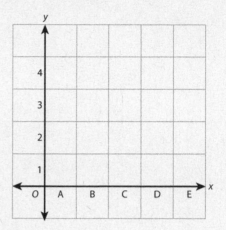

Dots Used

0 ☐☐☐☐   1 ☐☐☐☐   3 ☐☐☐☐

Nonlinear Association

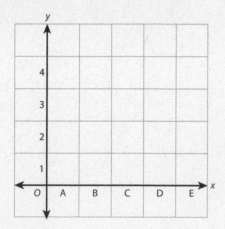

Dots Used

0 ☐☐☐☐   1 ☐☐☐☐   3 ☐☐☐☐

No Association

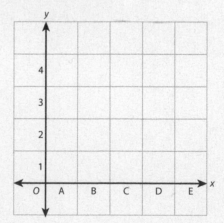

Dots Used

0 ☐☐☐☐   1 ☐☐☐☐   3 ☐☐☐☐

TR 9

Grid Section Cards

A1	A2	A3	A4
B1	B2	B3	B4
C1	C2	C3	C4
D1	D2	D3	D4
E1	E2	E3	E4